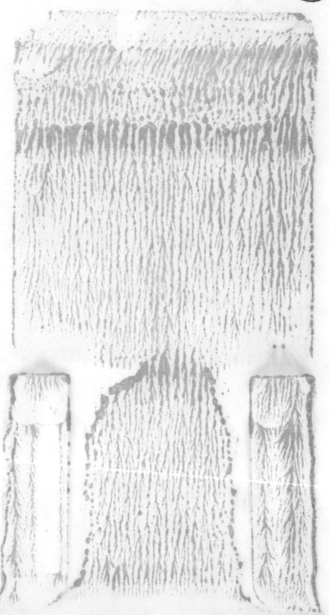

MATHEMATICAL
and PHYSICAL PRINCIPLES *of*
ENGINEERING ANALYSIS

MATHEMATICAL

and

PHYSICAL PRINCIPLES

of

ENGINEERING ANALYSIS

by WALTER C. JOHNSON

Professor of Electrical Engineering
Princeton University

McGRAW-HILL BOOK COMPANY, Inc.

NEW YORK AND LONDON

1944

MATHEMATICAL AND PHYSICAL PRINCIPLES OF ENGINEERING ANALYSIS

COPYRIGHT, 1944, BY THE
McGRAW-HILL BOOK COMPANY, INC.

PRINTED IN THE UNITED STATES OF AMERICA

171819202122 BP 10987

32600

PREFACE

This book is the outgrowth of a course in engineering analysis which the author has developed over the past six years for students in the several branches of engineering at Princeton University. The purpose of the book is to present the essential physical and mathematical principles and methods of approach that underlie the analysis of many practical engineering problems. The point of view is primarily utilitarian in an engineering sense but is aimed at a sound understanding of basic principles and designed to form a firm foundation for more advanced work. The book emphasizes basic physical principles and physical reasoning, and devotes considerable attention to methods of attack, the use of assumptions, procedures in setting up equations, the use of mathematics as a tool in accurate and quantitative reasoning, and the physical interpretation of mathematical results. Graphical methods are used freely, and reasonable approximations are encouraged provided that they lead to results within the required accuracy. Every effort is made to present the material from a broad and unspecialized point of view and to use material with which every graduate engineer should be familiar, whatever his field.

The problems have been drawn from numerous fields. Many of them have arisen in engineering practice and have been pared down no more than was thought necessary for inclusion in a textbook. Other, simpler, problems have been included as exercises for the student.

An attempt has been made to lead the student into building up a set of quantitative or semiquantitative physical concepts, such as, for example, quantitative ideas on the phenomena of mechanical and electrical oscillations, forced vibrations and resonance, and traveling waves in distributed systems. The development of physical intuition is regarded as one of the important functions of a course in engineering analysis.

This book presupposes a reasonable knowledge of elementary college physics and mechanics, and mathematics through calculus. A previous acquaintance with elementary differential equations is desirable but not essential, as the text includes considerable elementary material on this subject. Experience indicates that the course is most valuable in the upper-class years, when the students have had some background in a number of engineering subjects.

Much of the material was developed in class notes which were used in mimeographed and offset-printed form. Additional material has been added to make the book more adaptable to varied needs and to provide some leeway in the selection of material for a one-term course. In the course on which this text is based, the author has found that the practice of giving reasonably difficult but physically interesting problems, to be worked in a problem period under supervision, has been eminently successful.

It should be emphasized that this book is not intended to take the place of existing courses in mathematics, but is intended as a supplement from an engineering point of view. The author believes, however, that a course in fundamental engineering analysis can provide a type of training and promote a broad grasp of engineering problems which cannot be duplicated either in courses which are strictly mathematical or which stay closely within the boundaries of a single branch of engineering.

The author wishes to acknowledge his considerable debt to the Advanced Engineering Program of the General Electric Company, from which he received much of the inspiration for this book. He is indebted to Professor C. H. Willis, Chairman of the Department of Electrical Engineering at Princeton University, for his encouragement and his many valuable suggestions during the preparation of this manuscript. The author wishes to thank Professor S. Lefschetz of the Department of Mathematics at Princeton University for reading and criticizing the newer portions of the manuscript, and Professor J. W. Tukey of that department for his helpful suggestions.

WALTER C. JOHNSON.

PRINCETON, NEW JERSEY,
February, 1944.

CONTENTS

PAGE

PREFACE.   v

CHAPTER I

SECTION THE ANALYSIS OF ENGINEERING PROBLEMS

1. Introduction.   1
2. The First Requirement in Analysis.   3
3. Data   3
4. Method of Attack   3
5. Assumptions.   3
6. The Use of Mathematics   5
7. The Report   6
8. Summary: Point of View in Solving Problems   8

CHAPTER II

SOME BASIC PHYSICAL PRINCIPLES

9. Introduction. 10
10. Conservation of Energy. 11
11. Action Equals Reaction. 13
12. Principle of Superposition. 13
13. Newton's Laws of Motion. 14
14. Engineering Units of Force and Mass. 15
15. Rectilinear Translation and Rotation of Rigid Bodies. . . 16
16. D'Alembert's Principle 18
17. Conservation of Momentum. 19
18. Conservation of Angular Momentum 20
19. Electrical Systems; Kirchhoff's Laws 23
20. Induced Voltage 23
21. Principle of Constant Flux Linkages 26
22. Energy Stored in Inductive Circuits 30
23. Principle of Virtual Displacement 31

CHAPTER III

TRANSIENT AND STEADY-STATE CONDITIONS

24. The Nature of a Transient Condition. 40
25. Use of Differential Equations 41
26. Initial Conditions 43

CHAPTER IV

SETTING UP EQUATIONS

27. Introduction. 45
28. Coordinates 45

SECTION PAGE
29. Choice of Positive Directions 48
30. Electrical Systems 50
31. Mechanical Systems 56
32. Dual Systems 63
33. Mechanical and Electrical Analogies 67

CHAPTER V

GRAPHICAL AND NUMERICAL SOLUTION
OF DIFFERENTIAL EQUATIONS

34. Introduction. 75

A. GRAPHICAL AND NUMERICAL EVALUATION OF INTEGRALS

35. The Trapezoidal Rule. 76
36. Simpson's Rule. 78
37. Graphical Integration. 80

B. GRAPHICAL AND NUMERICAL SOLUTION OF DIFFERENTIAL EQUATIONS

38. Step-by-step Integration 82
39. Extensions. 84
40. Method of Isoclines. 86

CHAPTER VI

ORDINARY DIFFERENTIAL EQUATIONS

41. Introduction. 95

A. LINEAR EQUATIONS WITH CONSTANT COEFFICIENTS

42. Homogeneous Equation of First Order 97
43. Homogeneous Equation of Second Order 100
44. General Homogeneous Equation 109
45. Systems of Homogeneous Equations 110
46. The Nature of Nonhomogeneous Equations 117
47. Solution of Nonhomogeneous Equations. Reduction to Homo-
    geneous Form 119
48. Solution of Nonhomogeneous Equations. General Method . . . 127
49. Two or More Nonhomogeneous Terms 130
50. Systems of Nonhomogeneous Equations. 130
51. Change of Dependent Variable. 134
52. Operator Method of Determining Initial Derivatives 137
53. Hyperbolic Functions. 145

B. MISCELLANEOUS EQUATIONS

54. Equations with Variables Separable 155
55. Homogeneous Equation of First Order 157
56. Exact Differential Equations. 159
57. General Linear Equation of First Order. 161
58. Certain Equations of Second Order. 164
59. Euler's Equation. 167
60. Bessel's Equation and Bessel Functions. 168

CHAPTER VII

Sᴇᴄᴛɪᴏɴ VECTOR REPRESENTATION OF SINUSOIDS Pᴀɢᴇ

61. Introduction 182
62. Complex Numbers 182
63. Representation of Sinusoids 186
64. Derivatives and Integrals 187
65. Application to Steady-state Sinusoidal Response 188
66. Summary of the Method 193
67. Electrical Example 194
68. Mechanical Example Showing Resonance 196
69. Conclusion 201

CHAPTER VIII
THE CHECKING OF EQUATIONS

70. Introduction 206
71. Some Methods of Checking 206
72. Nature of Dimensional Checking 207
73. Equations Containing One Type of Quantity 207
74. Example of Tracing an Error 210
75. Equations Containing More Than One Type of Quantity . . . 211
76. Limiting-case Method 214

CHAPTER IX
DIMENSIONAL ANALYSIS

77. Introduction 218
78. Changing Units 218
79. Derivation of Formulas. The Buckingham π Theorem 219
80. Example: Velocity of Sound in a Gas 224
81. Example: Heat Transfer. Correlation of Data 226
82. Example: A Nonlinear Electrical Transient 229
83. Example: Force on Wing of Airplane. Use of Models 230
84. Dimensional Constants 234

CHAPTER X
FOURIER SERIES

85. Introduction 239
86. The Fourier Series 241
87. Restrictions 242
88. The Fourier Coefficients 242
89. Expansion of Even and Odd Functions 245
90. Expansion in Terms of Time or Distance 247
91. Expansion of Nonperiodic Function in an Interval 249
92. Convergence, Derivatives, and Integrals 249
93. Example: Application of Fourier Series 251
94. Complex Form of the Fourier Series 254
95. Numerical Methods of Harmonic Analysis 258

SECTION   PAGE
96. Estimation of Harmonic Content. 264
97. The Fourier Integral 266

CHAPTER XI

SYSTEMS WITH DISTRIBUTED CONSTANTS

98. Introduction. 280
99. Partial Derivatives. 282
100. The Nature of a Partial Differential Equation. The Vibrating
     String. 285
101. The Product Solution. Continuation of the Vibrating String
     Problem. 289
102. Extension to Other Boundary Conditions by Fourier Series . . . 296
103. Equations Homogeneous with Respect to Derivatives. 297
104. Variable One-dimensional Heat Flow 300
105. Two- and Three-dimensional Heat Flow. Laplace's Equation. . 305
106. Electrical Transmission Lines 311
107. Graphical Field Plotting. 317

INDEX. 337

MATHEMATICAL AND PHYSICAL PRINCIPLES OF ENGINEERING ANALYSIS

CHAPTER I

THE ANALYSIS OF ENGINEERING PROBLEMS

1. Introduction.—The analysis of engineering problems (or the analysis of physical problems in general) can be an exceedingly fascinating pursuit, as fascinating, say, as a game of bridge, a crossword puzzle, or a cryptogram. One starts with a supply of fundamental physical knowledge and, with mathematics and physical reasoning as tools, attempts to build the solution to his problem. First of all he must know just what he is trying to build, next he must have at his disposal the proper physical building materials for the task at hand and must select from these the ones that seem best suited for the job, then his mathematical tools must be sharp so that he can more easily manipulate his material, and finally he must know something of the technique by which the final product can be obtained. In the matter of technique he should be guided, but not ruled, by what others have done along similar lines.

The requirements for successful engineering analysis are therefore rather exacting. They include a working knowledge of physical and mathematical principles sufficient for the problem at hand and, in addition, a familiarity with the technique by which these principles can be applied to reasonably complex problems. The solution may or may not require considerable labor, depending sometimes upon the methods that the analyst uses or the accuracy required, and this labor the analyst must always be prepared to perform; however, most problems necessitate considerable mental effort, and here he must be ready to put forth his best efforts. It is this part of analysis which is the most fascinating and challenging.

1

The engineering student takes quite a number of courses in physics and mathematics, and in many of his engineering courses he can see some of the uses to which these principles have been put. However, in engineering work the most useful analyses frequently are those which do not appear in textbooks or which perhaps have never been made before. Here the engineer must go back to fundamental principles and, by use of the proper techniques, attempt to determine the solution. In this he frequently needs more of a guide in the matter of technique than is afforded by engineering literature in which the methods themselves are only incidental. One of the purposes of this book is to emphasize and correlate the techniques used in various types of engineering problems and to provide practice in solving engineering problems directly from fundamental principles.

The point of view of this book is primarily a physical one. It is physical in a quantitative sense and hence, of necessity, employs mathematics as an aid to clear and quantitative reasoning. The function of mathematics in the training of engineers is a much-discussed question. It should be pointed out here that mathematics has a dual role in engineering: that of providing a quantitative basis for analysis and computation and that of providing the background for a more clear and thorough physical understanding of engineering phenomena. The former function is an obvious one and of recognized importance in all branches of technical engineering, but it must be admitted that most practicing engineers use in their day-to-day work only a small portion of the mathematics that they once studied. This does not mean that the rest of their mathematical training is lost and of no value. On the contrary, it has served them as a basis for a clear quantitative understanding of the physical phenomena with which they work and has aided in developing the physical intuition with which the engineer can deal with many problems in a qualitative or semiquantitative manner. When mathematics aids the student in this physical understanding, it is performing one of its most valuable functions from the standpoint of the engineer. Thus, instead of regarding mathematics as an abstract tool for the few, we shall regard it as a key that will open the doors to a clear and quantitative understanding of many important physical concepts and phenomena. When this understanding has been attained, the phenomena can be dealt with more intelligently and more surely, and the mathematical concepts can fade into the background for the nonmathematical engineer or can be polished to new brilliance by the engineer who specializes in analysis.

2. The First Requirement in Analysis.—The first requirement in solving physical problems will seem rather obvious, but it is overlooked so frequently that it deserves close attention. It is: Understand just what the problem is and what results must be obtained. Problems often come to the engineer in a rather hazy form with inadequate description and data. He must then decide for himself the exact nature of the problem, and, unless he does this quite carefully, his efforts may be worthless. Sometimes the hardest part of a problem is to determine just what the problem is.

3. Data.—The next step is to obtain sufficient data and, if this cannot be done, to assume reasonable data to fill the gaps. The latter is of course undesirable but must sometimes be done. In many cases the greatest difficulty is not a lack of data but a superfluity of them. Here the engineer must "weed out" the data and decide which of them are really important.

4. Method of Attack.—With the nature of the problem and the available data well in mind and with a consideration of the required accuracy, the analyst should next decide on a tentative plan of attack. Sometimes the method of analysis is quite obvious, but in many cases it is not. If in pursuing his first line of attack the analyst encounters great difficulties, he should always be ready to back out and consider a new plan. In a problem in mechanics, for example, he may first decide to write the differential equations for the system and attempt to solve them. If the difficulties of solution are great, he may decide that the principle of the conservation of momentum will give him sufficiently accurate results with less labor, or he may decide that a graphical solution of the equations would be more practical than an analytic one. In any case he should balance the required accuracy against the labor of solution and the final usefulness of the result.

5. Assumptions.—It is hardly possible to overemphasize the importance of assumptions in engineering analysis. It is almost impossible to describe physical phenomena with absolute mathematical accuracy, and, in order to translate these phenomena into equation form, it is necessary to make some approximations.

The nature of these approximations should always be kept in mind.   When the engineer presents the results of his analysis, he should state the underlying assumptions clearly and explicitly, thus making clear the limitations of his solution and preventing its misuse.

Common assumptions in electrical-circuit calculations are that resistance, inductance, and capacitance are constant, *i.e.*, not dependent on the current flowing through them, and that an alternating voltage can be represented approximately by a sine wave.   The assumption of a constant inductance may lead to

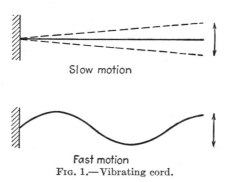

Slow motion

Fast motion
FIG. 1.—Vibrating cord.

erroneous results when the magnetic circuit of the inductor contains saturated iron and, in fact, may miss certain phenomena completely.   Any analysis based on a constant inductance should be prefaced by a statement pointing out this limitation.   Similarly, an analysis based on a sinusoidal electromotive force should state this assumption explicitly.

Figure 1 shows an elastic cord fastened at one end, with the other end given a vertical sinusoidal motion.   If the motion is slow, one can assume that the string remains straight, and the position of any point on the string can be calculated easily as a function of time.   However, if the motion of the end is rather fast, waves will be set up on the cord, and the previous assumption will be erroneous.   The analysis then involves partial differential equations and is considerably more difficult.

Figure 2 shows two air gaps in magnetic circuits.   In the upper sketch the gap length is small compared with the width of the pole face, and the reluctance of the gap can be calculated quite accurately by neglecting fringing flux and assuming the flux to pass straight across the gap.   The gap in the lower sketch is long and of small area, and any calculation made on the basis of the previous assumption would be worthless.   Here one must go to field theory with its more difficult equations or else use an approximate graphical method.

Furthermore, if the pole pieces in the lower sketch of Fig. 2 are of square cross section while the graphical method applies most easily to round pole pieces, the analyst may decide to assume that the square pole pieces can be replaced for purposes of calculation by round ones of equal area.   In this decision he must balance convenience against the required accuracy.

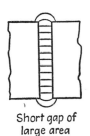

Short gap of
large area

The foregoing examples will serve to show how assumptions that are valid for one physical problem may be inaccurate and misleading in another problem of a somewhat similar nature.   It is therefore essential for the engineer to recognize his assumptions, to examine them carefully for validity, and to keep them in mind in his interpretation of the results.   It is also necessary for him to state the assumptions clearly in his presentation of the analysis so that others will not use his results where they do not

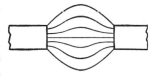

Long air gap

Fig. 2.—Air-gap flux.

apply.   The student will find it difficult at first to recognize his assumptions, but facility in this matter will increase with practice.

The use of simplifying assumptions often permits one to reduce a complicated problem to one of reasonable simplicity.   The assumptions should be chosen so as to stay within the required accuracy, at the same time making the problem as easy to handle as possible.

It will be evident that the method of attack will depend greatly upon the assumptions chosen, and vice versa.   The two go hand in hand and often should be chosen concurrently.

6. The Use of Mathematics.—With the method of attack and the pertinent physical laws decided upon, the analyst must next attempt to apply these physical laws to his particular problem. In the simplest cases this can be done mentally.   For example, if the physical system consists of a linear resistance in series with a constant inductance and the problem is to determine the effect on current of doubling the impressed alternating voltage, it can be seen immediately that the current will be doubled. If, however, the problem is to determine the effect of a change in frequency, the answer is not so easy to see, and one may have to resort to mathematics to obtain the solution. Here we decide that Kirchhoff's laws are the ones to use, and that the inductive reactance is directly proportional to frequency. By expressing the relations in equation form, we can solve for the current. The general procedure is to write in equation form the relations that must be satisfied by the physical system, and then let mathematical manipulation take the place of complicated physical reasoning. This has the advantage that, if one manipulates the mathematics correctly, then the solution will overlook nothing that has been included in the original equations. This, of course, is not always true of mental reasoning. Most important of all, mathematics permits the engineer to solve problems so complicated that he could not hope to cope with them by mental effort alone.

The main use of mathematics in engineering analysis is precisely that illustrated above. Using physical laws, the analyst writes equations expressing those relations which must hold for his particular problem. He then manipulates these equations according to the rules of mathematics so as to solve for the quantities in which he is interested. Finally, he translates the mathematical solution into physical terms, *i.e.*, he interprets the result.

After the result has been obtained, its usefulness must be evaluated: first, the solution should be checked (of this more will be said later) and, second, it should be examined in the light of the assumptions that were used in obtaining it, to determine the probable effect of the assumptions. Since some assumptions are almost always necessary in physical problems, the analyst cannot regard his result as *the* solution, but only as *a* solution, valid only under the limited conditions imposed by his assumptions.

7. The Report.—It has been said that a man who has something to tell, but cannot say it, may as well not have the knowledge at all. This may seem rather extreme, but it applies in some degree to engineering, where a great deal depends upon cooperative effort and an interchange of information. When an engineer has solved a problem, he should make a record of his solution, both for his own later reference and for the benefit of others. This record is usually made in the form of a report. It is rather enlightening to learn how much stress employers place on the writing of clear and concise reports.

Reports that present the results of engineering analysis are somewhat different from those presenting laboratory test results, although both are guided by the principles of clarity and conciseness. A logical order for presenting the results of analysis will often be as follows:

1. A concise statement of the problem to be solved. In most cases this will not contain specific numerical data but will indicate the general subject and scope of the analysis.

2. A list of the assumptions used in the analysis, including any necessary justification.

3. The complete results of the analysis. If the results consist of derived equations or formulas, the symbols should be defined unless their meaning is obvious. When the results contain a specific numerical application of derived formulas, it is often convenient to include the data if they are brief.

4. A discussion of the results and their significance.

5. Presentation of the data that form the basis of the results.

6. The analysis itself, which contains the reasoning and mathematics used to obtain the result. If the analysis is complex, it is desirable to summarize the method of attack before proceeding to details. Since an unbroken succession of equations and calculations is most difficult to follow, each major step in the analysis should be preceded by a brief explanation of the principles to be used. The details of obvious mathematical steps can be omitted, but on the other hand clearness should never be sacrificed for brevity. Symbols are preferably defined at the point where they are first used.

7. Detailed work not necessary to an understanding of the method and results should be placed in an appendix. If many symbols are used in the analysis, a tabulation of them in a separate section is helpful.

Each of these subdivisions of the report should be headed by an appropriate title such as "The Problem," "Assumptions," "Results," etc.

It should be observed that the order of presentation suggested above has a definite logic: the portions that would be of interest to a casual reader are placed at the beginning of the report so that one who is interested chiefly in results can obtain a reasonable understanding of the analysis by reading only the first portions; the assumptions are placed ahead of the results to warn the reader of the limitations of the solution; the analysis is placed near the end, because anyone who wishes to make himself intimately familiar with it will have to read most of the report in any case.

The writer of an engineering report will not go far wrong if he remembers the following principles: include everything that he himself would want to know if he were the reader of the report; state facts clearly so as to leave no doubts in the reader's mind; and conserve the reader's time by being as concise as possible without sacrificing the principles of completeness and clarity.

8. Summary: Point of View in Solving Problems.—The engineer starts the analysis of a problem with the knowledge that for every physical problem there exists a solution. He selects assumptions that will make the problem amenable to mathematical analysis without going beyond the limits of required accuracy, puts down his facts in equation form, and lets the mathematics take the place of complex physical reasoning. After obtaining the desired result in mathematical form, he interprets the physical meaning of the solution. He realizes that his result depends upon his assumptions, and that therefore it is *a* solution, not *the* solution. By judging the probable effect of his assumptions, he is able to estimate the limitations of his analysis. By presenting his results, assumptions, and analysis in written form, he enables others to utilize his work intelligently.

In outline form, his procedure will probably be as follows:
1. Understand just what is wanted.
2. Obtain the necessary data.
3. Decide on a method of attack and assumptions.
4. Translate the physical conditions into mathematical form.
5. Solve the equations for the desired quantities.
6. Make numerical calculations.
7. Check the results thoroughly.
8. Analyze the results.
9. Write the report.

In all of this work he should remember that a mistake in a decimal point or in arithmetic may have results just as disastrous as an error in method and that he cannot afford to tolerate essential mistakes of any kind.   The only way he can be sure that his results are correct is by checking them thoroughly, first by determining whether they are reasonable, second by mathematical methods to be described later, and third by comparing them with available test results.   In any case the essential thing is: results.

CHAPTER II

SOME BASIC PHYSICAL PRINCIPLES

9. Introduction.—The physical principles underlying many electrical, mechanical, and thermal phenomena are essentially the same, and many of the methods used in one branch of engineering can be applied equally well to others. For example, the law of the conservation of energy applies equally to mechanical, thermal, and electrical problems and is of great use in all three branches. This book will therefore aim to correlate the various types of problems as much as possible and will separate problems on the basis of the principles used in solution rather than according to the branch of engineering to which they are ordinarily considered to belong.

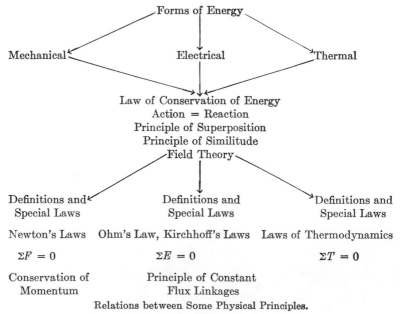

Relations between Some Physical Principles.

The purpose of this chapter is to present some of the more important basic physical concepts that are frequently used in engineering work. The principles are presented in forms that lead to direct application in engineering problems, rather than in forms that are most general or most compact in a mathematical sense.

The chart on page 10 is designed to aid the student in visualizing the relations between some of the fundamental laws that are of especial importance to engineers.

10. Conservation of Energy. *Definition.*—The total energy of an isolated system remains constant and cannot be changed in any way. This principle is an exceedingly useful one in many problems. In using it, one should be careful to include all the major changes of energy in the system. A frequent misuse is to attempt to apply the principle without properly taking into account a dissipation of energy.

Problems in which dissipation of energy should be considered include the impact of masses, a sudden change in velocity of a mass, switching operations in inductive circuits where a spark at the switch dissipates energy, and the charging of a condenser from a constant potential source.

Mechanical Energy.—The kinetic energy stored in a mass weighing W lb and moving at a velocity of v ft/sec is

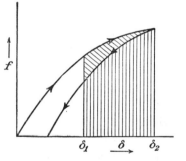

FIG. 3.—Nonlinear spring.

$$\mathcal{E} = \frac{1}{2}\frac{W}{g}v^2 \qquad \text{ft-lb,}$$

where g is the acceleration of gravity (32.2 ft/sec²).

The potential energy stored in a spring is equal to the integral of force with respect to displacement, which is the area under the force vs. displacement curve. Figure 3 shows such a curve for a nonlinear spring with energy losses. If the spring is initially compressed an amount δ_1, then the additional energy required to compress it to a displacement δ_2 is numerically equal to the total shaded area between the top curve and the zero axis. If the spring is then released to the original displacement δ_1, it will yield an energy equal to the shaded area between the bottom curve and the axis.

If the displacement of a spring is directly proportional to the applied force, the spring is said to be a "linear" system element. This relation can be expressed by $f = K\delta$, where δ is the displacement from the unstressed position and K is the "spring constant," or force per unit displacement. The total energy required to compress a linear spring a distance δ from the unstressed position is given by $\varepsilon = \int_0^\delta f\, d\delta = \int_0^\delta K\delta\, d\delta$, which when integrated yields

$$\varepsilon = \tfrac{1}{2}K\delta^2.$$

If K is expressed in pounds per foot and δ is in feet, then ε is in foot-pounds.

Electrical Energy.—The energy stored in the magnetic field of a linear inductance (see Sec. 22) is

$$\varepsilon = \tfrac{1}{2}Li^2 \qquad \text{watt-seconds or joules,}$$

where L is the self-inductance in henrys and i is the current in amperes. Compare this with the kinetic energy stored in a moving mass. If magnetic saturation is present, the inductance is said to be nonlinear, and the above expression cannot be used. For the stored energy in this case, and also when mutual inductance is present, see Sec. 22.

The energy stored in a perfect condenser can be expressed as

$$\varepsilon = \frac{1}{2}Ce^2 = \frac{1}{2}\frac{q^2}{C} \qquad \text{watt-seconds or joules,}$$

where C is the capacitance in farads, e is the potential difference in volts, and q is the stored charge in coulombs. The latter expression $(q^2/2C)$ can be compared with the energy stored in a perfect spring.

Example 1.—As an example of the use of the law in electrical problems, consider the discharge of a condenser through a linear inductance coil of negligible resistance. The maximum current will occur when all of the energy initially stored in the condenser has been transferred to the magnetic field of the inductance, *i.e.*, when

$$\tfrac{1}{2}CE_0^2 = \tfrac{1}{2}LI_m^2,$$

where E_0 is the initial condenser voltage and I_m is the maximum current in amperes. This can be solved for the maximum current:

$$I_m = E\sqrt{\frac{C}{L}} \qquad \text{amp.}$$

Example 2.—Another example is shown in Fig. 4. A mass M is held at a height h above the top of a spring and is then released. The problem is to determine the maximum deflection of the spring. If we assume that the mass falls freely, that it hits the spring perfectly true and does not fall off to one side, and that the mass and internal losses of the spring are negligible, then the conservation of energy is directly applicable.

Denote the maximum deflection of the spring by δ. Then at its lowest point the mass has lost a potential energy equal to $Mg(h + \delta)$, and the spring has gained an elastic energy $K\delta^2/2$. Equating the energy lost by the mass to that gained by the spring, there is

$$Mg(h + \delta) = \tfrac{1}{2}K\delta^2.$$

Solving this quadratic equation for δ and neglecting the spurious root, the maximum deflection is found to be

$$\delta = \frac{Mg}{K} + \sqrt{\frac{2Mgh}{K} + \frac{M^2g^2}{K^2}}.$$

This is the simplest and most direct method of finding the maximum spring deflection.

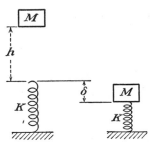

FIG. 4.—Example: conservation of energy.

11. Action Equals Reaction. *Definition.*—For every action there is always an equal and opposite reaction.

In a mechanical system every applied force results in an equal and opposite force of reaction. Thus, if a force is applied to a mass that is free to move without friction, it will accelerate along the line of force at such a rate that it will exert an equal backward force on the body that is propelling it. If a force is applied to a spring, the spring will compress until it exerts an equal counterbalancing force.

The principle of action equals reaction is also exceedingly useful in electrical calculations. For example, in a d-c motor the counter emf plus the IR drop in the armature must be equal and opposite to the applied voltage. In electrical work the principle is usually stated in another way: the algebraic sum of the voltages around any closed circuit must be equal to zero.

12. Principle of Superposition. *Definition.*—If effect is proportional to cause and several causes act simultaneously, then the total effect is the sum of the individual effects.

For example, if a steady force F_1 and an alternating force $F_2 \sin \omega t$ are simultaneously applied to a linear spring, the deflection caused by the steady force is

$$\delta_1 = \frac{F_1}{K}$$

and the deflection caused by the alternating force is

$$\delta_2 = \frac{F_2}{K} \sin \omega t.$$

By the superposition theorem the deflection caused by both forces acting simultaneously is $\delta_1 + \delta_2$, or

$$\text{Total } \delta = \frac{1}{K} (F_1 + F_2 \sin \omega t).$$

However, suppose that the deflection is not directly proportional to the applied force. For example, let

$$\text{Total } \delta = C(\text{total } F)^2.$$

In this case superposition cannot be used, as will be shown. The force F_1 acting alone would produce a deflection CF_1^2, and the alternating force acting alone would produce a deflection $CF_2^2 \sin^2 \omega t$. The sum of these two (by the incorrect use of the theorem) would be $\delta = C(F_1^2 + F_2^2 \sin^2 \omega t)$. However, the correct answer is obtained by first writing the total force at any instant: $F_1 + F_2 \sin \omega t$, and substituting this into the expression for total δ above.

$$\text{Total } \delta = C(F_1 + F_2 \sin \omega t)^2,$$

which is not equivalent to the expression obtained by superposition.

The superposition theorem requires that effect be directly proportional to cause and, before attempting to use the theorem, it is essential to make sure that this requirement is fulfilled. In general it holds for the determination of currents and voltages in linear electrical systems and of forces, motions, velocities, and accelerations in linear mechanical systems. It does not hold in the determination of energies when these are proportional to voltage squared, current squared, velocity squared, etc., and it does not in general apply to nonlinear physical systems such as inductive circuits where there is magnetic saturation.

13. Newton's Laws of Motion.—Newton's three laws of motion are fundamental in the study of dynamics and form much of the basis for investigating the behavior of moving mechanical systems.   These laws can be stated as follows:

1. A particle will continue to move at a constant speed in a straight line until acted upon by an external force.

2. When a force acts upon a particle, the particle is accelerated in the direction of the force by an amount proportional to the force.

3. For every action there is an equal and opposite reaction.

14. Engineering Units of Force and Mass.—Newton's second law concerning the acceleration of a particle can be expressed in a consistent set of units by the well-known relation

$$f = ma, \tag{1}$$

where f is the resultant force applied to the particle, a is the acceleration of the particle, and m is a measure of the inertia of the particle and is called its *mass*.

In engineering work the commonly used unit of force is the pound, which is the force exerted by gravity on a standard pound body.   This force varies slightly with location on the earth's surface and may be taken as standard at a given latitude and elevation but, as the variation is only about $\frac{1}{2}$ per cent, it can be neglected in most engineering work.

If a particle is allowed to fall freely (with negligible air resistance), the force of acceleration is evidently its own weight w, and by Newton's second law the acceleration will be constant at a value denoted by g.   For this condition Eq. (1) becomes $w = mg$, giving the relation between mass and weight

$$m = \frac{w}{g}. \tag{2}$$

If the weight is expressed in pounds and g is in ft/sec², the mass of the body will be expressed in lb-sec²/ft, or *slugs*.

This can be visualized further by imagining a body to be mounted on horizontal frictionless rails and given a horizontal accelerating force equal to its own weight.   This would cause the body to accelerate horizontally at the rate $g = 32.17$ ft/sec². Furthermore, any change in the accelerating force will produce a proportional change in the rate of acceleration.   In a consistent set of units the mass of a body is the factor of proportionality between the applied force and the resulting acceleration.   In engineering work this is usually denoted by W/g, although sometimes the symbol M is used for convenience.

15. Rectilinear Translation and Rotation of Rigid Bodies.—In this section we shall apply Newton's laws of the motion of a particle to two important types of motion of rigid bodies: rectilinear translation and rotation about a fixed axis.

In rectilinear translation every particle in the body moves in the same direction along a straight line. Consequently, all particles have the same acceleration a, their inertia forces are parallel

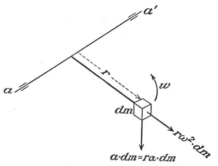

Fig. 5.—Particle of a rotating body.

and directed oppositely to the acceleration, and the resultant inertia force is

$$F = \sum ma = \left(\sum m \right) a = \frac{W}{g}\, a, \qquad (3)$$

in which W is the total weight of the body. Moreover, since the inertia forces of the particles are parallel in direction and for any given acceleration are proportional to their gravity forces, the resultant inertia force acts at the center of gravity (strictly speaking, the center of mass) of the body. Hence in rectilinear translation the body will behave like a particle concentrated at the center of gravity.

Consider next a rigid body rotating about a fixed axis with the angular velocity ω and being given an angular acceleration by an applied torque. An elementary particle of this body is shown in Fig. 5. The particle has a mass dm and is rotating about the axis a-a'. The angular velocity ω gives rise to a radial acceleration of the particle equal to $r\omega^2$ and, hence, the particle will exert a centrifugal force equal to $r\omega^2 \cdot dm$. This force will, however, cause no torque about the axis a-a', although it may cause undesirable forces on the bearings unless balanced by similar forces in a diametrically opposite portion of the body. If, however, the particle is being accelerated in the tangential direction with an instantaneous linear acceleration a, it will have a tangential inertia reaction equal to $a \cdot dm$ acting at right angles to the radius r, as shown in Fig. 5. This will give rise to an inertia torque about the axis a-a' equal to $ra \cdot dm$. Since the particle is rotating about a fixed axis, its angular acceleration α is given in radians per second per second by the relation $\alpha = a/r$. Hence the inertia torque of the particle can be written as $r^2\alpha \cdot dm$. The total inertia torque of the body about the axis of rotation is then given by the summation of all the torques of its elementary particles, or

$$T = \int r^2\alpha \, dm = \left(\int r^2 \, dm\right)\alpha, \tag{4}$$

in which α is the angular acceleration of the body in radians per second per second, and the integral is understood to extend over the entire volume of the body. The integral in this equation is called the *moment of inertia* of the body:

$$I = \int r^2 \, dm. \tag{5}$$

Hence we can write the inertia torque as

$$T = I\alpha, \tag{6}$$

which is similar to Eq. (3) for rectilinear translation.

Inspection of Eq. (5) shows that the moment of inertia has the dimensions of mass $\times$ length^2, or in engineering units, of slug-ft^2 or lb-ft-sec^2. If the moment of inertia is divided by the total mass of the body, the quotient has the dimensions of a distance squared. This distance is called the *radius of gyration* of the body with respect to the axis of rotation:

$$\text{Radius of gyration} = \sqrt{\frac{I}{M}}. \tag{7}$$

If the mass of the body were all concentrated at the radius of gyration, the moment of inertia with respect to the given axis would be unchanged.

In engineering work it is often convenient to specify the moment of inertia of a body in terms of its weight rather than its mass. This quantity is symbolized by WR^2, in which W is the total weight of the body and R is its radius of gyration. The WR^2 of a body must be divided by g to obtain the true moment of inertia.

When the moment of inertia is expressed in lb-ft-sec^2 and the angular acceleration is in radians per second per second, the inertia torque T of Eq. (6) is expressed in pound-feet. Inch units are sometimes used when the foot unit leads to inconveniently small numbers. The acceleration of gravity must then be expressed in terms of inches ($g \approx 386$ in./sec^2).

Example: Moment of Inertia.—As an example, we shall find the moment of inertia and the radius of gyration of a solid circular flywheel with respect to its axis of symmetry. The flywheel has a radius a and thickness h, and is made of a material with a weight w per unit volume. Referring to Fig. 6, the mass of an elementary ring of radius r is

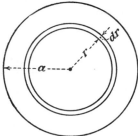

$$dm = 2\pi r \cdot dr \cdot hw/g.$$

Hence from Eq. (5) we have

Fig. 6.—Circular flywheel.

$$I = \frac{2\pi hw}{g} \int_0^a r^3 \, dr = \frac{\pi hwa^4}{2g}.$$

However, since the total weight is given by $W = \pi a^2 hw$, the moment of inertia can be written as

$$I = \frac{W}{g} \frac{a^2}{2}.$$

In engineering work this might be specified as

$$WR^2 = W \frac{a^2}{2}.$$

The radius of gyration is evidently $a/\sqrt{2}$.

16. D'Alembert's Principle.—It is a familiar principle in statics that, for a body in equilibrium, the algebraic sum of the forces in any given direction is equal to zero and, furthermore, that the sum of the moments about any axis is also zero. D'Alembert's principle states that the conditions of static equilibrium apply also to problems in dynamics provided that the inertia reaction of the body is considered in addition to the externally applied forces. Thus we can write equations in dynamics in much the same fashion as equations in statics provided that the inertia reactions are included in the same manner as applied forces. We shall find this principle of use in setting up the equations of both translatory and rotational mechanical systems.

17. Conservation of Momentum.—Equation (3) for the rectilinear translation of a body can be rewritten as

$$Ma = M\frac{dv}{dt} = \frac{d(Mv)}{dt} = F, \tag{8}$$

where M is the mass of the body, v is its velocity, F is the net external force acting on the body, and Mv is defined as the momentum of the body.

If a system contains a number of masses, there will be an equation of the form (8) for each of them. If we add together all the equations of the form (8) for the system, the sum can be expressed as

$$\sum \frac{d(Mv)}{dt} = \frac{d}{dt}\left(\sum Mv\right) = \sum F, \tag{9}$$

and since all the internal forces of the system cancel out through the principle of action equals reaction, Eq. (9) can be written as

$$\frac{d}{dt}\left(\sum Mv\right) = \sum \text{external forces} = \sum F_{\text{ext.}}. \tag{10}$$

Integrating Eq. (10) between the limits t_1 and t_2, we find that the change in momentum of the system during this period is

$$\Delta\left(\sum Mv\right) = \int_{t_1}^{t_2}\left(\sum F_{\text{ext.}}\right) dt. \tag{11}$$

Thus we find that the change in momentum of a system during any period of time is equal to the integral of the net external force (with respect to time) over that period. It should be observed that both force and momentum have direction as well as magnitude, that all the above equations are really vector equations, and that in adding either forces or momenta the relative directions must be taken into account.

From Eq. (11) we can draw at least two conclusions:

1. If the external forces acting on a system are quite small, then the total momentum of the system will change very slowly and may be considered constant over a relatively long period of time. For example, Fig. 7 shows two masses connected by a spring and resting on a surface with negligible friction; *i.e.*, the integral of

friction force with respect to time over the period of time that we are considering is very small compared with the maximum momentum of either mass. The two masses are pulled apart by hand, held stationary for a moment, and then released. At the moment before release their momentum was zero and, since there is negligible force acting on the system after release, the net momentum of the system must remain zero. Hence we can write

$$M_1v_1 - M_2v_2 = 0. \tag{12}$$

Therefore the two velocities are related by the expression:

$$v_1 = \frac{M_2}{M_1} v_2. \tag{13}$$

Observe that in writing Eq. (12) the momentum of the second mass has a negative sign since the two velocities are in opposite directions.

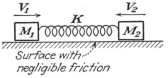

Fig. 7.—Example: conservation of momentum.

2. The second conclusion to be drawn from Eq. (11) is that, if the period of time that we are considering is very short, then the external forces can be neglected even if they are relatively large, and the net momentum of the system will remain constant over this short period. This follows from the fact that as the period of time $\Delta t = t_2 - t_1$ approaches zero, the integral in Eq. (11) approaches zero also, provided only that the net external force does not approach infinity. Thus, in calculating the velocities of two masses after impact, we are justified in neglecting such forces as those exerted by springs and by friction, and in equating the net momenta before and after the brief instant of impact. Physically this means that the force between the masses at the moment of impact is much larger than the external forces and that the latter can therefore be neglected.

It follows that the velocity of a single mass cannot be changed "instantaneously" except by an infinite force, *i.e.*, by impact with another mass.

18. Conservation of Angular Momentum.—The angular acceleration of a body or system of bodies is proportional to the net applied torque, or, in a consistent set of units, $T = I\alpha$, where I is the moment of inertia about the axis of rotation and α is the angular acceleration. Since the angular acceleration can be expressed as $\alpha = d\omega/dt$, where ω is the angular velocity, the foregoing equation can be integrated into

$$\Delta(I\omega) = \int_{t_1}^{t_2} T_{\text{ext.}} \, dt. \tag{14}$$

This says that the change in angular momentum of a rotating system over the period of time from t_1 to t_2 is equal to the integral of the net external torque (with respect to time) over that period. From this we can draw at least two conclusions, similar to those obtained concerning linear momentum:

1. If the net external torque acting on a system is small, then the angular momentum of the system will change slowly and can be considered constant until $\int T \, dt$ becomes appreciable within the limits of accuracy of the problem. For example, a person diving from a springboard starts with a certain amount of angular velocity. Once in the air he cannot change his angular momentum for there are no external torques except perhaps those of air resistance, which are small. However, by doubling up his body and thereby reducing his moment of inertia, he can increase his speed of rotation. Similarly, by straightening his body, he can increase his moment of inertia and greatly reduce his angular velocity. The relation that must be satisfied here is that $I_1\omega_1 = I_2\omega_2 =$ a constant, so that the larger the moment of inertia the smaller the angular velocity, and vice versa.

At the same time his linear momentum (Mv_h) remains nearly constant since the horizontal external forces are negligible, while his vertical linear momentum (Mv_v) increases downward according to Eq. (11), in which the external force is gravity.

Moreover, his change of angular velocity involves certain changes of energy. If in his doubled-up position he has a moment of inertia I_1 and rotates with an angular velocity ω_1, his energy of rotation is $I_1\omega_1^2/2$. In straightening out, his moment of inertia increases to I_2, his angular velocity decreases to $\omega_2 = I_1\omega_1/I_2$, and his final kinetic energy of rotation becomes

$$\mathcal{E}_2 = \frac{1}{2} I_2\omega_2^2 = \frac{1}{2} \frac{I_1^2}{I_2} \omega_1^2,$$

which is smaller than the previous energy. In straightening out, his muscles have had to provide some restraint against centrifugal force, thus absorbing the difference between the two energies.

Suppose that he now doubles up his body so as to regain his initial moment of inertia I_1. His speed of rotation will then increase to the original ω_1, and his kinetic energy of rotation will increase to its former value. Where does this additional energy come from? The answer is that it comes from his own muscles, for in doubling his body they had to do work against centrifugal force, and this work now appears in the form of additional kinetic energy. The foregoing considerations will not reduce the art of diving to a science, but they do serve as an interesting example of the conservation of momentum.

2. The second conclusion to be drawn from Eq. (14) is that over a short period of time it is permissible to neglect external torques provided that they are not extremely large, and the net angular momentum will remain constant over this small interval. For example, if we wished to apply the conservation of angular momentum to two rotating systems that were being coupled together rather quickly, we could neglect all minor torques such as friction since they would have small effect during a short period. Physically this means that the coupling torque is assumed to be much larger than the torque of friction.

One should be extremely careful in applying the conservation of angular momentum to systems that are coupled together by gears, for the principle as stated by Eq. (14) assumes that the internal torques of the system are equal and opposite. Thus, if two systems are rotating separately and are then suddenly coupled through gears, the principal internal torque is the coupling torque transmitted by the gears, and this torque may be different on the two systems. Here one must go back to the more fundamental relation $T = I\,d\omega/dt$ for each of the systems separately, introduce the effect of the gear ratio on both torque and speed, and then integrate the resulting expression between the limits of known initial velocity and unknown final velocity to obtain the correct relation.

Similarly, linear momentum and angular momentum cannot be added or equated directly. In problems involving the coupling of rotating and translatory systems, the correct relation can be found by using the fundamental equations $F = M\,dv/dt$ and $T = I\,d\omega/dt$, introducing the relation between coupling torque and force, and integrating between proper limits.

19. Electrical Systems; Kirchhoff's Laws.—Kirchhoff's experimental laws form the basis for writing the equations of electric circuits and can be stated as follows:

1. In any network the algebraic sum of all currents flowing toward any point is zero at all times.

2. The algebraic sum of all voltages acting around any closed circuit is zero at all times.

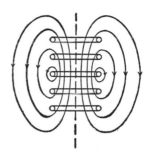

20. Induced Voltage.—A flux linkage is defined as one line or maxwell of flux interlinking with one turn of wire. Figure 8 shows a cross section of a coil together with interlinking lines of magnetic flux. If all of the flux linked all the turns of wire, the flux linkages would be the product of the number of turns and the number of lines of flux. However, in Fig. 8 some of the flux does not link all the turns and a summation process must be used:

FIG. 8.—Flux linkages.

Turn	Flux Linkage
1	4 lines
2	6 lines
3	8 lines
4	6 lines
5	4 lines

Total flux linkages = 28 maxwell-turns

One can, therefore, express flux linkages as

$$\text{Flux linkages} = \psi = \Sigma N \phi. \tag{15}$$

The flux linking the coil can come from at least three sources: from permanent magnets, from near-by current-carrying coils (mutual induction), or it may be caused by current in the coil itself (self-induction). Equation (15) will hold regardless of the source of the flux.

It has been found experimentally that a change in flux linkage of 10^8 maxwell-turns per second will induce an emf of 1 volt. The values of flux linkages as expressed in maxwell-turns (flux lines times turns) are ordinarily very large, and it is more convenient to use the weber-turn as a unit, where one weber of flux equals 10^8 ordinary lines or maxwells. A change in flux linkage of 1 weber-turn per second will induce 1 volt.

A familiar method of expressing the induced voltage is

$$e = -N \, d\phi/dt,$$

but this can also be written as

$$e = -\frac{d\psi}{dt}, \tag{16}$$

where ψ is expressed in weber-turns. If all the flux does not link all the turns, the voltage calculated by $N \, d\phi/dt$ will be somewhat too large; however, the voltage given by $d\psi/dt$ will be correct. Experiment has shown that if the familiar right-hand screw relation shown in Fig. 9 is used to define the positive directions of flux and voltage, then an increase of flux in the positive ϕ-direction will cause an induced voltage opposite to the positive e-direction. This gives rise to the negative sign in Eq. (16).

FIG. 9.—Positive directions.

In self-induction the flux that induces the voltage is caused by current in the coil itself, while in mutual induction the flux comes from one or more near-by current-carrying coils. Moreover, both self-induction and mutual induction may be present simultaneously. If the magnetic circuits of the coils contain saturated iron, there is no very convenient way of expressing the relation between flux and current except with a graph, or "saturation curve" (see Fig. 13). If the effects of saturation are not appreciable, some exceedingly useful relations can be written.

Consider a single coil with no magnetic saturation. The flux produced by the current in the coil will be directly proportional to the current, and the coil is said to be a *linear* circuit element. Flux linkages will be equal to the current times a constant of proportionality. This constant of proportionality is called the *coefficient of self-induction* or the *self-inductance* of the coil. Furthermore, experiment shows that if the right-hand screw convention is used to relate the positive directions of current and flux, then positive current will produce positive flux. Thus we can write

$$\psi = Li, \tag{17}$$

where L is the self-inductance in henrys.

Substituting Eq. (17) into Eq. (16) for induced voltage, we find that the self-induced voltage in the coil is

$$e = -L\frac{di}{dt},\qquad(18)$$

provided that the magnetic circuit is linear.

If there are near-by current-carrying coils, each of these will send flux into the first coil. If the magnetic circuits are linear, the flux sent into the first coil by a current in the second coil will be proportional to that current, and in this case the constant of proportionality is called the *coefficient of mutual induction* or the *mutual inductance*. The coefficient is denoted by the letter M and carries two subscripts, the first denoting the coil in which the voltage is induced and the second denoting the coil in which the current is flowing. Depending upon the relative orientation and winding of the two coils and also upon the positive directions selected for the currents, positive current in the second coil may send flux into the first coil in either the positive or negative ϕ-direction. This can be taken into account in either of two ways: the mutual inductance can be regarded as either a positive or negative numerical quantity, or it can always be used as a positive number if the proper algebraic sign is affixed to the symbol M. The former procedure will be used consistently in this text. There are advantages to both methods, and it may be found that in certain types of problems the latter convention is more convenient. The flux linkages of the first coil caused by current in the second coil can then be written as

$$\psi_1 = M_{12}i_2,\qquad(19)$$

where M_{12} is the mutual inductance between coils 1 and 2 in henrys.

The voltage induced in coil 1 by current in coil 2 is obtained by substituting Eq. (19) into Eq. (16):

$$e_1 = -M_{12}\frac{di_2}{dt}.\qquad(20)$$

The mutual inductance M will be a positive number if positive currents in both circuits produce fluxes that mutually aid, and will be a negative number if positive currents produce opposing fluxes.

If there are a number of coils carrying current simultaneously and their magnetic circuits are linear, the flux linkages of each coil can be found by superposition to be

$$\left. \begin{aligned} \psi_1 &= L_1 i_1 + M_{12} i_2 + M_{13} i_3 + \cdots \\ \psi_2 &= M_{21} i_1 + L_2 i_2 + M_{23} i_3 + \cdots \\ &\quad\dots\dots\dots\dots\dots\dots\dots\dots\dots\dots\dots\dots\dots \end{aligned} \right\} \tag{21}$$

The voltages induced in each coil are obtained by Eq. (16):

$$\left. \begin{aligned} e_1 &= -\left(L_1 \frac{di_1}{dt} + M_{12} \frac{di_2}{dt} + \cdots \right) \\ e_2 &= -\left(M_{21} \frac{di_1}{dt} + L_2 \frac{di_2}{dt} + \cdots \right) \\ &\quad\dots\dots\dots\dots\dots\dots\dots\dots\dots\dots\dots\dots\dots \end{aligned} \right\} \tag{22}$$

It can be shown by the principle of the conservation of energy that the coefficient of mutual induction between two coils is the same in either direction, *i.e.*,

$$M_{ij} = M_{ji}. \tag{23}$$

It should be emphasized again that Eqs. (17) to (23) hold only when the magnetic circuits are substantially linear. For non-linear systems the relation between flux linkages and current can be shown graphically, and Eq. (16) will still apply.

At this point it may be interesting to note an analogy between mechanical mass and electrical inductance. The inertia force of a single mass can be written as $f = Ma$ or as $f = M\,dv/dt$, where v is the velocity. Compare the latter expression with Eq. (18) for the self-induced voltage of a single coil: $e = -L\,di/dt$. Here voltage is analogous to force, current is analogous to velocity, and self-inductance is analogous to mass. Furthermore, the inertia force of the mass opposes a change in velocity, while in the electrical circuit the self-inductance opposes a change in current. We shall observe further parallels between mechanical and electrical systems in later sections.

21. Principle of Constant Flux Linkages.—Consider an electrical network such as that shown in Fig. 10 and write an equation for the voltage around any one of the several closed circuits in the network, for example the closed circuit *abcda*. There are four types of voltage that we must consider: resistance drops,

$-ir$; induced voltages, $-d\psi/dt$; voltage drops across condensers, $-q/C$, where q is the charge in coulombs and C is the capacitance in farads; and applied voltages, e. By Kirchhoff's second law the algebraic sum of the voltages around the closed circuit must be equal to zero, hence,

$$-\sum ir - \sum \frac{d\psi}{dt} - \sum \frac{q}{C} + \sum e = 0,$$

or, transposing and removing the derivative outside the summation sign,

$$\frac{d}{dt}\left(\sum \psi\right) = -\sum ir - \sum \frac{q}{C} + \sum e. \qquad (24)$$

The right side of Eq. (24) represents a voltage which may vary with time but which is, in general, of finite value. Represent this voltage by e' and integrate both sides of the equation between the limits t_1 and t_2. This results in

$$\Delta\left(\sum \psi\right) = \int_{t_1}^{t_2} e'\,dt. \qquad (25)$$

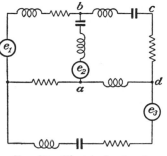

FIG. 10.—Electrical network.

This equation has a familiar form, for it is similar to Eq. (11) for linear momentum and Eq. (14) for angular momentum. From it we can state a theorem which is similar to the conservation of mechanical momentum, which might be called the conservation of electrical momentum, but which is more generally called the *principle of constant flux linkages*. For very short intervals of time the integral in Eq. (25) reduces to zero, so, therefore:

The algebraic sum of the flux linkages around a closed circuit cannot be changed instantaneously.

Observe that the foregoing principle has been derived without reference to the linearity or nonlinearity of the circuit and therefore holds when magnetic saturation is present.

The principle of constant flux linkages is a more precise statement of the well-recognized principle that under ordinary conditions the current through an inductance cannot be changed suddenly, just as the conservation of momentum generalizes the principle that under ordinary conditions the velocity of a mass cannot be altered suddenly. Moreover there are certain conditions under which the velocity of a mass can be changed suddenly, for example by impact with another mass, and the principle of the conservation of momentum enables one to calculate the velocities after impact. Similarly there are conditions under which the current in an inductance can be changed suddenly, for instance by quickly changing the inductance of the circuit, and the constant-flux-linkage theorem enables one to calculate the effect.

It is interesting to observe that for a single mass, momentum is expressed as Mv, while for a single linear inductance the flux linkages are expressed as Li [Eq. (17)]. We have already noted an analogy between velocity and current, and between mass and inductance, and we now find that their products, momentum and flux linkage, also have analogous meanings.

Example 1.—As an example of the use of the principle, consider the circuit of Fig. 11, in which current is flowing in steady state with a value E/R. The switch S is then opened quickly. Find the current in the circuit the instant after the switch has opened.

By Eq. (17) the flux linkages in the circuit before the switch was opened were

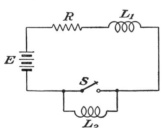

FIG. 11.—Circuit of example 1.

$$\psi_1 = L_1 I_1 = L_1 \frac{E}{R}. \tag{26}$$

If the switch is opened quickly, the flux linkages will remain constant. The flux linkages the instant after opening are

$$\psi_2 = (L_1 + L_2)I_2. \tag{27}$$

Equating Eqs. (26) and (27) and solving for the current at the instant after the switch has opened, we obtain

$$I_2 = \frac{L_1}{L_1 + L_2} \cdot \frac{E}{R}. \tag{28}$$

The current will gradually increase from this value to the steady-state value of E/R along an exponential curve as shown in Fig. 12.

If the switch is not opened very quickly, the flux linkages will change somewhat, and the current just after opening the switch will be higher than indicated by Eq. (28). If the principle is to yield accurate quantitative results, the time required for the physical change in the circuit should be much less than the time of recovery of the system. In the simple series circuit of Fig. 11 the time of recovery can be expressed as a *time constant* equal to L/R sec, which gives the time required for the current to recover 63.2 per cent of the way toward its steady-state value.

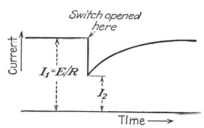

FIG. 12.—Current in circuit of Fig. 11.

If the inductance of Fig. 11 were nonlinear, the relation between flux linkage and current could be shown graphically as in Fig. 13. The constant-flux-linkage theorem could then be applied graphically. Referring to Fig. 13, if the original current is I_1, then L_1 contains flux linkages equal to ψ_1, and L_2 has zero current and zero flux linkages. After the switch is open, the current is the same in both inductances and will drop temporarily to the value I_2, at which point the sum of the flux linkages in L_1 and L_2 is equal to the original value ψ_1.

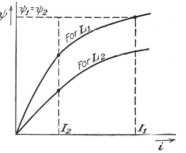

FIG. 13.—Saturation curves.

Example 2.—Another example is shown in Fig. 14, in which a short-circuited coil with an area of A in.² and an inductance of L henry has its plane parallel to a magnetic field of B lines per square inch. The coil is then turned suddenly so that its plane is perpendicular to the lines of flux.

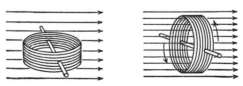

FIG. 14.—Short-circuited coil.

If the coil has N turns, calculate the initial value and the direction of the induced current, assuming that the coil is turned in a time considerably shorter than its time constant L/R.

The flux linkages before turning were zero. After turning, a transient current will be induced such that the flux linkages will temporarily remain zero.   The flux passing through an area A would be equal to $BA \times 10^{-8}$ weber, hence,

$$\psi = BAN \cdot 10^{-8} - LI = 0,$$

or
$$I = BAN \cdot \frac{10^{-8}}{L} \quad \text{amp},$$

flowing in the direction of the arrow in Fig. 14 so as to oppose the entering flux.

Observe that the resistance of the coil does not enter into the calculations except that, for the theorem to hold quantitatively, the time of turning must be much less than L/R sec.   The induced current will, of course, die out along an exponential path from the maximum value calculated above, thus permitting the external flux to enter the coil.

22. Energy Stored in Inductive Circuits.—The energy expended in building up a magnetic field in an inductance is equal to the

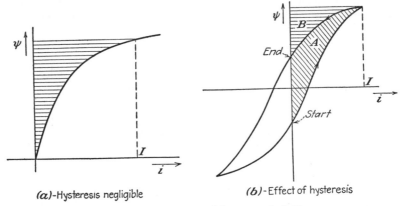

(a)-Hysteresis negligible   (b)-Effect of hysteresis

Fig. 15.—Energy stored in magnetic field.

time integral of applied voltage times current.   Since the applied voltage can be expressed as $d\psi/dt$, the energy can be expressed as

$$\varepsilon = \int i \frac{d\psi}{dt} dt = \int i \, d\psi \quad \text{watt-sec or joules.} \quad (29)$$

This integral evidently represents the area between the saturation curve and the ψ-axis.   Such an area is shown in Fig. 15a and represents the watt-seconds of energy stored in the magnetic field of the inductance when the current is $i = I$, neglecting the effects of hysteresis.

Refer now to Fig. 15b, which shows a cyclic hysteresis loop. If the current is brought from zero to a value I, the energy required to produce the magnetic field is represented by the area A plus the area B, expressed in weber-turns times amperes, or watt-seconds. Now if the current is allowed to return to zero, the flux will follow the left-hand path and will return to the circuit an energy represented by the area B. The area within the loop is lost and represents the hysteresis loss of the iron.

In the case of a single *linear* inductance, the flux linkages are expressed by $\psi = Li$ [Eq. (17)]. Substituting this into Eq. (29) and integrating, there results for the energy stored in a single linear inductance

$$\varepsilon - \tfrac{1}{2}Li^2. \tag{30}$$

When there is mutual inductance between two coils with *linear* magnetic circuits, the total energy stored in the magnetic fields of both coils can be found as follows: Consider the second coil to be open-circuited, and bring the current in coil 1 to the value i_1, thus storing the energy $L_1 i_1^2 / 2$. Now bring the current in coil 2 to the value i_2, meanwhile holding i_1 at its previous value. The only voltage induced in coil 2 will be self-induced, thereby adding an energy $L_2 i_2^2 / 2$. However, while the current in coil 2 is rising, it will induce a voltage in the first coil equal to $-M_{12}\, di_2/dt$. To hold the current i_1 constant, coil 1 must have an equal and opposite applied voltage, and the first circuit will then add an energy equal to

$$\int i_1 \left(M_{12} \frac{di_2}{dt} \right) dt = M_{12} i_1 i_2.$$

The total stored energy is, therefore,

$$\varepsilon = \tfrac{1}{2}(L_1 i_1^2 + 2M_{12} i_1 i_2 + L_2 i_2^2). \tag{31}$$

The mutual inductance M_{12} will be a negative number if positive currents in the two circuits produce fluxes in opposition.

Similar expressions can be derived for any number of linear coupled circuits.

23. Principle of Virtual Displacement.—If a force F is exerted on any part of a mechanical system and if the amount of displacement in the direction of the force is the infinitesimal dx, then the amount of work done by the force is

$$d\varepsilon = F\, dx. \tag{32}$$

This can be solved for the force F:

$$F = \frac{d\mathcal{E}}{dx}. \tag{33}$$

This provides a means of calculating the force on a system by means of the energy change that would take place if the force were given an infinitesimal displacement. The displacement does not need to exist physically, hence the name *virtual displacement*.

Definition.—The force on a body in a given direction is the ratio of the work done in displacing the body an infinitesimal amount in this direction, to the amount of the displacement. In a similar manner the torque on a body can be expressed by the ratio:

$$T = \frac{d\mathcal{E}}{d\theta}. \tag{34}$$

Example 1.—Figure 16 shows two coils numbered 1 and 2, with self-inductances L_1 and L_2 and a mutual inductance M and carrying currents I_1 and I_2 in opposite directions as shown. The problem is to find the force of repulsion F between the two coils.

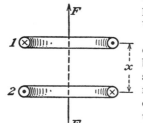

FIG. 16.—Force between coils.

The energy stored in the magnetic fields of the coils is given by Eq. (31). If the distance between the two coils x is imagined to increase a small amount dx, the self-inductances will remain the same but the mutual inductance will change an amount dM. If the currents are maintained constant, the change in stored energy will be, from Eq. (31),

$$d\mathcal{E}_s = I_1 I_2 \, dM. \tag{35}$$

We shall next find the energy delivered by the sources in keeping the currents constant. The flux linkages of the first coil are $\psi_1 = L_1 I_1 + M I_2$, and the displacement dx will cause a change in flux linkages equal to $d\psi_1 = I_2 \, dM$. This will induce a voltage equal to $-d\psi_1/dt$ which must be balanced by an equal and opposite applied voltage to keep the current I_1 constant. Thus, the source will supply an energy to coil 1 equal to

$$d\mathcal{E}_1 = -e_1 I_1 \, dt = I_1 \, d\psi_1 = I_1 I_2 \, dM. \tag{35a}$$

In a similar manner we can show that in order to keep the current I_2 constant, the source supplying coil 2 must deliver an energy equal to

$$d\mathcal{E}_2 = I_1 I_2 \, dM. \tag{35b}$$

We now have the following energy balance:

(Electrical energy supplied to coils) − (increase in stored energy)
$$= \text{total work done by } F,$$
or, by Eqs. (35), (35a), and (35b),

$$d\mathcal{E}_t = 2I_1I_2\,dM - I_1I_2\,dM$$
$$= I_1I_2\,dM. \tag{36}$$

Hence by Eq. (33) the force of repulsion is

$$F = \frac{d\mathcal{E}_t}{dx} = I_1I_2\frac{dM}{dx}. \tag{37}$$

By calculating or measuring the variation of M with x, the value of dM/dx can be found from the slope of the M vs. x curve at the proper value of x. The units of the force F in Eq. (37) will depend on the unit of length used for x. If I is in amperes, M in henrys, and x in inches, the force will be expressed in watt-seconds (or joules) per inch. An appropriate conversion factor can be used to change this force into pounds. If x is measured in meters, F will come out in the MKS unit of newtons, or joules per meter.

It will be observed that in the derivation above we have used an energy balance which considered all pertinent changes of energy. However, comparison of Eqs. (35) and (36) shows that the net change in energy caused by the force F moving through a distance dx ($d\mathcal{E}_t$) is numerically equal to the change in stored energy ($d\mathcal{E}_s$). This gives rise to a commonly used short-cut procedure in which the force is found from the derivative of the stored energy, neglecting the electrical input energy which is exactly twice as great. Then taking the derivative of Eq. (31) and recalling that all quantities except M are constant, we obtain

$$F = \frac{d\mathcal{E}_s}{dx} = I_1I_2\frac{dM}{dx}.$$

The direction of the force can be found by physical reasoning.

Example 2.—The cam shown in Fig. 17 is cut so that its radius can be expressed as

$$r = k_1 + k_2\theta^2, \tag{38}$$

where θ is in radians. A force F is exerted at the end of the rod. Neglecting friction (which could be taken into account later), what is the torque required to turn the cam at any angle θ?

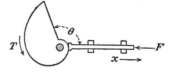

Fig. 17.—Torque on cam.

The displacement at the end of the rod is equal to the increase in radius of the cam, i.e., $x = r$. If the cam is turned through a virtual angle $d\theta$, the amount of work done by the torque is equal to that done on the force: $d\mathcal{E} = T\,d\theta = F\,dx$. Then

$$T = F\frac{dr}{d\theta}. \tag{39}$$

Substituting Eq. (38) into (39), the torque as a function of θ is found to be

$$T = 2Fk_2\theta. \tag{40}$$

If F is in pounds and r is in inches, T will be in pound-inches.

Problems

In general, the problems given here will involve certain physical assumptions. These assumptions should be stated explicitly in presenting the solution of the problem, even when they have been suggested in the problem statement.

Certain of the problems may involve an excess of data, and the student should not assume that all the data need always be used to obtain a proper solution.

1. The compound spring shown in Fig. P1 has a top spring with a force constant of 5 lb/in. and a bottom spring with a force constant of 15 lb/in. The latter comes into effect only when the top spring has been depressed 4 in. from its unstressed position. A 10-lb weight is dropped on the spring from a height 5 in. above the top spring. Find the maximum deflection of the top spring.

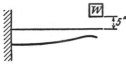

Fig. P1.—Compound spring.

2. A round body (sphere, disk, or hoop) with a radius of r ft is released at the top of an inclined plane and rolls without slipping to the bottom. The vertical height of the incline is h ft. Find the linear velocity at the bottom for

a. A sphere, moment of inertia $I = \dfrac{2}{5}\dfrac{W}{g}r^2$.

b. A disk, $I = \dfrac{1}{2}\dfrac{W}{g}r^2$.

c. A hoop, $I = \dfrac{W}{g}r^2$.

3. When two bodies collide in a direct central impact, the elasticity of the collision can be indicated by a coefficient of restitution e, which depends mainly on the materials of which the bodies are made. The coefficient of restitution is defined as

$$e = \frac{V_1' - V_2'}{V_2 - V_1} = -\frac{\text{difference between velocities after impact}}{\text{difference between velocities before impact}},$$

where positive velocity is measured in the same direction for both bodies. For a perfectly inelastic collision $e = 0$, and for a perfectly elastic collision $e = 1$. Practical values range somewhere between and can be found in handbooks for various materials.

A sphere of weight w is dropped from a height h_1 on to the horizontal surface of a large body of the same material resting on the ground. The sphere rebounds to a height h_2. Develop a formula for the coefficient of restitution of the impact.

4. A 5-lb weight slides with a velocity of 21 ft/sec over a relatively frictionless surface and collides in a direct central impact with a stationary

10-lb weight. Calculate the velocities of the weights just after impact and the energy lost in impact for the following conditions:

a. If the weights couple together upon collision so that the impact is, in effect, completely inelastic with a coefficient of restitution $e = 0$ (see Prob. 3 above).

b. If the collision is completely elastic with $e = 1$.

5. The buffer mechanism of a machine is to arrest the motion of the sliding weight W_1 by impact with the movable steel block W_2 as shown in Fig. P5. Using the data below, calculate

a. The velocity of W_1 after impact (indicate direction).

b. The velocity of W_1 after impact and the maximum compression of the spring from the position shown, neglecting frictional losses.

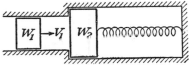

Fig. P5.—Buffer mechanism.

c. The amount of energy in Btu dissipated as heat at the moment of impact.

Data: $W_1 = 9$ lb; $W_2 = 20$ lb; initial velocity of W_1 is $v_1 = 50$ ft/sec; initial compressive force of the spring as shown $= 55$ lb; spring constant $K = 19.2$ lb/in.; specific heat of steel $c = 0.11$ Btu/lb-°F; coefficient of restitution for steel impact on steel $e = 0.55$.

6. A monkey weighing 10 lb stands at the edge of a circular turntable which is free to turn about its axis with relatively small friction. The turntable has a WR^2 of 600 lb-ft². With the turntable originally stationary, the monkey starts to run around the periphery, 6 ft from the axis, at a speed of 5 ft/sec. What is his speed with respect to a stationary observer?

7. A motor with its attached flywheel has a WR^2 of 105 lb-ft² and is rotating at a speed of 1,170 rpm. It is then suddenly coupled by means of a clutch to a stationary flywheel with a WR^2 of 45 lb-ft². The time of coupling is 0.2 sec. Find the speed of rotation of the combination the instant after coupling and the energy dissipated in the clutch.

8. The centrifugal device shown schematically in Fig. P8 is to be used to reclose a large circuit breaker after it has been tripped. The rotating weights are latched in position *a* and are slowly brought up to speed by a small electric motor. When the rotating system has accumulated sufficient energy, the catch is released and the weights fly out to position *b*, raising a collar which closes the breaker.

a. Calculate the kinetic energy in the rotating system before the weights are released.

b. Calculate the energy available to close the breaker.

c. The reclosing mechanism, by means of an appropriate linkage, does the equivalent of the following work in closing the breaker: (1) It raises a weight of 117 lb a distance of 1.5 ft against gravity, (2) compresses a spring 1.5 ft from an initial compression of 150 lb (the spring constant is 14 lb/in.), (3) moves a distance of 1.4 ft against a frictional force of 8 lb and, when the contacts are closing, an additional distance of 0.1 ft against a frictional force of 75 lb. Discuss quantitatively the utilization and dissipation of all the available energy. Does the energy that is finally dissipated perform a useful function?

Data: WR^2 of motor $= 185$ lb-in.^{2}

WR^2 of centrifugal mechanism in position $a = 790$ lb-in.^{2}

WR^2 of centrifugal mechanism in position $b = 1,490$ lb-in.^{2}

Rotational speed before release $= 2,000$ rpm.

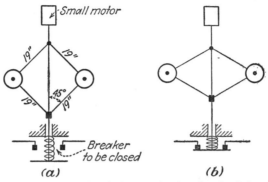

Small motor

45°

Breaker
to be closed

(a)   (b)

Fig. P8.—Centrifugal reclosing mechanism for circuit breaker.

9. A wheel with a moment of inertia I, weight W, and radius R is suspended above a horizontal floor and is spinning with an angular velocity ω. It is then dropped vertically onto the floor. Find the linear velocity of the wheel after slippage has stopped.

Hint: When the wheel is slipping on the floor and coming up to speed, the frictional force with the floor causes translational acceleration of the wheel and at the same time produces a torque which causes rotational deceleration. Equate the two expressions for force and integrate between proper limits.

10. A flywheel with moment of inertia I is connected through gears to a shaft. If the gear ratio is G (see below), find the angular acceleration of the shaft caused by an applied shaft torque T. What is the apparent moment of inertia of the flywheel as viewed through the gears from the shaft?

$$\text{Gear ratio } G = \frac{\text{flywheel speed}}{\text{shaft speed}}.$$

11. A shaft is driven by a heavy motor and rotates at a constant speed of 600 rpm. An initially stationary flywheel with a WR^2 of 2,500 lb-in.^{2} is brought up to speed by engaging a clutch that connects it to the shaft. Neglecting bearing friction and windage, how much energy must the shaft supply, how much is stored in the flywheel, and what amount is dissipated in the clutch?

12. A small test car for a hydraulic towing tank has a total weight, including wheels, of 95 lb. The wheels weigh a total of 23 lb. Each wheel has a radius of 6 in. and a radius of gyration of 4.07 in. If a horizontal accelerating force F is applied to the car, set up an expression for the resulting acceleration and find the effective mass of the car, including the effect of the moment of inertia of the wheels.

13. The torsion exerted by the moving coil of a ballistic galvanometer is proportional to the current flowing through it: $T = Ci$. The moment of inertia of the moving system is I and the torsional spring constant of the suspension is K. A relatively large current of brief duration is sent through the coil. Assume that the discharge is over before the coil deflects appreciably. For simplicity neglect damping. Develop an expression for the maximum angular deflection of the coil and show that this will be proportional to the total quantity of electricity discharged through the coil: $Q = \int i\, dt$.

14. A coil with N turns and an inductance of L henrys has its circuit completed through a resistance R ohms. A magnetic flux of ϕ webers from an external source of flux links the coil and is suddenly reversed in direction. Find an expression for the initial current in the circuit and observe the assumptions.

The current decreases from its initial value according to the exponential law $i = I_0 \epsilon^{-Rt/L}$ (see Chap. VI). Find the total quantity of electricity discharged through the circuit: $Q = \displaystyle\int_0^\infty i\, dt$.

15. In example 1, Sec. 21, find the energy dissipated at the switch when it is opened very quickly, using the following values: $L_1 = 0.1$ henry, $L_2 = 0.05$ henry, $R = 1.5$ ohms, $E = 3.0$ volts.

16. In the generator field circuit shown in Fig. P16, the switch S_1 is closed and the current is flowing in steady state. The switch S_2 is then closed and S_1 is opened very quickly. Find the direction and initial magnitude of the current flowing the instant after the switch is opened, and the direction and initial magnitude of the voltage across the switch.

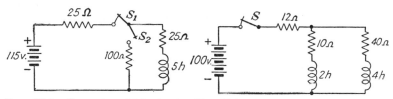

Fig. P16.— Generator field circuit   Fig. P17.—Parallel inductance coils.
with discharge resistor.

17. The circuit shown in Fig. P17 has the switch S closed with the current flowing in steady state. The switch is then opened quickly. Find the direction and initial magnitude of the current that flows the instant after the switch is opened. Observe that the direction of the flux linkages, as determined by the direction of the current, must be taken into account in algebraically summing the linkages around a closed circuit.

Compute the energy lost in the switch when it is opened. Estimate the order of magnitude of the time in which the switch must be opened to have the foregoing results hold with reasonable accuracy.

18. Repeat the calculations of Prob. 17 for the mutually coupled circuit shown in Fig. P18. The two coils are connected so that, when the current flows through them in series, their fluxes will oppose, hence the mutual inductance must be taken to be numerically negative. Observe that the mutual inductance causes L_2 to have flux linkages even when the switch is closed.

19. A certain nonlinear inductance has a saturation curve that can be expressed approximately by the relation

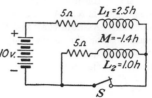

$$i = K_1\psi + K_3\psi^3,$$

where i is in amperes and ψ is in weber-turns. A 12.4-μf condenser is charged to a voltage of 140 volts and is discharged

Fɪɢ. P18.—Circuit with mutual inductance.

through the inductance. Find the maximum current that can be expected in the resulting oscillation if $K_1 = 0.41$ amp/weber-turn and $K_3 = 3.50$ amp/ (weber-turn)^3. The resistance of the circuit is quite small.

20. A magnetic solenoid is mounted vertically and has an iron plunger weighing 11 lb. The coil draws a d-c current of 19 amp.

a. If the plunger is inserted at the bottom, find the position at which it will be drawn into the coil.

b. If the plunger is floating in the coil, find the maximum downward force that it can support, and the position that the plunger will take under this condition.

Length of coil = 18 in.
Length of plunger = 18 in.
Resistance of coil = 1.5 ohm.

Distance plunger is inserted into coil, in.....	0	6	8	10	12	14	16	18
Inductance, henry.......	0.050	0.065	0.082	0.113	0.160	0.218	0.251	0.260

21. An electrostatic voltmeter is shown schematically in Fig. P21. When a d-c voltage is applied to the plates of the condenser, the resulting attraction causes the pointer to move up the scale against the restraining action of a spring.

a. If the capacitance varies linearly with deflection according to the relation

$$C = A_1 + A_2\theta \qquad \text{farads},$$

develop an expression for the angular deflection of the pointer as a function of the applied d-c voltage E. Let

θ = angular deflection, radians.
K = spring constant, dyne-cm/radian.

Fɪɢ. P21.—Electrostatic voltmeter.

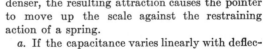

b. If $A_1 = 7.02 \times 10^{-12}$ farad, $A_2 = 55.2 \times 10^{-12}$ farad per radian, $K = 455$ dyne-cm/radian, find the angular deflection in degrees caused by an applied potential difference of 1,000 volts.

22. Two parallel cylindrical copper conductors are carrying d-c current in opposite directions.   Find the force of repulsion between them, expressed in pounds per foot length, for the data given below:

Radius of the conductors $= r = 0.230$ in.
Distance between centers $= s = 1.00$ in.

The inductance of the conductors per unit length is given by

$$L = \left[1.219 \log_\epsilon \left(\frac{s}{r}\right) + 0.3048 \right] \times 10^{-7} \text{ henrys per foot length.}[1]$$

Calculate the force for (*a*) a normal current of 230 amp, (*b*) a short-circuit current of 4,600 amp.

[1] See WOODRUFF, L. F., "Electric Power Transmission and Distribution," 2d ed., John Wiley & Sons, Inc., New York, 1938.

CHAPTER III

TRANSIENT AND STEADY-STATE CONDITIONS

24. The Nature of a Transient Condition.—A steady-state condition is one in which all the various parts of the system are in equilibrium. A transient condition is a state of transition between two steady-state conditions and, as its name implies, is of more or less limited duration. Figure 18 shows a circuit in which, with the switch S closed, the steady-state current is

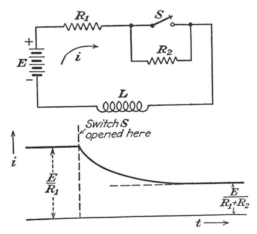

Fig. 18.—Transient current.

equal to E/R_1. If the switch is opened, the final condition of equilibrium (the new steady state) occurs when the current is equal to $E/(R_1 + R_2)$. Because of the inductance in the circuit the current cannot decrease instantly to its new steady-state value but, instead, drops along a curve such as that shown in the figure. This intermediate state is a transient condition and is solved by differential equations.

It should be observed here that, if the solution at some end point is desired rather than the total solution as a function of time, it is sometimes possible to avoid the use of differential equations and obtain the solution in a more simple manner.   The examples of Sec. 10 would involve differential equations if it were necessary to determine the current or displacement as a function of time.   However, only maximum values were desired and were obtained most easily by applying the principle of the conservation of energy.   Such short cuts should be used wherever applicable.   However, many problems do not lend themselves to this treatment, and sometimes it is necessary to find the solution as a function of time.   Such problems may require the use of differential equations.

25. Use of Differential Equations.   If the circuit of Fig. 18 had zero inductance, the current would be able to change to its new steady state instantly and there would be no transient. Transients occur when the system is not in equilibrium, provided that the instantaneous value of the variable depends to some extent upon its own rate of change, or perhaps upon the rate of change of some variable in another part of the system.   The equations that express the relations between the various quantities in the system will then contain derivatives and are therefore differential equations.

For example, in the circuit of Fig. 18, the voltage across the inductance can be expressed as $-L\,di/dt$, and after the switch is opened the voltage across the resistance is $-(R_1 + R_2)i$.   By Kirchhoff's second law, the algebraic sum of the voltages around the circuit must be equal to zero, so we can write

$$-L \frac{di}{dt} - (R_1 + R_2)i + E = 0. \tag{41}$$

This equation contains a derivative and is therefore a differential equation.   We have already pointed out that the final steady-state current is $E/(R_1 + R_2)$.   This is constant in value, so its derivative is zero.   Substitute this current into the differential equation to see whether the equation is satisfied:

$$0 - (R_1 + R_2) \frac{E}{(R_1 + R_2)} + E = 0. \tag{42}$$

This is an identity, so the steady-state solution satisfies the differential equation.   The initial value of current (just after the switch was opened) was E/R_1, but in order for this value of current to satisfy the differential equation (41), the rate of change of current di/dt must have a negative value.   To find this value, solve the differential equation for di/dt:

$$\frac{di}{dt} = \frac{1}{L} [E - (R_1 + R_2)i]. \tag{43}$$

Define $t = 0$ as the time at which the switch is opened.   At this time the current was E/R_1.   By substitution into Eq. (43) we obtain

$$\frac{di}{dt}\Big|_{t=0} = -\frac{ER_2}{LR_1}. \tag{44}$$

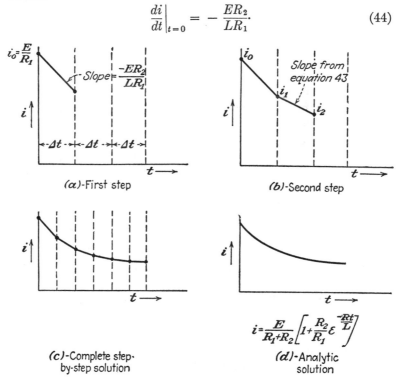

(a)-First step

(b)-Second step

(c)-Complete step-by-step solution

(d)-Analytic solution

$$i = \frac{E}{R_1 + R_2}\left[1 + \frac{R_2}{R_1}\varepsilon^{\frac{-Rt}{L}}\right]$$

FIG. 19.—Solution for circuit of Fig. 18.

Therefore, as soon as the switch is open, the current starts to decrease at a finite value, the beginning of the transient.   Moreover Eq. (43) shows that as the current changes, the rate of decrease will also change.   It is possible to build up an approximate solution in a step-by-step manner as shown in Fig. 19.

Here the instantaneous value of current i is plotted against time t.   A small increment of time Δt is first chosen.   Starting at the initial value E/R_1 at $t = 0$, the curve of current is drawn downward across the first increment at the slope indicated by Eq. (44). By the end of the first increment the current has changed to a new value i_1.[1] Substituting $i = i_1$ into Eq. (43) we can calculate a new slope (smaller than before) for $t = \Delta t$:

$$\frac{di}{dt}\bigg|_{t=\Delta t} = \frac{1}{L}[E - (R_1 + R_2)i_1].$$

Now continue the curve across the second increment, using the new slope. Read the current i_2 from the scale, calculate the slope for the third increment from Eq. (43), and proceed across the third increment. The final result will be that shown in Fig. 19c.

It can be seen that the accuracy of such a step-by-step solution will depend greatly upon the size of the increments and that an accurate solution would involve considerable labor. Fortunately analytic methods exist for the solution of the differential equations of linear systems with constant parameters. However, for nonlinear systems or for those with variable parameters, it is sometimes necessary to use step-by-step, graphical, or mechanical methods of solution. The analytical solution for the foregoing problem is

$$i = \frac{E}{R_1 + R_2}\left(1 + \frac{R_2}{R_1}\epsilon^{-Rt/L}\right),\tag{45}$$

where $R = R_1 + R_2$.

26. Initial Conditions.—It will be observed in the differential equation (41) or (43) that the equation expresses merely the relation between the current and its derivative without any reference to the starting point at $t = 0$. In the previous problem we knew that the current just before switching was E/R_1, and because of the inductance in the circuit the current just after switching had to be E/R_1 also. This gave us the starting point for Fig. 19a, and was an essential part of that particular solution of differential equation (41).

The steady-state conditions in a system do not depend upon the starting point but, since the transient represents the transition between the initial conditions and the final steady state, the transient will depend greatly upon the starting point. For

---

[1] See Chap. V for a more detailed discussion of some graphical and numerical methods of solving differential equations.

example, if the initial conditions for the previous problem had been that $i = 0$ at $t = 0$, the final steady-state solution would have been the same as in Eq. (45) above: $E/(R_1 + R_2)$. However, the transient would have been

$$- \frac{E}{R_1 + R_2} \, \epsilon^{-Rt/L} \text{ instead of } \frac{E}{R_1 + R_2} \cdot \frac{R_2}{R_1} \, \epsilon^{-Rt/L} \text{ as above.}$$

The particular solution would then be

$$i = \frac{E}{R_1 + R_2} (1 - \epsilon^{-Rt/L}). \tag{46}$$

Analytic methods for obtaining these solutions will be discussed later.

If a differential equation contains second derivatives as well as first derivatives and the variable itself, the equation merely states the relationship between these three quantities. For a particular solution two of them must be known at the beginning, *i.e.*, we must have two initial conditions to determine the manner in which the curve starts at $t = 0$. The initial conditions might be the values of i and di/dt at $t = 0$, or the values of di/dt and d^2i/dt^2 at $t = 0$. Similarly, if the differential equation contains the nth derivative, we must have n initial conditions in order to know everything about the solution at $t = 0$. The *order* of a differential equation is the order of the highest derivative contained in the equation: if the highest derivative is the nth, the equation is of the nth order. The number of necessary initial conditions is therefore equal to the order of the equation.

It will be seen in Eqs. (45) and (46) that the transient portions of the solution are of the exponential form $\epsilon^{-\alpha t}$ and therefore die out as time t becomes large. In linear systems with constant parameters the transient parts of the solution are always of this form.

CHAPTER IV

SETTING UP EQUATIONS

27. Introduction.—In many problems the most difficult task is to write the equations for the system correctly, and this process therefore deserves special attention. The relations to be satisfied by the system usually take the form of simultaneous equations with one equation for each of the dependent variables in the system. The equations frequently involve rates of change and are then differential equations.

28. Coordinates.—The first step in setting up the equations for a system should be to make a sketch showing the relation

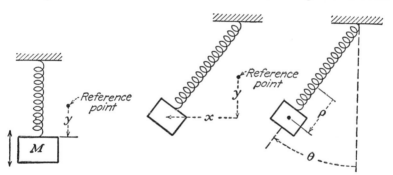

FIG. 20.—Mass oscillating vertically.　FIG. 21.—Oscillating mass with two degrees of freedom.

between its various parts. This will be an invaluable aid in visualizing the relations that are to be written in equation form.

The next step is to choose the dependent variables that are to be used. The number of variables that is necessary depends entirely on the problem to be solved. For example, Fig. 20 shows a mass suspended on a spring. If the mass oscillates straight up and down, it will be evident that one should choose the vertical displacement of the mass (from any convenient reference point) as the dependent variable. Since the vertical position of the mass will be a function of time, time will be the independent

45

variable.   In this problem the system is said to have one *degree of freedom* since it is necessary to specify only one variable (the vertical displacement) in order to know the exact position of every part of the system.

Figure 21 shows the same system except that here the mass can swing in pendulum fashion as well as stretching the spring lengthwise.   Here one must know two quantities in order to specify the position of every part of the system.   These two quantities may be chosen in a number of ways: we might choose the vertical and horizontal displacements of the mass, or the

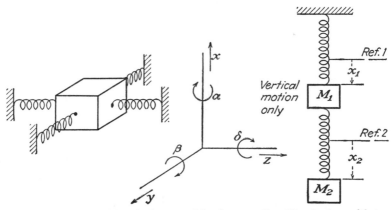

FIG. 22.—Mass with six degrees of freedom.   FIG. 23.—System with two degrees of freedom.

amount of elongation of the spring and the angle from the vertical position.   The choice of variables should be made so as to yield the simplest form of the equations.   Sometimes this choice is difficult to make, and several trials may be necessary.

In Fig. 22 the mass is suspended on springs so that it can move or turn in any direction.   Six dependent variables are necessary to specify the position of the mass, since its motion can have components along three perpendicular axes (x, y, and z) as well as rotation about these three axes (angles α, β, and δ).   The system therefore has six degrees of freedom.

As a final mechanical example, consider the system of Fig. 23. Here the only possible motion is assumed to be vertical.   Two variables are necessary here, *i.e.*, the displacements of the two masses from their reference positions.   This system therefore has two degrees of freedom.

In electrical systems the choice of variables often is simpler than in mechanical systems and usually can be made in a routine manner.   In the network of Fig. 24a we would wish to know the six currents $i_1, i_2, \ldots, i_6$ in order to know all about the currents and voltages in every part of the system.   But by Kirchhoff's first law (Sec. 19) we see that

$$
\left.
\begin{aligned}
i_4 &= i_1 - i_2 \\
i_5 &= i_2 - i_3 \\
i_6 &= i_1 - i_3.
\end{aligned}
\right\}
\tag{47}
$$

Hence, we need to know only three currents, $i_1, i_2,$ and i_3 in order to know the currents everywhere, and the system has three degrees of freedom.   These three currents are redrawn in Fig. 24b so as to encircle the three open spaces, or *meshes*, of the net-

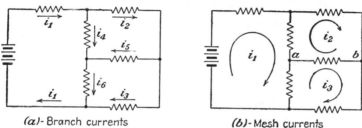

(a)- Branch currents   (b)- Mesh currents
FIG. 24.—Currents in a network.

work, and when so drawn are called *mesh currents*.   The current in an internal branch of the system is correctly given by the difference between the mesh currents drawn on opposite sides of the branch, as reference to Fig. 24a and Eqs. (47) will show. By setting up the equations in terms of these mesh currents we automatically take care of Kirchhoff's first law and need concern ourselves only with his second law.

For the common case of networks that can be drawn without crossovers on a flat surface, the following rule for determining the number of degrees of freedom and for deciding upon the mesh currents will be found convenient.   First draw a circuit diagram as in Fig. 24b and indicate a mesh current in each of the "windowpanes" of the diagram.   The number of degrees of freedom of the network is equal to the number of "windowpanes."   In setting up the equations for the system one should remember that the current in any internal branch is equal to the difference between the two mesh currents on opposite sides; for example, in branch a-b of Fig. 24b the current is $i_2 - i_3$. This automatically takes care of Kirchhoff's first law that the algebraic sum of the currents approaching any junction in a network must be equal to zero.

The mesh currents shown in Fig. 24b are not the only choice one could make in this network. If we wished to solve only for the current in branch a-b, a different choice might be desirable. With the original choice we would have to solve the system for i_2, then for i_3 and finally subtract the two to obtain the desired current. The work of finding the current in branch a-b would be

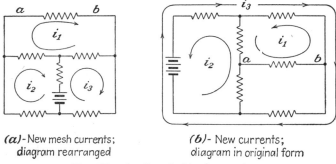

(a)- New mesh currents;   (b)- New currents;
diagram rearranged   diagram in original form

Fig. 25.—Another choice of currents.

diminished by rearranging the diagram as shown in Fig. 25a, choosing new mesh currents as shown, and solving for i_1. Figure 25b shows the way the new currents would look if the diagram were returned to its original configuration. One could, if he wished, have chosen the currents in this way in the beginning.

For the beginner, at least, it is usually better to draw the diagram so that the branch (or branches) in which he is particularly interested fall on the outside, and then choose the mesh currents in the conventional "windowpane" manner shown in Figs. 24b and 25a.

29. Choice of Positive Directions.—The choice of signs in writing equations probably causes more needless worry than any other single point, although the matter is a simple and fundamental one once it is understood. Before writing any equations, it is essential first to choose a *positive direction* for each of the dependent variables, and to indicate clearly this positive direction on the sketch of the system. In Fig. 21 the positive direction of y has been chosen downward, and x has been chosen positive to the left. It would have been all right to choose y positive upward or x positive to the right but, whatever the choice, it should be indicated clearly and adhered to throughout the analysis. In Fig. 24b the positive directions of all the mesh currents are clearly shown by arrows. Here again one could choose one or more of the positive directions to be opposite to those shown, provided that he clearly indicated his choice and stuck to it.

The choice of positive directions has no connection with the direction in which the current will actually flow, or with the direction of the actual motion in a mechanical system, but merely forms a basis by which one can choose the signs of the various terms in his equations and later interpret the meaning of the signs in his results. This may be made more clear by the following hypothetical event:

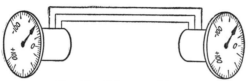

Fig. 26.—Selsyn machines.

An observer situated by a roadside wishes to signal to a companion who is out of sight of the road and tell him the direction and speed of all of the vehicles that pass by. Their signaling apparatus consists of a pair of Selsyn machines which will accurately transmit an angular motion over a considerable distance by electrical means. The observer has a Selsyn transmitter with a scale marked 0 in the center and going up to $+100$ in one direction and to -100 in the other. The scale of the receiver is similarly marked, as in Fig. 26. When a vehicle passes by, the observer notes its speed and turns the pointer of his transmitter to the proper number of miles per hour; the pointer of the receiver follows it and indicates to the companion the speed of the passing vehicle. However, in order to indicate the direction in which the vehicle is going, the observer and his companion must first decide what "plus" and "minus" are to mean. It does not matter whether they decide on "plus" to mean east and "minus" to mean west or vice versa, but once they make their choice they must stick to it. Let us suppose that they choose west to be the positive direction.   Then, when the man at the receiving end sees his pointer move to -30, he knows that there is a vehicle moving eastward at 30 mph.   If the pointer moves to $+45$, it evidently means that a vehicle is moving westward at 45 mph.   Observe that the chosen positive direction has no necessary connection with the direction of motion of the first car, the second car, or any other car and could have been chosen equally well in the opposite direction.   It merely affords a means of signaling direction as well as magnitude.

Of course if the observer had a particular fondness for positive numbers and knew beforehand that the main traffic would be eastward, he might choose east as the positive direction, but there would be no real necessity for doing this.

In the case of an analysis, the analyst is the person to whom the messages are being sent, and his equations are analogous to the Selsyn apparatus and the roadside observer combined.   (After all a human observer would be unnecessary; a photoelectric apparatus might do better.)   The analyst first chooses positive directions, sets up his equations consistent with this choice, and is then able to interpret the algebraic signs that appear in his result.   If he thinks that a current or a motion is going to be in a certain direction, he may choose that to be his positive direction, but this is not essential.

30. Electrical Systems.—With the circuit diagram drawn, the variables selected (currents, or possibly charges), and the positive directions chosen, one can next write the voltage relations from Kirchhoff's second law that the algebraic sum of the voltages around any closed loop must be equal to zero.   The number of equations required is equal to the number of dependent variables. Each branch of the network must be included in the equations at least once in order for these equations to be truly independent.

A convenient way of doing this is to write one equation around the outline of each "windowpane" in the diagram.   It is better to write all the voltage terms, whether generated voltages or impedance drops, on the left side of the equation and equate to zero on the right.   The sign of each term is correctly determined by assuming that all mesh currents are flowing in their positive directions.   A suitable convention is

If the direction of travel through a circuit element is from $-$ to $+$ (a voltage rise), the sign of the term is positive.

If the direction of travel through a circuit element is from $+$ to $-$ (a voltage drop), the sign of the term is negative.

The opposite convention is equally satisfactory and will merely serve to reverse all signs in the equation.

The following voltages across lumped impedances in an electrical circuit are expressed algebraically as voltage drops in the positive direction of current:

1. Resistance R: Voltage drop $= Ri = R\dfrac{dq}{dt}$,

where $R =$ resistance.

$i =$ instantaneous current, amp.,

$q =$ charge, coulombs.

The resistance R frequently can be assumed to be constant, but cases arise where the resistance is a function of current, giving rise to nonlinear equations, or it may occasionally be a function of time, giving rise to equations with variable coefficients.

2. Capacitance C: Voltage drop $= \dfrac{q}{C} = \dfrac{1}{C}\displaystyle\int i\, dt$,

where $C =$ capacitance, farads.

3. Induced voltage: Voltage drop $= \dfrac{d\psi}{dt}$ (see Sec. 20),

where $\psi =$ net flux linkage, weber-turns.

When the magnetic circuit is linear, more convenient expressions are obtained by using coefficients of self- and mutual induction:

Self-induced voltage drop $= L\dfrac{di}{dt} = L\dfrac{d^2q}{dt^2}$.

Mutually induced voltage drop in circuit j due to change of

$$\text{current in circuit } k = M_{jk}\frac{di_k}{dt} = M_{jk}\frac{d^2q_k}{dt^2}.$$

The algebraic sign of the mutually induced voltage can be written the same as that of the self-induced voltage provided that the mutual inductance M is regarded as a positive or negative number according as positive fluxes in the two circuits aid or oppose each other.

Example 1.—The voltage equations for the circuit of Fig. 27 will now be set up. There are two "windowpanes," therefore two degrees of freedom, and two dependent variables, i_1 and i_2. Two simultaneous equations will be necessary.

Write the voltages around the outlines of the two "windowpanes." For the first, start at point a and work around the loop until point a is reached again, progressing clockwise (the direction of progression does not matter).

R: If the current i_1 flows in the positive direction, the left end of R will be $+$. Proceeding clockwise through it we go from $+$ to $-$ as shown on the diagram. Therefore, the sign is negative:

$$\text{Voltage} = -Ri_1.$$

Observe that, if the current i_1 actually flows in the opposite direction, it will be represented by a negative number, say $i_1 = -I$ amp, where I is a positive number. The voltage across the resistor will then be

$$-Ri_1 = RI,$$

with the positive sign indicating that the voltage across the resistor has reversed. Thus the algebraic sign of the term $-Ri_1$ as determined by assuming that i_1 is flowing in the positive direction is correct for either direction of current flow.

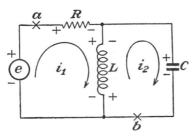

FIG. 27.—Electrical network. The $+$ and $-$ signs indicate the direction of voltage caused by positive current, by positive charge, or by current increasing in the positive direction in the respective meshes.

L: The net current downward through the inductance is $i_1 - i_2$. If the net current downward increases, the top end of the inductance will be positive, since the induced voltage will oppose the change in current. Proceeding clockwise through L we go from $+$ to $-$, so the sign is negative:

$$\text{Voltage} = \frac{-L\,d(i_1 - i_2)}{dt}.$$

The $+$ and $-$ signs shown on the diagram indicate the direction of the voltages caused by current increasing in the positive direction in each of the respective meshes.

e: The positive direction of the impressed voltage e is shown in the sketch. This voltage may be direct current, alternating current, or of any form whatsoever. If at any time the applied voltage is directed oppositely, then e becomes merely a negative number. Proceeding clockwise through the circuit we go through e from $-$ to $+$. Therefore the sign is positive:

$$\text{Voltage} = +e.$$

We have now arrived at the starting point a, and by Kirchhoff's second law the algebraic sum of the above voltages must be equal to zero. Therefore the first of our two voltage equations is

$$-Ri_1 - L\frac{d}{dt}(i_1 - i_2) + e = 0. \tag{48}$$

Now starting at any point b in the second loop and proceeding, say, clockwise completely around the loop, the second voltage equation can be written. The signs are determined as before. For example, proceeding upward through L the net current upward is $i_2 - i_1$. If the current increases in this direction, the bottom end of the inductance will be positive and we shall be going from $+$ to $-$. Therefore the sign of the term is negative:

$$\text{Voltage} = -L\,d(i_2 - i_1)/dt.$$

Let us now derive the voltage across the inductance by considering instead the net current *downward*, $i_1 - i_2$. If the net current downward increases, the top end of the inductance will be positive and, proceeding clockwise or upward, we shall be going from $-$ to $+$. Therefore the sign of the term is positive: Voltage $= +L\,d(i_1 - i_2)/dt = -L\,d(i_2 - i_1)/dt$. This is identical with the expression derived in the preceding paragraph and shows that as long as one uses the positive conventions consistently the signs will take care of themselves.

Positive current i_2 through the condenser C will charge it positive at the top as shown on the diagram, and the sign of the term is negative. With these considerations we can write the other voltage equation:

$$-L\frac{d}{dt}(i_2 - i_1) - \frac{1}{C}\int i_2\,dt = 0. \tag{49}$$

With a little practice the proper signs can be written down immediately after the positive directions have been chosen. However, one should always be sure of the signs. In cases of doubt the method shown above for the first loop is helpful.

The two differential Eqs. (48) and (49) can be rewritten as follows:

$$\left.\begin{aligned}
Ri_1 + L\frac{di_1}{dt} - L\frac{di_2}{dt} &= e \\
-L\frac{di_1}{dt} + L\frac{di_2}{dt} + \frac{1}{C}\int i_2\,dt &= 0.
\end{aligned}\right\} \tag{50}$$

A convenient method of rewriting these equations is to use the symbol p to signify the operation d/dt, in which case a second derivative would be symbolized by $(d/dt)(d/dt)$ or p^2, etc. Similarly, the integral with respect to time, being the operation that cancels the first derivative, could be symbolized by $1/p$. The symbol p is called the *differential operator*. In many elementary treatments of linear differential equation theory the symbol D is used instead of p. The use of the differential operator will be discussed in Chap. VI. For our present purposes

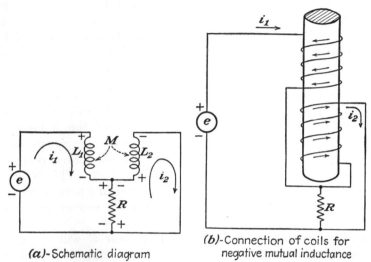

(a)-Schematic diagram

(b)-Connection of coils for negative mutual inductance

FIG. 28.—Network with mutual inductance.

it may be regarded as a convenient shorthand means of writing differential equations.

Using the differential operator, Eqs. (50) can be written in more compact form as follows:

$$\left. \begin{aligned} (R + Lp)i_1 - (Lp)i_2 &= e \\ -(Lp)i_1 + \left(Lp + \frac{1}{pC}\right) i_2 &= 0. \end{aligned} \right\} \qquad (51)$$

Observe that the coefficient of i_1 in the first equation is the total impedance in circuit 1, while the coefficient of i_2 is the mutual impedance between the two circuits, with a negative sign because i_1 and i_2 are indicated oppositely in the mutual branch. Similarly, in the second equation the coefficient of

i_1 is the mutual impedance with a negative sign attached (the same as the coefficient of i_2 in the first equation), while the coefficient of i_2 is the total impedance in loop 2. This is a general rule in static networks with lumped parameters.

Example 2.—Figure 28 shows a network with two degrees of freedom in which there is coupling by mutual inductance. The net flux linkages of the first coil are given by Eq. (21):

$$\psi_1 = L_1 i_1 + M_{12} i_2.$$

The induced voltage in coil 1 is then

$$-\frac{d\psi_1}{dt} = -L_1 \frac{di_1}{dt} - M_{12} \frac{di_2}{dt}.$$

Referring to the schematic diagram we can then write the voltage equation for the first loop:

$$-L_1 \frac{di_1}{dt} - M_{12} \frac{di_2}{dt} - R(i_1 - i_2) + e = 0. \tag{52}$$

Similarly, the flux linkages of the second coil are expressed by $\psi_2 = L_2 i_2 + M_{21} i_1$, and the voltage equation for the second loop can be written as

$$-L_2 \frac{di_2}{dt} - M_{21} \frac{di_1}{dt} - R(i_2 - i_1) = 0. \tag{53}$$

Now $M_{12} = M_{21}$ (see Sec. 20), so both subscripts can be dropped without ambiguity. The voltage equations can be written using the differential operator p to symbolize the operation d/dt:

$$\left. \begin{array}{l} (R + L_1 p)i_1 - (R - Mp)i_2 = e \\ -(R - Mp)i_1 + (R + L_2 p)i_2 = 0. \end{array} \right\} \tag{54}$$

These are the desired differential equations.

The mutual inductance will be a negative numerical quantity if positive currents in the two circuits produce fluxes in opposition as in Fig. 28*b*. This is of importance in obtaining numerical results for mutually coupled circuits that have further interconnections, such as the network of Fig. 28 where the relative directions of the currents in the resistance element determine some of the signs in the voltage equations. When there are no further interconnections between the two circuits, the relative directions of the currents are not so important, and the mutual inductance is often chosen arbitrarily to be a positive numerical quantity.

31. Mechanical Systems.—After the sketch of the system has been made, the variables selected (usually displacements or velocities), and the positive directions chosen, the equations of motion for the system can be written with the aid of D'Alembert's principle that for any body the algebraic sum of the applied and inertia forces in any given direction is zero and that the sum of the applied and inertia torques about any axis is also zero. One equation is needed for each of the dependent variables.

For the equations of the system to be ordinary (rather than partial) differential equations, the following conditions must be satisfied reasonably well:

The masses must be rigid.

The springs must have inappreciable distributed mass.

It is comparatively difficult to solve the differential equations when friction and other damping forces are not directly proportional to velocity. If the damping force is not actually proportional to the first power of velocity, an "equivalent damping constant" sometimes is found that will dissipate the same amount of energy per cycle, and the damping force is then put into the equations as proportional to velocity. The difficulty with other types of damping is this: The damping force always opposes the motion and is thus a function of velocity. If the force is not directly proportional to velocity, the equations will turn out to be nonlinear, and an analytic solution may be difficult to obtain. Some graphical and numerical methods of solving such equations are discussed in Chap. V. The assumption of linear damping (sometimes called *viscous damping*) often is not serious, but if the damping forces are especially important, the effects of the assumption should be considered carefully. When the damping force is relatively independent of velocity (as is often the case with ordinary friction), it is usually given the name *solid damping*.

An exception to the foregoing discussion occurs when the motion is always in the same direction and the damping force is nearly independent of velocity. Here the direction of the frictional force will always be the same, and its effect can be represented in the force equation by a constant term.

The three primary types of force in translational mechanical systems are

1. Spring force, directed oppositely to displacement. When the force is directly proportional to displacement it can be written as

$$f_K = Kx = K\int v\, dt, \tag{55}$$

where K = spring constant, force per unit deflection.

   x = net displacement of one end of the spring relative to the other.

   v = relative velocity of the two ends of the spring.

   t = time.

2. Damping force, in the direction opposite to velocity. When the damping force is directly proportional to velocity it can be written as

$$f_D = D\frac{dx}{dt} = Dv, \tag{56}$$

where D = damping constant, force per unit velocity.

3. Inertia force, proportional to acceleration and in the opposite direction.

$$f_M = M\frac{d^2x}{dt^2} = M\frac{dv}{dt}, \tag{57}$$

where M = mass, force per unit acceleration (see Sec. 14).

In engineering work, forces are usually expressed in pounds. Displacements are expressed in feet or inches, velocities in feet per second or inches per second, spring constants K in pounds per foot or pounds per inch, damping constants D in lb-sec/ft or lb-sec/in., and mass in lb-sec^2/ft (slugs) or lb-sec^2/in.

In rotating systems the primary torques are

1. Spring torque, directed oppositely to angular displacement. If the spring torque is proportional to angular displacement, then

$$t_K = K\theta = K\int \omega\, dt, \tag{58}$$

where t = torque.

   K = torsional spring constant, torque per radian.

   θ = net displacement, radians.

   ω = net angular velocity, radians per unit time.

2. Damping torque, in opposition to the angular velocity. If the damping torque is directly proportional to angular velocity

it can be written as

$$t_D = D\frac{d\theta}{dt} = D\omega, \tag{59}$$

where D = torsional damping coefficient, torque per unit angular
   velocity.

3. Inertia torque, opposite in direction to the angular acceleration:

$$t_I = I\frac{d^2\theta}{dt^2} = I\frac{d\omega}{dt}, \tag{60}$$

where I = moment of inertia about the axis of rotation, torque
   per unit angular acceleration (see Sec. 15).

The customary engineering unit of torque is the pound-foot,
although the pound-inch is also sometimes used. Torsional
spring constants are correspondingly expressed in lb-ft/radian or
in lb-in./radian, torsional damping coefficients in lb-ft-sec/radian
or lb-in.-sec/radian, and moments of inertia in lb-ft-sec^2 (slug-ft^2)
or lb-in.-sec.^{2} Observe that radians are a ratio of arc to radius
and have no dimensions.

In mechanical systems one dependent variable is generally
necessary at each junction between two or more system elements,
and also at any other movable points where force is applied. A
thorough consideration of the sketch of the system is the best
method of determining the necessary variables. At each point
where a variable has been assigned, the forces are summed and
equated to zero. A positive direction for force should be chosen
for each variable to assist in the determination of the proper
algebraic signs.

It will be seen in the following examples that if the system
can have an equilibrium position in which all the masses would
be supported statically on springs, then by choosing the coordinates so that all displacements are zero at this equilibrium
position, the gravity forces will not enter equations written
for an interior part of the system. This occurs because in the
equilibrium position the downward forces of gravity are balanced
by equal upward forces in the spring supports.

Example 1.—Figure 29 shows a mass M suspended by a spring
with a force constant K. The mass is equipped with damping
vanes with a damping coefficient D and has a force F applied to
it. This force can vary with (be a function of) time. The

dependent variable x is measured downward from the equilibrium position of the mass, and the positive direction for force on the mass has been taken downward also.

The forces on the mass are as follows:

Spring force: The force in the spring is equal to the weight of the mass plus the force caused by stretching an additional amount x. If the bottom of the spring is displaced in the positive direction (downward), the force on the mass will be upward (negative), so the spring force is expressed by $f_K = -(Mg + Kx)$.

Damping force: This is equal to the damping coefficient times the velocity. If the velocity is in the positive direction (downward), the damping force will be opposite, or upward (negative):

$$f_D = -D \, dx/dt.$$

Inertia force: If the acceleration of the mass is in the positive direction (downward) the inertia force will be upward (negative):

$$f_M = -M \, d^2x/dt^2.$$

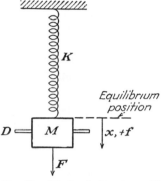

FIG. 29.—Mechanical system with one degree of freedom.

Gravity force on the mass: This is downward, or positive, and can be written $f_g = +Mg$.

Applied force: This has been taken positive downward: $f_{\text{app.}} = +F$.

The algebraic sum of the forces on the mass must be equal to zero, so we obtain

$$\sum f = -(Mg + Kx) - D\frac{dx}{dt} - M\frac{d^2x}{dt^2} + Mg + F = 0.$$

This can be rewritten as

$$M\frac{d^2x}{dt^2} + D\frac{dx}{dt} + Kx = F, \qquad (61)$$

or, in operator form (as in the examples of Sec. 30),

$$(Mp^2 + Dp + K)x = F. \qquad (62)$$

This can be solved by differential equation theory. As the equation is of the second order, two initial conditions must be known if the complete solution is desired. These conditions would probably be the initial displacement and velocity of the mass.

If the external force is constant, the steady-state response will merely be a constant displacement to a new equilibrium position. Superposed on this displacement will be a transient response which may be either an oscillation or a combination of exponential motions, depending on the damping. If the applied force varies periodically, the motion of the mass may be a sustained oscillation with an amplitude depending greatly upon the frequency of the applied force, superposed upon which will be a transient of the form described above.

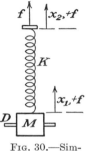

FIG. 30.—Simple system with two degrees of freedom.

Example 2.—Figure 30 shows a system similar to that of Fig. 29 except that the upper end of the spring is free to move and the force f is applied there. In order to know the position of every part of the system we must know two quantities: (1) the position of the top of the spring where the force is applied and (2) either the amount of stretching of the spring or the position of the mass. The position of the top of the spring and the position of the mass have been chosen as dependent variables. If the only possible motion is vertical, the system evidently has two degrees of freedom. Since two equations are necessary, we shall sum the forces about the upper end of the spring and also the forces acting on the mass.

Consider first the forces acting at the upper end of the spring.

Applied force: This is acting upward (in the assumed positive direction): $f_{\text{app.}} = +f$.

Spring force: If displacements are measured from the equilibrium position, the force in the spring is the weight of the mass plus the force caused by additional stretching. The net stretching is equal to $x_2 - x_1$. The force of the weight and the force caused by additional stretching are both downward at the top of the spring, *i.e.*, negative: $f_K = -Mg - K(x_2 - x_1)$.

The summation of forces at the top of the spring yields

$$\Sigma f = +f - Mg - K(x_2 - x_1) = 0. \qquad (63)$$

Next consider the forces acting on the mass.

Spring force: $Mg + K(x_2 - x_1)$.

Damping force: $-D \dfrac{dx_1}{dt}$.

Inertia force: $-M \dfrac{d^2x_1}{dt^2}$.

Gravity force: $-Mg$.

$$\sum f = Mg + K(x_2 - x_1) - D \frac{dx_1}{dt} - M \frac{d^2x_1}{dt^2} - Mg = 0. \quad (64)$$

Equations (63) and (64) can be rewritten as

$$\left. \begin{array}{c} M \dfrac{d^2x_1}{dt^2} + D \dfrac{dx_1}{dt} + Kx_1 - Kx_2 = 0 \\[2mm] -Kx_1 + Kx_2 = f - Mg = f - W, \end{array} \right\} \quad (65)$$

where W is the weight of the body.

Using the differential operator, these equations become

$$\left. \begin{array}{c} (Mp^2 + Dp + K)x_1 - Kx_2 = 0 \\[1mm] -Kx_1 + Kx_2 = f - W. \end{array} \right\} \quad (66)$$

When the force f is specified as a function of time, these are two simultaneous differential equations involving two unknowns, x_1 and x_2. Methods for solving such systems of equations are discussed in Chap. VI. It should be observed, however, that if the upper end of the spring is given a specified motion as a function of time (perhaps by a cam), there remains only one degree of freedom, one dependent variable (x_1), and the first of Eqs. (66) is sufficient to describe the motion. This equation could then be rewritten as

$$(Mp^2 + Dp + K)x_1 = Kx_2, \quad (67)$$

and the quantity Kx_2 could be regarded as a driving force [compare with Eq. (62)].

Example 3: Free-body Method.—In the free-body method the system to be analyzed is divided into groups of elements, with the interconnections between elements replaced by appropriate (but unknown) forces. Each group of elements is then considered to be a free body. When the equations for the free bodies have been written, the unknown forces of interconnection can be eliminated between them by the principle that action equals reaction, thus yielding the desired equations for the system.

This method is of considerable aid in writing the equations for systems that contain gears, pulleys, or other means of obtaining mechanical advantage, since it concentrates attention on the individual groups of elements and introduces the complication of mechanical advantage afterward.

Consider, for example, the system of Fig. 31. If the pulley rope is relatively inextensible, the system has two degrees of freedom, *i.e.*, if we know the position of both masses, we can then find the extension of the spring. The pulleys will be assumed

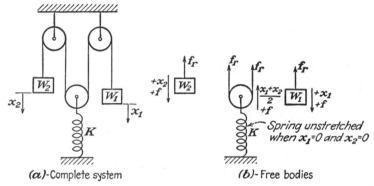

(a)-Complete system   (b)- Free bodies

Fig. 31.—Free-body method.

to be massless and frictionless for simplicity. It then follows that the tension will be the same in all parts of the rope. In setting up the equations for the system, we shall choose free bodies as shown in Fig. 31b. Denote the tension in the rope by f_r and sum the forces on the first weight:

$$-f_r - \frac{W_1}{g}\frac{d^2x_1}{dt^2} + W_1 = 0. \tag{68}$$

For the second weight:

$$-f_r - \frac{W_2}{g}\frac{d^2x_2}{dt^2} + W_2 = 0. \tag{69}$$

If W_1 and W_2 move, respectively, x_1 and x_2, the spring will be extended an amount $(x_1 + x_2)/2$. Thus for the spring we have

$$2f_r - K\frac{x_1 + x_2}{2} = 0. \tag{70}$$

Solving Eq. (70) for the tension in the rope and substituting into Eqs. (68) and (69) to eliminate f_r, the following two simultaneous equations are obtained:

$$\left.\begin{array}{l}\left(\dfrac{W_1}{g}p^2 + \dfrac{K}{4}\right)x_1 + \left(\dfrac{K}{4}\right)x_2 = W_1 \\[2mm] \left(\dfrac{K}{4}\right)x_1 + \left(\dfrac{W_2}{g}p^2 + \dfrac{K}{4}\right)x_2 = W_2. \end{array}\right\} \tag{71}$$

32. Dual Systems.—The equations for both mechanical and electrical systems often exhibit an interesting and useful type of symmetry in which the equations for one system are identical with those for another system except that all coefficients and dependent variables have been interchanged symmetrically. To understand how this could happen, consider first the expressions relating velocity and force for simple linear mechanical elements:

$$\left.\begin{array}{c}M\dfrac{dv}{dt} = f \\[2mm] Dv = f \\[2mm] K\int v\,dt = f. \end{array}\right\} \tag{72}$$

If each of these expressions is solved for v. the relations can be written in the following form:

$$\left.\begin{array}{c}\dfrac{1}{K}\dfrac{df}{dt} = v \\[2mm] \dfrac{1}{D}f = v \\[2mm] \dfrac{1}{M}\int f\,dt = v. \end{array}\right\} \tag{73}$$

Observe now that Eqs. (73) are identical in form with Eqs. (72), and that in comparing symbols the following interchanges become apparent:

f for v and v for f, $\dfrac{1}{K}$ for M and $\dfrac{1}{M}$ for K, $\dfrac{1}{D}$ for D.

Because of this symmetrical and mutual interchange of symbols, the two sets of Eqs. (72) and (73) might be called the *duals* of each other.

Next examine the mechanical system of Fig. 32a, which consists of a mass suspended from a spring, with a driving force applied to the mass.   Damping is neglected.

The force equation is

$$M \frac{dv}{dt} + K \int v \, dt = f_{\text{app.}}. \tag{74}$$

Now consider the system of Fig. 32b, in which the upper end of the spring is caused to move with a known velocity.   The velocity of the top of the spring is equal to the sum of the velocity of the mass and the net velocity at which the spring is being stretched.   Denoting the spring force by f, we can use relations (73) to write the velocity equation:

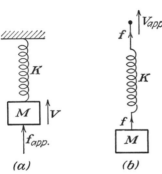

$$\frac{1}{K} \frac{df}{dt} + \frac{1}{M} \int f \, dt = v_{\text{app.}}. \tag{75}$$

Equations (74) and (75) are of the same form and have the symmetrical and mutual interchange of parameters previously noted in comparing Eqs. (72) and (73). These are dual equations, and the systems of Figs. 32a and 32b are said to be *dual systems*.

FIG. 32.—Dual systems.

Since the equations are dual, it follows that the steady-state solutions will be dual also, *i.e.*, of the same form but with an interchange of parameters.   Furthermore, if the initial conditions of the two systems are dual, the transient solutions will also be dual.

For example, it is known that if the applied force in **Fig.** 32a is sinusoidal with time, there will be a certain frequency of application at which the system will go into resonance.   Under this condition the motion of the mass will become very great and the ratio of force in the spring to applied force will be large. Observe that the displacement of the mass is given by $x = \int v \, dt$ and that the dual of spring force $K \int v \, dt$ is the velocity of the dual mass $(1/M) \int f \, dt$.   Applying this result to the dual system of Fig. 32b we see that if the velocity of the top of the spring is caused to vary in a sinusoidal manner, there will be a certain frequency at which resonance will occur, and that for this condition we can expect a large ratio between velocity of the mass and applied velocity.

Figure 33 shows two other mechanical systems that are duals. A small damping coefficient in Fig. 33a is the dual of a large damping coefficient in Fig. 33b, and the larger the mass in either system, the weaker the spring in the dual system.

The principle of duality has a number of practical types of application. It permits the results of experience or calcula-tion obtained with one type of system to be applied directly to its dual. If the solution for a particular system is desired and the solution of its dual is known, the desired solution can be ob-tained merely by an interchange of symbols. Furthermore, oc-casions arise where a certain type of result is desired and the means of obtaining the dual

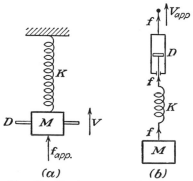

FIG. 33.—Dual systems with damping.

result is already known. The process of devising the proper system is then reduced to a deduction of the correct dual device.

Next consider the duality of the following expressions for voltage across lumped electrical elements:

$$\left.\begin{array}{cc} L\dfrac{di}{dt} = e & C\dfrac{de}{dt} = i \\[2mm] Ri = e & \dfrac{1}{R}e = i \\[2mm] \dfrac{1}{C}\displaystyle\int i\,dt = e & \dfrac{1}{L}\displaystyle\int e\,dt = i. \end{array}\right\} \qquad (76)$$

Here it is evident that dual quantities are voltage and current, inductance and capacity, resistance and reciprocal resistance (or conductance).

The voltage equation for the series circuit of Fig. 34a can be written from Kirchhoff's second law that the algebraic sum of the voltages around the circuit is equal to zero, resulting in

$$L\frac{di}{dt} + Ri + \frac{1}{C}\int i\,dt = e_{\text{app.}}. \qquad (77)$$

Now imagine that in the parallel circuit of Fig. 34*b* there is a generator capable of supplying a given form of current. This might be accomplished in practice by supplying the circuit from a voltage generator through a series impedance high enough to determine the form of current. By Kirchhoff's first law the

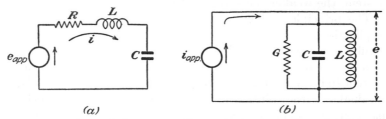

(*a*)   (*b*)

Fig. 34.—Dual electrical systems. *G* = conductance = reciprocal resistance.

algebraic sum of the currents approaching the junction is zero; so by Eqs. (76) we can write

$$C \frac{de}{dt} + \frac{1}{R} e + \frac{1}{L} \int e \, dt = i_{\text{app.}}, \tag{78}$$

where *e* is the instantaneous voltage across the parallel elements.

Thus the dual of a series circuit is seen to be a parallel system composed of dual elements, and vice versa. This principle serves to correlate the concepts of the impedance of a series circuit

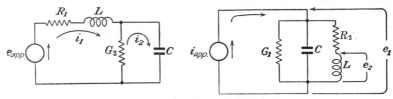

Fig. 35.—Electrical duals.

and the admittance of the corresponding parallel elements, and explains the remarkable similarity between impedance and admittance relations. Another set of dual electrical systems is shown in Fig. 35.

It will be observed that in setting up Eq. (78) for the parallel system of Fig. 34, we have used as our dependent variable the voltage *e* between the junction points ("nodes") of the branches. We then used Kirchhoff's first law concerning the algebraic sum of the currents flowing toward the junction, rather than his

second law concerning the algebraic sum of the voltages around
a loop.   This is the *node method* of setting up equations, as distinguished from the *loop method* which we have used previously.
In general, a given electrical network can be solved by either the
loop or the node method, and, depending on the network, one
method or the other may lead to fewer equations.   We shall
concentrate our attention here primarily on the more commonly
used loop method and shall refer the reader to the literature for
further consideration of the node method.[1]

33. Mechanical and Electrical Analogies.—There are many
interesting parallels between the characteristics of mechanical
systems and those of electrical circuits.   The similarity between
mechanical mass or inertia and electrical inductance is well
known for, while a mass tends to maintain a constant velocity,
an inductance tends to maintain a constant current.   In Sec. 21
the analogy between momentum in a mechanical system (Mv)
and flux linkages in a linear inductance (Li) was noted.   In
fact the same differential equation relates the force applied to
a mass and the resulting velocity as applied to the voltage
impressed on a linear inductance and the resulting current:

$$M \frac{dv}{dt} = f \quad \text{and} \quad L \frac{di}{dt} = e \left.\begin{array}{c}\\\\\\\end{array}\right\}$$

or $\quad M \frac{d^2x}{dt^2} = f \quad \text{and} \quad L \frac{d^2q}{dt^2} = e.$ (79)

The minus sign has not been used in the electrical equation
because e represents applied rather than induced voltage, the two
being equal and opposite.

In a similar way, viscous damping in a mechanical system
can be considered analogous to resistance in an electrical circuit,
as can be seen by comparing the expressions for damping force
and for voltage across a resistance:

$$Dv = f \quad \text{and} \quad Ri = e \left.\begin{array}{c}\\\\\end{array}\right\}$$

$$D \frac{dx}{dt} = f \quad \text{and} \quad R \frac{dq}{dt} = e. \quad (80)$$

---

[1] See "Electric Circuits," by the M.I.T. Department of Electrical Engineering, John Wiley & Sons, Inc., New York, 1940.

GARDNER, M. F., and J. L. BARNES, "Transients in Linear Systems,"
Vol. I, Chap. II, John Wiley & Sons, Inc., New York, 1942.

The compression of a spring and the charge on a condenser are expressed by similar equations:

$$\left. \begin{array}{lcl} Kx = f & \text{and} & \dfrac{q}{C} = e \\[2em] K \displaystyle\int v \, dt = f & \text{and} & \dfrac{1}{C} \displaystyle\int i \, dt = e. \end{array} \right\} \tag{81}$$

From an examination of these equations, we could say that the following quantities can be considered analogous:

Mechanical System	Electrical System
Force f	Voltage e
Velocity v	Current i
Displacement x	Charge q
Mass M	Inductance L
Viscous damping coefficient D	Resistance R
Spring constant K	Reciprocal capacity $\dfrac{1}{C}$

A word of warning is appropriate here: The foregoing analogies should be used with care, for they are based merely upon the fact that under certain assumptions (viscous damping, constant inductance, etc.) the equations for one type of system can have the same form as equations for the other. Furthermore, the assumptions underlying analogous equations should be examined carefully, as assumptions that are reasonably accurate for one type of system may not be tolerable in another. Systems that have equations of the same form will have analogous steady-state solutions, and if in addition the initial conditions are analogous, the transient solutions will be of the same form also.

Analogies serve a number of useful purposes. Their most common use is as an aid in visualizing relations in an unfamiliar type of system by reducing it to more familiar terms. They are of aid in calculation, for if two systems are rigorously analogous their solutions are analogous also, thus permitting the theorems and solutions that have been built up in one branch of engineering to be extended to problems in other branches. Finally, if a particular type of result is desired, while the means of obtaining an analogous result is already known, the analogy may be an extremely suggestive aid in devising the proper system.

The system of analogies relating mechanical force to electrical voltage and velocity to current appears to be quite a natural one, but it should not be inferred that this is the only possible set of electrical-mechanical analogies. In some problems other analogies may be more convenient. We have based our criterion for an analogy on a similarity between equations, but we have already found that dual systems have equations that are identical in form, so that for a given electrical system there must be at least two analogous translational mechanical systems: one analogous in the sense given previously and its dual. Thus we

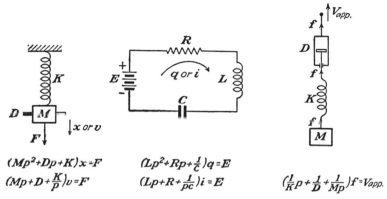

$$(Mp^2+Dp+K)x = F \qquad (Lp^2+Rp+\tfrac{1}{C})q = E$$

$$(Mp+D+\tfrac{K}{p})v = F \qquad (Lp+R+\tfrac{1}{pc})i = E \qquad\qquad (\tfrac{1}{K}p+\tfrac{1}{D}+\tfrac{1}{Mp})f = V_{app}.$$

FIG. 36.—Analogous mechanical and electrical systems.

are led to an entirely separate set of analogies based on the similarity between the following fundamental relations:

$$\left.\begin{aligned}
\frac{1}{K}\frac{df}{dt} &= v \qquad \text{and} \qquad L\frac{di}{dt} = e \\
\frac{1}{D}f &= v \qquad \text{and} \qquad Ri = e \\
\frac{1}{M}\int f\,dt &= v \qquad \text{and} \qquad \frac{1}{C}\int i\,dt = e.
\end{aligned}\right\} \qquad (82)$$

In this system the following quantities could be considered analogous: velocity and voltage, force and current, reciprocal spring constant and inductance, reciprocal damping coefficient and resistance, mass and capacitance.

Furthermore, it can be shown that, under proper conditions, voltage and current in electrical systems are analogous to torque and angular velocity in rotating mechanical systems, or to pressure and rate of flow in hydraulic systems. The choice of an analogy is based on convenience and utility, and the demonstration of its correctness is based on a correspondence between equations.

Examples of analogous systems and their equations are shown in Figs. 36 and 37. In the analogy of Fig. 37 observe that the reciprocal capacity $1/C$ is analogous to the spring constant of the mechanical system *divided by four*. The factor of four

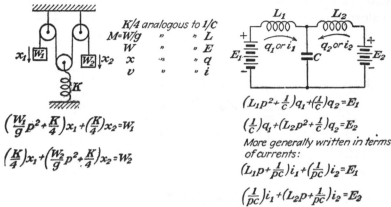

$$\left(\frac{W_1}{g}p^2+\frac{K}{4}\right)x_1+\left(\frac{K}{4}\right)x_2=W_1$$

$$\left(\frac{K}{4}\right)x_1+\left(\frac{W_2}{g}p^2+\frac{K}{4}\right)x_2=W_2$$

$$\left(L_1p^2+\frac{1}{C}\right)q_1+\left(\frac{1}{C}\right)q_2=E_1$$

$$\left(\frac{1}{C}\right)q_1+\left(L_2p^2+\frac{1}{C}\right)q_2=E_2$$

More generally written in terms of currents:

$$\left(L_1p+\frac{1}{pC}\right)i_1+\left(\frac{1}{pC}\right)i_2=E_1$$

$$\left(\frac{1}{pC}\right)i_1+\left(L_2p+\frac{1}{pC}\right)i_2=E_2$$

Fig. 37.—Analogous systems.

enters because of the mechanical advantage of the pulley. This illustrates the necessity for care in the use of analogies.

Problems

1. Set up the two voltage equations for the d-c network shown in Fig. P1 and solve for both currents. On a sketch of the network, show the magnitude and direction of the current in each of the three branches, and also the voltage from point a to point b.

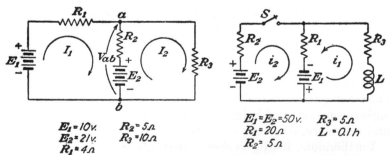

$E_1 = 10v.$ $R_2 = 5\Omega$
$E_2 = 21v.$ $R_3 = 10\Omega$
$R_1 = 4\Omega$

$E_1 = E_2 = 50v.$ $R_3 = 5\Omega$
$R_1 = 20\Omega$ $L = 0.1h$
$R_2 = 5\Omega$

Fig. P1.—Direct-current network.   Fig. P2.—Network with inductance.

2. In the network shown in Fig. P2 the switch S is open and the current i_1 is flowing in steady state. At $t = 0$ the switch is closed.

a. Set up the differential equations for the system after the switch is closed.

b. These equations hold for all positive values of time, including $t = 0+$ (just after the switch is closed) and can be solved as simultaneous algebraic equations for conditions at this instant. Substitute into the differential equations the known initial condition $(i_1)_0 = E_1/(R_1 + R_3)$ and solve the resulting algebraic equations for the initial value of i_2, denoted by $(i_2)_0$, and for the initial rate of change of i_1, denoted by $(di_1/dt)_0$.

c. Take the first derivatives of the original differential equations, substitute known initial values including the value of $(di_1/dt)_0$ found above, and solve for $(di_2/dt)_0$.

3. The switch S in Fig. P3 is originally open and is closed at $t = 0$.

a. Set up the differential equations for the network.

b. Substitute into the differential equations the known initial values $(i_1)_0 = 0$ and $(i_2)_0 = 0$ and solve for the initial rate of change of both currents, $(di_1/dt)_0$ and $(di_2/dt)_0$. See the discussion in Prob. 2*b*.

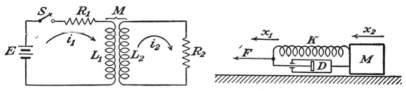

Fig. P3.—Network with mutual inductance.   Fig. P4.—Mechanical system.

4. In the mechanical system of Fig. P4 the mass is initially at rest at $x_2 = 0$, and a constant force F is suddenly applied at $t = 0$.

a. Write the differential equations for the system.

b. Substitute the known initial values $(x_1)_0 = 0$, $(x_2)_0 = 0$, and $(dx_2/dt)_0 = 0$ into the differential equations (see Prob. 2*b*) and solve for the initial velocity $(dx_1/dt)_0$ and for the initial acceleration of the mass $(d^2x_2/dt^2)_0$.

c. Take the first derivatives of the original equations, substitute the known initial values including those obtained in part *b*, and solve for $(d^2x_1/dt^2)_0$.

5. *a.* Find the dual of the electrical system shown in Fig. P5.

b. If the current in the system of Fig. P5 is initially zero and a constant voltage E is applied at $t = 0$, it is known that the resulting current, the voltage across the resistance, and the voltage across the inductance are given, respectively, by

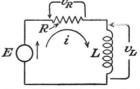

Fig. P5.—Problem in dual systems.

$$i = \frac{E}{R}\,(1 - \epsilon^{-Rt/L}),$$
$$v_R = E(1 - \epsilon^{-Rt/L}),$$
and
$$v_L = E\epsilon^{-Rt/L}.$$

From these equations, write the corresponding solutions for the dual network.

6. Figure P6*a* shows a simple a-c constant-current network. It is known that, if an a-c voltage of constant amplitude is applied to the system and if the constants of the circuit are adjusted so that $2\pi fL = 1/2\pi fC$, where f is the frequency in cycles per second, then a current of constant amplitude will be forced through the load regardless of the load impedance.

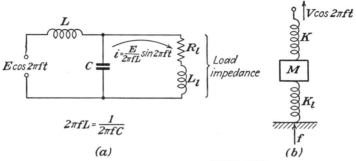

$$2\pi fL = \frac{1}{2\pi fC}$$

(a)   *(b)*

Fig. P6.—Problem in duals and analogies, constant-current network.

This current is given by

$$i = \frac{E}{2\pi fL} \sin 2\pi ft.$$

a. Deduce the electrical dual to this system that will receive power from a constant-current a-c source and deliver constant voltage to a linear electrical load of any impedance. If the received current is $I \cos 2\pi ft$, specify the output voltage and the relation that must hold between f and the parameters of the circuit.

b. Using the dual circuit found in (*a*), show that an analogous mechanical system is that of Fig. P6*b*. Show by means of the analogy that, if a velocity $V \cos 2\pi ft$ is applied to the top end of the upper spring and if the proper relation holds between the parameters of the system, then an alternating force f of constant amplitude will be applied to the supporting structure at the bottom regardless of the size of the bottom spring. Show the relations that must hold between the parameters, and write the expression for the force f.

7. Add to the mechanical system of Fig. P4 a viscous damping force with a coefficient D_2 between the mass and the floor and find an analogous electrical system.

8. Set up the differential equation of motion for the mechanical system shown in Fig. P8 and find the magnitude of the downward acceleration of W_1 if $W_1 = 10$ lb, $W_2 = 6$ lb, the WR^2 of the pulley is $WR^2 = 18$ lb-in.^{2}, and $R = 3$ in.

9. A pulley is supported from the end of a flat spring which provides flexibility in the vertical direction as shown in Fig. P9. The distance x_2

is measured from the equilibrium position of the pulley alone resting on the spring.

a. Set up the two simultaneous differential equations of motion for the system.

b. Initially the weight W_1 is resting on the floor with no force in the cord. At $t = 0$ a constant downward force F is suddenly applied to the free end of the cord. For the data given below, find the initial upward acceleration of the weight and the initial downward acceleration of the pulley wheel (see

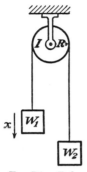

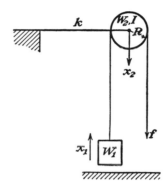

FIG. P8.—Pulley system.

FIG. P9.—Pulley system with spring support.

the discussion in Prob. 2*b*). Known initial conditions are that $(x_1)_0 = 0$ and $(x_2)_0 = 0$.

Data: $W_1 = 5$ lb, $W_2 = 4$ lb, pulley $WR^2 = 18$ lb-in.², $R = 3$ in., $F = 20$ lb, $K = 30$ lb/in.

10. An electromechanical system is one that converts mechanical energy into electrical energy and vice versa, for example, galvanometers, electrical motors and generators, and microphones and loud-speakers. A certain d-c motor has constant field excitation and is running with zero shaft load. Its armature is supplied with a variable voltage e. The armature has a resistance R and an inductance L, and the moment of inertia of the rotating parts is J.

a. Set up the differential equations for this system, neglecting frictional losses. Assume that the counter emf is given by $e_c = K_1\omega$ where ω is the speed in radians per second, and that the electrical torque exerted on the rotor is given by K_2i lb-ft where i is the armature current in amperes.

b. Eliminate the speed ω between the two equations and obtain a single differential equation expressed in terms of current i. (A convenient method of doing this is to manipulate the differential operator p as an algebraic coefficient and use algebraic methods to eliminate the undesired variable. This is discussed in Chap. VI, Sec. 45.) Show that the resulting differential equation is of the same form as that obtained for an *RLC* series circuit and that the moment of inertia J enters as a capacitance term. Sketch the equivalent electrical circuit and specify the equivalent capacitance in terms of the parameters of the motor.   Explain the capacitive action in terms of the storage of energy as a function of applied voltage.

11. A shaft is driven with a torque that pulsates in a periodic manner. It is desired to design a rotational mechanical filter which will transmit the steady component of torque but which will filter out the pulsation.   An analogous two-section low-pass electrical filter is shown in Fig. P11*a*, and the desired mechanical construction is shown in Fig. P11*b*, in which the flywheels and end collars are free to rotate on the shaft.   The cutoff frequency of the electrical filter is given by

$$f_c = \frac{1}{\pi \sqrt{LC}} \qquad \text{cycles per second.}$$

The cutoff frequency for the mechanical filter should be 20 cycles per second, and for purposes of rigidity the center spring should have a constant of 150 lb-ft/radian.

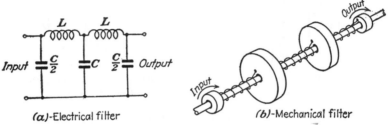

(a)-Electrical filter   *(b)*-Mechanical filter

Fig. P11.—Analogous systems, low-pass filter.

a. Specify the required constants for the flywheels and for all three springs.

b. If the flywheels are to be solid disks with a diameter equal to five times their thickness and are to be made of steel weighing 0.28 lb/in.[3], find the approximate size of the disks required, neglecting the hole in the center. The radius of gyration of a solid disk is $R/\sqrt{2}$.

12. Set up the equation for V_{ab} in Fig. P1 on the node basis, *i.e.*, equate to zero the algebraic sum of the currents approaching node *a*.   For example, the current approaching from the left is given by $\dfrac{E_1 - V_{ab}}{R_1}$.   Solve for V_{ab}, using the numerical data given, and from this find the magnitude and direction of the currents in all three branches.

CHAPTER V

GRAPHICAL AND NUMERICAL SOLUTION OF DIFFERENTIAL EQUATIONS

34. Introduction.—After expressing in equation form the relations that must be satisfied by the system, the next step is to solve the equations for the dependent variables. When the equations are algebraic, as for example the equations in Sec. 10, the methods of algebra can be used to solve them. Sometimes it is difficult to determine the solution by ordinary mathematical processes, in which case approximate graphical or numerical methods can be used to advantage. If the equations contain derivatives, there are several possibilities:

1. If there is a single equation that can be put into the form $dy/dx = f(x)$, the solution can be expressed as $y = \int f(x)\,dx$.

   a. If $f(x)$ can be expressed in equation form, the solution $y = \int f(x)\,dx$ often can be evaluated by the methods of integral calculus.

   b. If $f(x)$ is expressed empirically, then the solution $y = \int f(x)\,dx$ can be evaluated by graphical or numerical integration.

2. The equations may involve derivatives in such a manner that they cannot be put into the foregoing simple form. In this case the methods of differential equations must be used.

   a. If all the terms can be written explicitly in equation form, and if the equations are of certain types, an analytic solution can be obtained. Linear differential equations with constant coefficients occur frequently in engineering work and can be solved with relative ease.

   b. If an analytic solution cannot be obtained, graphical, numerical, or mechanical methods of integration must be used to solve the differential equations.

The graphical, numerical, and mechanical methods mentioned above yield a result in graphical rather than equation form, and for each case a new solution must be started from the beginning.

75

Hence they are used only as a last resort after mathematical methods fail. However, they are very useful in the solution of nonlinear systems such as those involving saturated magnetic circuits, elastic systems where deflection is not directly proportional to force, systems with nonlinear damping, and many others.

We shall first study some methods of numerically and graphically integrating equations of the form $y = \int f(x) \, dx$, and then examine some numerical and graphical methods of solving more complicated differential equations. Next we shall devote considerable attention to the analytic solution of linear constant-coefficient differential equations. Analytic methods of solving certain other types of differential equations have useful but comparatively limited application to engineering problems and will be discussed briefly. The graphical and numerical solution of differential equations will be studied before the analytic methods, since the former permits the student to visualize more readily the meaning of differential equations and their solution.

A. GRAPHICAL AND NUMERICAL EVALUATION OF INTEGRALS

35. The Trapezoidal Rule.—The definite integral $y = \int_a^b f(x) \, dx$ can be evaluated by plotting $z = f(x)$ vs. x and determining the area under the curve between the limits $x = a$ and $x = b$. If the interval $a < x < b$ is divided into n equal small increments Δx and adjacent ordinates are joined by straight lines, then the sum of the areas of the resulting trapezoids is approximately equal to the area under the curve $f(x)$.

The areas of the trapezoids in Fig. 38 are

$$A_1 = \frac{z_0 + z_1}{2} \Delta x$$

$$A_2 = \frac{z_1 + z_2}{2} \Delta x$$

$$\cdots \cdots \cdots \cdots \cdots$$

$$A_n = \frac{z_{n-1} + z_n}{2} \Delta x.$$

The sum of the above areas is

$$A = \int_a^b f(x) \, dx \approx \Delta x \left(\frac{z_0 + z_n}{2} + z_1 + z_2 + \cdots + z_{n-1} \right). \quad (83)$$

This is the trapezoidal rule.   Computations using this method are most conveniently handled on a calculating machine.   It will be evident that smaller values of Δx will produce greater accuracy at the expense of more labor.

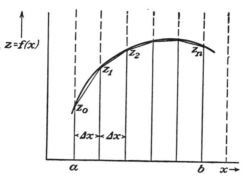

FIG. 38.—Integration by trapezoids.

Example: Trapezoidal Rule.—The buffer mechanism of a machine is to arrest the motion of a 15-lb weight which is moving initially at a velocity of 12 ft/sec.   The damping force of the mechanism, including friction, is given in the following table:

Velocity, ft/sec.............	12	10	8	6	4	2	0
Damping force, lb............	9.4	7.3	5.6	4.2	3.1	2.4	2.1

Determine the time required to bring the weight to rest.
   The equation of motion is

$$\frac{W}{g}\frac{dv}{dt} + f_d = 0.$$

Since the damping force f_d is a function of velocity, it is advantageous to invert the equation:

$$\frac{dt}{dv} = -\frac{W}{g}\cdot\frac{1}{f_d}.$$

Integrating, there results

$$t = -\frac{W}{g}\int_{v=12}^{v=0}\frac{1}{f_d}\,dv. \qquad (84)$$

The integral in Eq. (84) can be evaluated by the trapezoidal rule (83) as follows, choosing an increment $\Delta v = 2$ ft/sec:

$$\int_{v=12}^{v=0}\frac{1}{f_d}\,dv = -2\left[\frac{1}{2}\left(\frac{1}{9.4}+\frac{1}{2.1}\right)+\frac{1}{7.3}+\frac{1}{5.6}+\frac{1}{4.2}+\frac{1}{3.1}+\frac{1}{2.4}\right],$$
$$= -3.17 \text{ ft/lb-sec,}$$

where the negative sign arises because the integration is performed in the direction of decreasing velocity. The time required to bring the weight to rest is obtained from Eq. (84):

$$t = - \frac{W}{g} (-3.17) = 0.0985W \qquad \text{sec,}$$

where W is the weight in pounds. For a 15-lb weight the required time is 1.48 sec.

If it is desired to find the time required to bring the weight to rest with various initial velocities, the integration of Eq. (84) could be performed for various lower limits—for example, limits of $v = 12$ to 0, 10 to 0, 8 to 0, etc.—and the required times could then be plotted against initial velocity.

If it is desired to determine instantaneous velocity vs. time for an initial velocity of 12 ft/sec, the integration of Eq. (84) could be performed for various upper limits—for example $v = 12$ to 10, $v = 12$ to 8, $v = 12$ to 6, etc.—from which the instantaneous velocity could be plotted against time. Integration of this curve would yield the distance traveled by the weight.

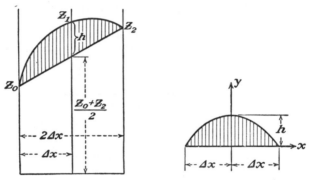

Fig. 39.—Approximation by second-degree equation.

36. Simpson's Rule.—The trapezoidal method amounts to fitting a linear equation between each set of adjacent points. Greater accuracy can be obtained by fitting a second-degree equation (parabola) to three points.[1] Referring to Fig. 39, it will be seen that the area of the trapezoid is equal to

$$A_t = \frac{z_0 + z_2}{2} (2 \, \Delta x). \tag{85}$$

If the curve is parabolic, the height of the curve above the trape-

---

[1] Although we shall derive Simpson's rule on the basis of a second-degree curve passing through three equidistant points, it can be shown that the rule also gives exact results for a third-degree curve passing through these points.

zoid is given by

$$y = h\left[1 - \frac{x^2}{(\Delta x)^2}\right], \tag{86}$$

if the x-axis is shifted so that z_1 occurs at $x = 0$. The area between the trapezoid and the curve is obtained by integrating Eq. (86) between the limits $x = -\Delta x$ and $x = \Delta x$ and is

$$A_p = (\tfrac{2}{3}h)(2\,\Delta x). \tag{87}$$

This equation shows that the average height of the portion above the trapezoid is equal to two-thirds the height in the center. The center height is $h = z_1 - (z_0 + z_2)/2$. Substituting this in Eq. (87) and adding the areas A_t and A_p, we obtain for the total approximate area over two space increments (base $= 2\,\Delta x$):

$$A_1 = \frac{\Delta x}{3}(z_0 + 4z_1 + z_2). \tag{88}$$

Proceeding to the next two increments the area would be found similarly to be

$$A_2 = \frac{\Delta x}{3}(z_2 + 4z_3 + z_4). \tag{89}$$

It will be seen that each of these areas covers two space increments, so to apply this method the number of increments must be even. The total area is then given by

$$A = \int_a^b f(x)\,dx \approx \frac{\Delta x}{3}(z_0 + 4z_1 + 2z_2 + 4z_3 + 2z_4$$
$$+ \cdots + 4z_{n-1} + z_n). \tag{90}$$

This is Simpson's rule.

Example: Simpson's Rule.—Apply Simpson's rule to the example of Sec. 35. Note that there are six increments. Then,

$$\int_{v=12}^{v=0} \frac{1}{f_d}\,dv \approx -\frac{2}{3}\left(\frac{1}{9.4} + \frac{4}{7.3} + \frac{2}{5.6} + \frac{4}{4.2} + \frac{2}{3.1} + \frac{4}{2.4} + \frac{1}{2.1}\right),$$
$$= -3.17 \quad \text{ft/lb-sec.}$$

From Eq. (84) the time required to stop the weight is $0.0985W$ sec, or 1.48 sec for a 15-lb weight.

One advantage of Simpson's rule is that the increments can be chosen larger than in the trapezoidal method and still obtain the same accuracy. Another is that if the curve does not have a point of inflection, the trapezoidal rule gives errors that are always in the same direction, while with Simpson's rule this is not necessarily so.

37. Graphical Integration.—The method of integration to be described is essentially a graphical application of Simpson's rule. The procedure is simple and has the advantage that the size of the increments can be varied continually to suit the requirements of various portions of the curve without introducing additional labor. For example, if a large portion of the curve is nearly linear, the area of that part can be found by using one large increment.

Referring to Fig. 40 and assuming as in the previous section that the curve $z = f(x)$ can be approximated within the interval C to D by a second-degree equation, it will be seen that the average height of the trapezoid $ABDCA$ is equal to MP, where M is the mid-point of line AB. According to Eq. (87) the average height of the area above the trapezoid is approximately equal to two-thirds of the height PE, or PO. The mean ordinate of the curve from C to D is therefore the height MO.

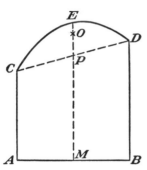

FIG. 40.—Determination of mean ordinate.

Therefore, to find the area under the curve CED, first draw the straight line CD, next draw the middle vertical ME, and locate (by eye) the point O two-thirds of the way from P to E. The area is equal to the average height times the base, or $MO \times AB$.

The function to be integrated should be divided by vertical lines into sections that can be approximated by parabolic curves. Since a parabola has no point of inflection, lines of division should pass through all inflection points, and further subdivisions should be used as necessary to make the sections approach parabolic curves. The areas of all sections could then be found separately and the several areas added together. However, a practical method of adding these areas with a minimum of labor has been described by Moore[1] and is as follows:

The average heights of the various sections are found by the method just described. The area of the first two sections could then be found by (refer to Fig. 41a)

$$A_{12} = b_1 h_1 + b_2 h_2. \tag{91}$$

[1] MOORE, A. D., Fast Method for Finding Areas or Mean Ordinates of Curves, *J. Eng. Educ.*, March, 1941, pp. 452–459.

However, draw the straight line O_1O_2 and locate the point O_{12} above the mid-point of the base b_{12}. This weights the average heights h_1 and h_2 according to the breadth of their bases, and it is

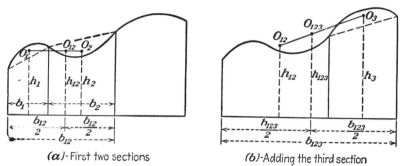

(a)- First two sections   *(b)*-Adding the third section

Fig. 41.—Graphical method of adding areas.

easily shown by geometry that

$$b_{12}h_{12} = b_1h_1 + b_2h_2,$$

which, by Eq. (91), is equal to the area A_{12}.

Proceeding to the third section, the point O_{12} is joined to point O_3 by a straight line as in Fig. 41b, and the point O_{123} located

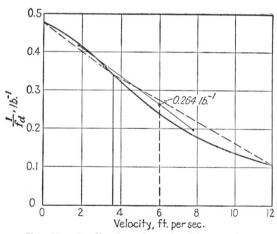

Fig. 42.—Application of graphical integration.

above the mid-point of the total base b_{123}. The area of the three sections is then given by the average height h_{123} times the total base b_{123}.

This procedure can be continued indefinitely, and only one calculation need be made: the multiplication of the final average height by the total base.

Example: Graphical Integration.—Solve the example of Sec. 35 by graphical integration. Using Eq. (84), the reciprocal of damping force is plotted against velocity in Fig. 42. When the curve is divided at its point of inflection, the sections are judged not to depart greatly from parabolic curves. The average height of each section is found and these points joined by a straight line. The average height of the total area is located above the mid-point of the total base line and is read from the scale as 0.264 lb^{-1}. The total base is 12 ft/sec, so the total area is $0.264 \times 12 = 3.17$ ft/lb-sec. Since the integration proceeds toward negative velocity, the integral is negative. Using Eq. (84), the time required to stop the weight is $0.0985W$ sec, or 1.48 sec for a 15-lb weight. This checks with the previously obtained results.

B. GRAPHICAL AND NUMERICAL SOLUTION OF DIFFERENTIAL EQUATIONS

38. Step-by-step Integration.—If the differential equation can be put into the form $dy/dx = f(x, y)$, the solution y vs. x can be evaluated by a step-by-step integration.

Suppose that the initial condition is that $y = y_0$ at $x = 0$. Select a small increment Δx such that the variable y will not change more than, say, 10 per cent, depending upon the accuracy needed.

1. Substitute the initial condition $y = y_0$ and $x = 0$ into the differential equation $dy/dx = f(x, y)$ and calculate the slope dy/dx at $x = 0$.

2. Calculate an approximate value of y at $x = \Delta x$ by assuming that the slope remains constant over the increment:

$$y_1 = y_0 + \Delta x \cdot \frac{dy}{dx}\bigg|_0 .$$

3. Calculate the slope $dy/dx|_1$ at y_1 by substituting $y = y_1$ and $x = \Delta x$ into the differential equation.

4. The value of y_1 as obtained above will be somewhat in error because the slope will not remain constant throughout the increment. A better value to use would be

$$\frac{dy}{dx}\bigg|_{\text{av.}} = \frac{1}{2}\left(\frac{dy}{dx}\bigg|_0 + \frac{dy}{dx}\bigg|_1\right).$$

Recalculate y_1 using this average slope:

$$y_1 = y_0 + \Delta x \cdot \frac{dy}{dx}\bigg|_{av.}$$

5. Using the new value of y_1, recalculate $dy/dx|_1$, compute the average value of dy/dx again, and recalculate y_1 using the new value of average slope. This process should be continued until successive values of y_1 are reasonably constant (within the required accuracy). If the increment Δx is chosen small enough, a very few operations will produce a constant y_1.

6. Repeat the process across the next increment to find the value of y_2, and, when successive values converge, proceed across the third increment, and so on until the entire solution is obtained.

The number of steps necessary to produce a constant y_1 can be decreased considerably by estimating the slope at the next point instead of considering the slope to be constant (step 2 above).

Example: Step-by-step Integration.—In the example of Sec. 35 a 15-lb weight moving at an initial velocity of 12 ft/sec was brought to rest by a damping force which was a function of velocity. If in addition the weight is subjected to a forward force of $f_w = 4(1 - t)$ lb, find the resulting motion.

The equation of motion is

$$\frac{W}{g}\frac{dv}{dt} + f_d = f_w$$

and, numerically, $dv/dt = 2.14[4(1 - t) - f_d(v)]$.   (92)

A time increment $\Delta t = 0.1$ sec will be chosen. The initial condition is that $v = 12$ ft/sec at $t = 0$. Substituting these figures and the corresponding damping force of 9.4 lb into Eq. (92) we find that the initial slope is $dv/dt|_0 = -11.6$ ft/sec². As a first approximation the velocity at $t = 0.1$ sec is

$$v_1 = 12 + (0.1)(-11.6) = 10.84 \text{ ft/sec.}$$

Substituting $t = 0.1$ sec, $v = 10.84$ ft/sec, and the damping force corresponding to this velocity (8.15 lb) into Eq. (92) we find that, approximately, $dv/dt|_1 = -9.73$ ft/sec².

The average value of dv/dt between points 0 and 1 is then approximately the average of $dv/dt|_0$ and $dv/dt|_1$, or -10.67 ft/sec². A better value of v_1 is

$$v_1 = 12 + (0.1)(-10.67) = 10.93 \text{ ft/sec.}$$

Recalculating the derivative at point 1, we find $dv/dt|_1 = -9.95$ ft/sec², giving a new average slope over the increment of -10.78 ft/sec², from which a new approximation to v_1 is 10.92 ft/sec. This is nearly equal to the preceding approximation, and completes the calculations for point 1. The results to $t = 0.3$ sec are tabulated below. Final approximations are printed in bold-faced type.

t	v	dv/dt	Average dv/dt
0	12.00	−11.6	
0.1	10.84	− 9.73	−10.67
	10.93	− 9.95	−10.78
	10.92		
0.2	9.92	− 8.66	− 9.31
	9.99	− 8.78	− 9.37
	9.98		
0.3	9.10	− 7.92	− 8.35
	9.14	− 8.02	− 8.40
	9.14		
...	.....	....	....

39. Extensions.—The extension of step-by-step integration to differential equations other than the simple type $dy/dx = f(x, y)$ is facilitated by the use of the so-called "normal" form of the differential equations. The original differential equations are broken up by a routine process into a system of equations in which the left-hand members contain only a single first derivative, while the right-hand members contain no derivatives. This is done by substituting a new variable of the form $m = dy/dx$ wherever derivatives occur in the equations, thus reducing the order of the derivatives but introducing the new equation $dy/dx = m$. Then, by making the substitution $n = dm/dx$, the order of the derivatives is again reduced by one, at the cost of introducing the new equation $dm/dx = n$. This process can be continued until all equations contain only a single first derivative.

As an example, reduce to normal form the equation

$$\frac{d^3y}{dx^3} + A\frac{d^2y}{dx^2} + B\frac{dy}{dx} + Cy = f(x), \tag{93}$$

where the coefficients A, B, and C can be functions of x and y.

First introduce the variable $m = dy/dx$. Substituting this into Eq. (93) we find that it reduces to

$$\frac{d^2m}{dx^2} + A\frac{dm}{dx} + Bm + Cy = f(x). \tag{94}$$

Next introduce the variable $n = dm/dx$.   Then Eq. (94) reduces to

$$\frac{dn}{dx} = f(x) - An - Bm - Cy. \tag{95}$$

In addition we can write

$$\frac{dm}{dx} = n \qquad \text{and} \qquad \frac{dy}{dx} = m. \tag{96}$$

The three Eqs. (95) and (96) constitute the normal form of the original differential Eq. (93).

Equations of the form $d^2y/dx^2 + A\, dy/dx + B = 0$, where A and B are not functions of x, can be solved step by step in a simple manner by first putting the equation into normal form:

$$\left. \begin{array}{l} \dfrac{dz}{dx} = -(Az + B) \\[2mm] \dfrac{dy}{dx} = z. \end{array} \right\} \tag{97}$$

Now divide the first equation by the second, obtaining

$$\frac{dz}{dy} = -\frac{Az + B}{z},$$

which, if A and B are functions of y but not of x, is of the form solvable by the method of Sec. 38.   After z has been found as a function of y, either or both of Eqs. (97) can be employed to find x as a function of y:

$$x = \int \left(\frac{1}{z}\right) dy,$$

or

$$x = -\int \frac{1}{Az + B}\, dz.$$

The methods of Secs. 35 to 37 may be required in performing the integration.

Equations of more complicated form can be solved step by step by first placing them in normal form, then solving each equation in a step-by-step manner, carrying the solutions to all equations forward at the same time.

The step-by-step method of Sec. 38 amounts to fitting a polynomial of the second degree to each pair of adjacent points.

More accurate results can be obtained by fitting higher degree polynomials to more points.[1]

40. Method of Isoclines.—The method of isoclines is a quite satisfactory graphical method of solving equations that can be

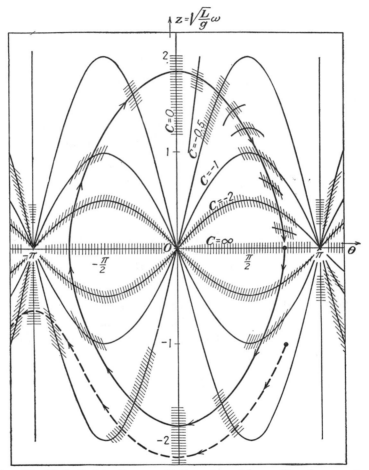

Fig. 43.—Method of isoclines: oscillation of pendulum. The sine curves are isoclines.

put into the form $dy/dx = f(x, y)$. Since dy/dx is the slope of the solution y vs. x, the equation $f(x, y) = C$ will represent a

[1] For further information on numerical integration, see, for example, J. B. Scarborough, "Numerical Mathematical Analysis," The Johns Hopkins Press, Baltimore, 1930.

curve on the x-y plane along which the slope of the solution must be constant at the value C. Such a curve is called an *isocline*. Whenever the solution of the differential equation crosses an isocline, it must do so at the slope C, and this direction can be indicated by a series of short direction lines as shown in Fig. 43.

To use the method, choose a series of values of the slope C, and for each of these draw the isocline $f(x, y) = C$. Next draw short direction lines at the slope C for each isocline. Starting at the initial condition $y = y_0$ at $x = x_0$, follow the direction of the short strokes, thus drawing in the solution. If the isoclines are reasonably close together, the direction lines will nearly join, and the eye will automatically follow the proper path of the solution. It is necessary to draw the isoclines and direction lines only in the expected region of the solution. The method of isoclines has the advantage of permitting the solutions to be drawn for several initial conditions without greatly increasing the labor. As in all graphical methods, the work must be done carefully to produce good results.

In some problems the differential equation is of the form $dy/dx = f(y)$, in which the slope depends on y only and not on x. Here the isoclines will be horizontal straight lines. It should be observed, however, that equations of this form can be inverted and integrated by the methods of Secs. 35 to 37.

Example: Method of Isoclines.—A simple pendulum has a weight W suspended on an arm of length L. It is given an initial displacement θ_0 from the vertical and is permitted to oscillate. Find the period of oscillation.

The differential equation of motion is

$$\frac{d^2\theta}{dt^2} + \frac{g}{L} \sin \theta = 0. \tag{98}$$

This equation can be put into normal form:

$$\left.\begin{aligned} \frac{d\omega}{dt} &= -\frac{g}{L} \sin \theta \\ \frac{d\theta}{dt} &= \omega. \end{aligned}\right\} \tag{99}$$

Dividing the first of these equations by the second, there results

$$\frac{d\omega}{d\theta} = -\frac{g \sin \theta}{L\omega},$$

which is more conveniently expressed in dimensionless form as

$$\frac{d}{d\theta}\left(\sqrt{\frac{L}{g}}\,\omega\right) = -\frac{\sin\theta}{\sqrt{\frac{L}{g}}\,\omega}.$$

Denote the quantity $\omega\sqrt{L/g}$ by the letter z for convenience. Then

$$\frac{dz}{d\theta} = -\frac{\sin\theta}{z}. \qquad (100)$$

Along an isocline, $-(\sin\theta)/z = C$, or $z = -(1/C)\sin\theta$. Figure 43 shows the isoclines for slopes of $C = 0$, ±0.5, ±1.0, ±2.0, and infinity, together with direction lines indicating the slope of the solution at these points. Observe that a slope of unity does not indicate that the direction lines are at 45°, since the scales along the two axes are different. A line with a slope of unity will move upward one unit on the scale of the z-axis while moving a distance of 1 radian on the scale of the θ-axis. In Fig. 43 a particular solution is drawn in for an initial condition of $z = 0$ (*i.e.*, $\omega = 0$) and $\theta = 3\pi/4$ at $t = 0$, and shows the relation between angular position and velocity of the pendulum. Notice how easily the solutions for other initial conditions could be drawn. For example, an initial condition of $z = -1.0$ and $\theta = 3\pi/4$ at $t = 0$ would result in an irregular spinning motion rather than in oscillation, as shown by the dotted line in Fig. 43. The velocity of the weight varies from a minimum at the top of the motion to a maximum at the bottom. If damping had been included in Eq. (98), the resulting curve would spiral inward toward the origin.

Returning to the solution for the initial conditions $z = 0$ and $\theta = 3\pi/4$, it is desired to find the period of oscillation. This can be done by employing Eqs. (99). Inverting and integrating these equations we obtain

$$t = -\int \frac{L}{g\sin\theta}\,d\omega,$$

and

$$t = \int \frac{d\theta}{\omega},$$

or, in terms of z,

$$t\sqrt{\frac{g}{L}} = -\int \frac{dz}{\sin\theta} \qquad (101)$$

and

$$t\sqrt{\frac{g}{L}} = \int \frac{d\theta}{z}. \qquad (102)$$

Corresponding values of θ and z can be obtained from the solution of Fig. 43, and the time can be found by a graphical integration. However, it will be seen that the integrand of Eq. (101) becomes infinite at $\theta = 0$, and graphical integration of the equation will fail in this region. Furthermore, Eq. (102) has a similar difficulty at $z = 0$. This difficulty can be avoided by using Eq. (102) in the region where Eq. (101) fails, and vice versa. The integrals can join at any convenient point, say at $\theta = \pi/4$ corresponding to $z = -1.68$. Denoting the time for a whole period by T and integrating over the first quarter period only, we can then write

$$\frac{T}{4}\sqrt{\frac{g}{L}} = -\int_{z=0}^{z=-1.68}\frac{dz}{\sin\theta} + \int_{\theta=\pi/4}^{\theta=0}\frac{d\theta}{z}. \tag{103}$$

The integrands are plotted against their respective variables of integration in Fig. 44, using points selected from the first quarter cycle of the solution in Fig. 43. Graphical integration then yields an area corresponding to the first integral of $1.16 \times 1.68 = 1.95$, and for the second integral we

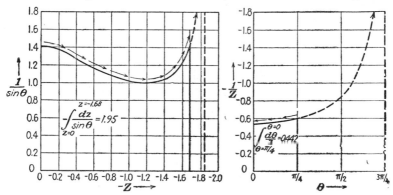

FIG. 44.—Integration to find period.

obtain $0.562 \times \pi/4 = 0.442$. The sum of the two integrals is

$$1.95 + 0.44 = 2.39.$$

So by Eq. (103) the period of oscillation for an initial displacement of $3\pi/4$ radians (135°) is obtained from

$$\frac{T}{4}\sqrt{\frac{g}{L}} = 2.39.$$

Then
$$T = 9.56\sqrt{\frac{L}{g}}\ \text{sec},$$

if L is expressed in feet and g is in ft/sec².

It happens that this particular problem can be solved analytically by means of elliptic integrals. The analytical solution shows a period of $9.6004\sqrt{L/g}$ sec, less than 1 per cent higher than that obtained by the method of isoclines. Note that the simple pendulum theory, which assumes small vibrations, would give the result $T = 6.28\sqrt{L/g}$ sec.

Problems

1. A mass weighing 4,000 lb is to be accelerated horizontally from rest at $x = 0$ by a force that varies with displacement as given in the table which follows. Find the velocity of the mass at $x = 40$ ft.

x, ft..........	0	5	10	15	20	25	30	35	40
Force, lb......	7,200	10,650	13,950	17,100	19,200	20,000	18,500	12,900	0

2. The velocity of a fluid flowing in a 6-in.-diameter cylindrical pipe has been found experimentally and is given in the table below as a function of radius. Find the total rate of flow in cubic feet per minute.

Radius r, in.................	0	0.6	1.2	1.8	2.4	2.7	2.85	3.0
Velocity v, ft/sec.............	1.17	1.15	1.09	0.992	0.838	0.702	0.599	0

Hint: Show the relation between rate of flow and $\int v \, d(r^2)$, plot or tabulate v vs. r^2, and integrate graphically or numerically.

3. A boat weighing 3,500 lb is traveling at a speed of 14 ft/sec when the propulsion is stopped. The water resistance vs. velocity is given in the table below. Plot a curve of velocity vs. time and show how long it takes for the boat to come to a stop.

Velocity v, ft/sec...................	14	12	10	8	6	4	2	0
Resisting force f, lb................	497	280	113	48.3	28.2	22.0	19.0	18.0

4. A nonlinear inductor with a resistance of 128 ohms is connected at $t = 0$ to a 74-volt d-c source. The magnetization curve is given in the accompanying table for two conditions: with the inductor initially demagnetized and with a residual flux in the positive direction. Set up the differential equation for the circuit, put it in a form suitable for graphical integration, and integrate to find current vs. time. Plot the results for the two conditions shown in the table.

Current, amp	Flux linkages, weber-turns	
	Initially de-magnetized	With residual flux
0	0	11.0
0.02	12.0	13.8
0.04	15.1	15.6
0.10	18.1	18.2
0.20	19.5	19.5
0.40	20.9	20.9
0.60	21.9	21.9
0.80	22.8	22.8
1.00	23.4	23.4
1.20	24.0	24.0

5. A self-excited d-c generator is running at 1,200 rpm with the field switch open and with no load connected to the armature circuit. At $t = 0$ the field switch is closed. Using graphical or numerical integration, plot a curve of armature voltage vs. time and specify the time required for the machine to build up to 90 per cent of its final voltage.

Data: The total resistance of the field circuit including the field rheostat is 75.0 ohms.

A test shows that at 1,200 rpm the open-circuit armature voltage and the flux linkages of the field are related by the expression $e_a = 4.18\psi$ where ψ is in weber-turns.

The open-circuit saturation curve of the machine at 1,200 rpm is given in the accompanying table.

Field current, amp	Armature voltage	Field current, amp	Armature voltage
0	5.3	0.60	99.2
0.04	9.0	0.80	111.1
0.08	17.5	1.00	118.0
0.20	43.8	1.50	131.6
0.30	65.0	2.00	139.8
0.40	80.2	2.50	144.9
0.50	90.9		

6. A 30-μf condenser is charged to a potential difference of 310 volts and is then discharged through a nonlinear inductor. Using the saturation

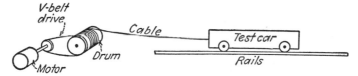

FIG. P7.—Test-car drive.

curve given in Prob. 4 for the initially demagnetized condition and neglecting hysteresis and resistance:

a. Set up the differential equation for the system and reduce to normal form, expressing the equation in terms of ψ, $i = f(\psi)$, and $e = d\psi/dt$.

b. Using the method of isoclines, draw a curve of e vs. ψ for the first quarter cycle of oscillation.

c. Find the period of oscillation. Qualitatively, how will the frequency of oscillation vary as the maximum voltage across the condenser becomes lower on successive cycles of a damped oscillation?

d. Sketch the wave form of current.

7. The small test car shown schematically in Fig. P7 is to be used in a hydraulic towing tank. The car is towed along the rails by means of a cable, the opposite end of which is wrapped around a drum.   The drum is driven through *V*-belts by a d-c motor.

In starting, the cable is initially taut and the motor is thrown on full line voltage.   The problem is to find the velocity of the car as a function of time after the switch is closed and to find the distance required for the car to reach 90 per cent of final speed.   Set up the differential equation for velocity of the car and integrate graphically or numerically.

Data: The motor is rated 3 hp, 220 volts, 13.25 amp.

Pulley ratio, $P_r = 2.0$ (motor on high-speed side).

Radius of drum, $R = 5$ in.

Equivalent weight of car including effect of the moment of inertia of the wheels, $W = 210$ lb.

WR^2 of the rotating parts, all referred to the motor shaft, is 9.5 lb-ft².

Frictional force required to move the car along the rails is about 15 lb.

Frictional torques including belt friction are estimated to be about 3.5 lb-ft referred to the motor.

Steady-state test at 220 volts shows the following relation between speed and torque of the motor:

Rpm	Torque, lb-ft	Rpm	Torque, lb-ft
0	121	1,000	54
200	114	1,100	38
400	103	1,150	26.9
600	91	1,200	14.8
800	75	1,250	0

8. The d-c motor shown schematically in Fig. P8 is to be brought to rest quickly by dynamic braking.   Switch 1 is opened, disconnecting the motor

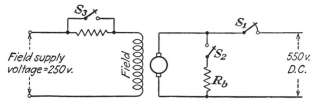

Fig. P8.—Dynamic braking.

from the line.   Switch 2 is closed, connecting the braking resistor.   Switch 3 is closed to increase the field current and produce greater braking effort. These operations take place in quick succession.   The transient build-up of field flux caused by the closing of switch 3 has already been calculated and is given in the accompanying table.

Using the method of isoclines, plot speed vs. time and find the time required to reach a speed of 70 rpm.

Data: When switch **3** is closed, the field flux builds up as follows:

Time, sec	0	1	2	3	4	5	Steady state
Flux per pole, megalines	6.49	8.55	10.1	11.4	12.2	12.8	13.0

The motor rating is 8 pole, 1,000 hp, 350/700 rpm, 550 volts.
The initial speed of the motor is 700 rpm.
The total WR^2 on the motor shaft is 23,000 lb-ft².
The braking resistor has 0.305 ohm resistance.
The armature resistance is 0.0086 ohm.

Calculation shows that the generated voltage of the armature is related to the speed and field flux by

$$e_a = 1.16\phi\omega \qquad \text{volts,}$$

where ϕ is the field flux in megalines per pole, and ω is the angular velocity in radians per second.

The electrical torque is related to the field flux and armature current by

$$T = 0.810\phi i_a \qquad \text{lb-ft,}$$

where i_a is armature current in amperes, and ϕ is in megalines per pole.

9. Friction is ordinarily supposed to damp out oscillations and cause stability. However, dry friction, which decreases in magnitude with increasing velocity, can under proper conditions cause self-excited oscilla-

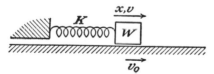

Fig. P9.—Self-excited oscillations.

tions. This can explain the chattering of lathe tools, the intermittent slip of locomotive driving wheels, and the violent vibration of poorly lubricated machine parts.

A specific example is represented schematically in Fig. P9. A weight W is lowered onto the moving surface, which exerts dry friction as shown in the following table of data. The weight initially has zero velocity and displacement.

Using the method of isoclines, plot velocity vs. displacement and show whether self-excited oscillations will build up. If so, show the maximum and minimum displacement and velocity. Also, by a rough sketch of the isoclines, show the effect of friction which increases in magnitude with increasing slip.

Data: $W = 5$ lb, $K = 1,000$ lb/ft, $v_0 = 6$ ft/sec.

Relative velocity of slip, ft/sec	Friction force, f_f, lb	Relative velocity of slip, ft/sec	Friction force, f_f, lb
16	30.4	2	56.9
12	32.6	+0	75.0
8	37.9	−0	−75.0
6	41.9	−2	−56.9
4	47.8	. . .	. . . . . .

Note: If the isoclines for slopes of $C = 0$ and $C = 100$ are plotted, it will be seen that the isoclines for other slopes can be found by direct proportion along the x-direction, using dividers.

CHAPTER VI

ORDINARY DIFFERENTIAL EQUATIONS

41. Introduction.—There is considerable advantage in solving differential equations analytically rather than numerically. An analytic solution will apply over a wide range of parameters and will indicate the effect of a change in parameters, while in a numerical solution each new condition will generally require a new start from the beginning. Furthermore, there are a number of physically important types of differential equations for which an analytical solution is much less laborious than a numerical solution. Therefore, we shall try to obtain an analytic solution whenever possible and reserve the graphical and numerical methods for those problems where mathematical methods fail.

We have defined the *order* of a differential equation in Sec. 26 as the order of the highest derivative contained in the equation. The *degree* of a differential equation is defined as the degree of the derivative of highest order, provided that the equation has been cleared of all fractions and radicals that involve derivatives. In the following examples, Eq. (104) is of the second order and first degree, Eq. (105) is of the third order and second degree, and Eq. (106) is of the second order and second degree:

$$\frac{d^2y}{dx^2} + Ay = 0. \tag{104}$$

$$\left(\frac{d^3y}{dx^3}\right)^2 + A\frac{dy}{dx} + By = 0. \tag{105}$$

$$\frac{\dfrac{d^2y}{dx^2}}{\left[1 + \left(\dfrac{dy}{dx}\right)^2\right]^{\frac{3}{2}}} = K. \tag{106}$$

An *ordinary differential equation* is one that involves only one independent variable and derivatives with respect to it, such as the equations above. A *partial differential equation*

95

is one that involves more than one independent variable and derivatives with respect to them, as illustrated by Eq. (107):

$$\frac{\partial^2 y}{\partial x^2} - a \frac{\partial y}{\partial t} = 0. \tag{107}$$

In this chapter we shall be concerned only with ordinary differential equations.

A solution of a differential equation is a relation between the variables, free from derivatives, that will satisfy the differential equation identically. In Sec. 26 we reached the conclusion that for an nth-order differential equation we would have to know the initial values of the variable and its first $n - 1$ derivatives (or equivalent information) in order properly to start a graphical solution of the equation. Thus we might expect that the most general analytic solution of an nth-order differential equation would contain n constants of integration which would be entirely arbitrary from a mathematical standpoint, but which could be evaluated for a physical system from the initial conditions. This can also be seen mathematically by taking the first n derivatives of such a solution, thus obtaining $n + 1$ equations between which the arbitrary constants could be eliminated to yield the original differential equation. Since no more than n constants could be eliminated in this manner to yield an nth-order differential equation, the solution containing this number of constants must be the *general solution*. A *particular solution* is obtained from the general solution by assigning values to the arbitrary constants. In most physical problems we shall do this by the application of initial conditions.

A linear differential equation is one of the general form[1]

$$a_0 \frac{d^n y}{dt^n} + a_1 \frac{d^{n-1} y}{dt^{n-1}} + \cdots + a_n y = f(t), \tag{108}$$

in which the a's can be constants or functions of t. When the $f(t)$ on the right is identically zero, the equation is said to be *homogeneous*, since each term of the equation contains y in a linear manner. When $f(t)$ is not identically zero, Eq. (108) is called *complete* or *nonhomogeneous*. When the parameters of a

---

[1] Throughout most of this chapter we shall use the symbol t for the independent variable. This will not necessarily represent time, although in a great many of our problems it will do so.

linear system do not vary with time, its equations will be of the form of Eq. (108), and the a's will be constants. Linear differential equations with constant coefficients are comparatively easy to solve, and fortunately a large number of engineering problems fall into this classification. We shall consider this type first, in some detail.

A. LINEAR EQUATIONS WITH CONSTANT COEFFICIENTS

42. Homogeneous Equation of First Order.—This equation arises in such problems as the deceleration of a mass with viscous damping and without driving force, and the decay of current through an inductance and resistance connected in series without driving voltage. The equation is of the form

$$a_0 \frac{dy}{dt} + a_1 y = 0, \tag{109}$$

where the a's are constants. This particular equation can be rewritten so as to be solved by straight integration, but we shall obtain the result by a method that will apply also to equations of higher order. Examination of Eq. (109) shows that to satisfy the equation for all values of time, the derivative of the solution must have the same form as the solution itself. This leads us to try an exponential solution of the form

$$y = C\epsilon^{mt}, \tag{110}$$

where C and m are undetermined constants. To check the validity of the assumed solution (and to evaluate one of the constants if possible), substitute it back into the differential equation. We then obtain

$$a_0 m C \epsilon^{mt} + a_1 C \epsilon^{mt} = 0, \tag{111}$$

which is satisfied for all values of time and for any given value of C provided that

$$a_0 m + a_1 = 0. \tag{112}$$

Equation (112), called the *characteristic equation* of the differential equation (109), must be satisfied if Eq. (110) is to be a solution. From it we obtain $m = -a_1/a_0$, and the solution turns out to be

$$y = C\epsilon^{-(a_1/a_0)t}, \tag{113}$$

where C is the single arbitrary constant which we expect from a first-order equation. Observe that since the differential equation was homogeneous (had zero on the right side), it would correspond to a dynamic system with no driving force or voltage. Hence we would expect the steady state to be zero, and the only response would be a transient caused by lack of initial equilibrium. This is precisely what the solution (113) indicates, for the exponential will approach zero for large values of time. Theoretically, the solution will not reach zero in finite time, but it will become extremely small in a reasonable length of time,

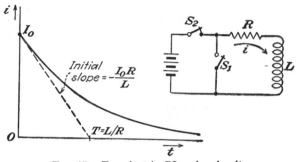

FIG. 45.—Transient in RL series circuit.

after which the assumptions underlying the differential equation may no longer be valid and the solution will lose its physical meaning.

Let us return for a moment to the characteristic equation (112). If we write the differential equation (109) in terms of the differential operator introduced in Sec. 30 ($p \equiv d/dt$), it becomes

$$(a_0 p + a_1)y = 0. \tag{114}$$

If we compare this with the characteristic equation $a_0 m + a_1 = 0$, we see that the latter can be obtained from the operator form of the differential equation merely by replacing the differential operator p by the algebraic coefficient m and dropping the dependent variable y. This is one of the conveniences of the operator form. We shall find others as the differential equations become more complicated.

Example.—Consider an inductance L and a resistance R connected in series with a battery and drawing a current I_0 as in Fig. 45. At $t = 0$ the series combination is short-circuited by closing switch S_1 and the battery is removed by opening S_2. Determine the resulting current as a function of time. The differential equation after $t = 0$ is

$$L \frac{di}{dt} + Ri = 0. \tag{115}$$

We could write the general solution immediately by comparison with Eqs. (109) and (113). However, since the method itself is as easy to remember as the formula and is of far greater usefulness, we shall start with the differential equation and use the procedure that is applicable to equations of higher order. Write the differential equation in operator form:

$$(Lp + R)i = 0. \tag{116}$$

The characteristic equation can be written by inspection of Eq. (116) and is

$$Lm + R = 0, \tag{117}$$

from which $m = -R/L$ and the general solution is

$$i = C\epsilon^{-(R/L)t}. \tag{118}$$

To evaluate the constant of integration, substitute the initial condition $i = I_0$ at $t = 0$:

$$I_0 = C\epsilon^0,$$

from which $C = I_0$ and the particular solution is

$$i = I_0\epsilon^{-(R/L)t}. \tag{119}$$

The solution is pure transient, and its general form is shown in Fig. 45.

Let us examine an interesting property of the solution. Its initial slope can be found by taking the first derivative of Eq. (119) and setting $t = 0$, which yields $-I_0R/L$. It is easy to show that a straight line drawn from the starting point with this slope (*i.e.*, tangent to the curve at the beginning) will intersect the time axis at a time $T = L/R$ sec, as shown in Fig. 45. This is known as the *time constant* of the circuit and affords a convenient measure of the length of the transient. Substitution of this value of time into the solution (119) will show that the transient current at this instant is given by $I_0\epsilon^{-1}$, *i.e.*, the current is then 63.2 per cent of the way toward its final steady-state value of zero. All linear constant-parameter systems which are described by first-order equations have this property even when constant driving forces are present.

43. Homogeneous Equation of Second Order.—This equation is of special interest, since it arises in electrical problems involving inductance and capacity and in mechanical problems involving a mass and spring, and provides the possibility of free oscillations. The equation is of the form:

$$a_0 \frac{d^2y}{dt^2} + a_1 \frac{dy}{dt} + a_2 y = 0. \tag{120}$$

This can also be written in the operator form:

$$(a_0 p^2 + a_1 p + a_2)y = 0. \tag{121}$$

Since the equation is of the second order, we shall expect two constants of integration in the general solution. Following the reasoning of Sec. 42, we again decide that the solution and its derivatives must have the same form. So, neglecting the requirement of two constants of integration for a moment, we shall try an exponential solution of the form:

$$y = C\epsilon^{mt}. \tag{122}$$

To check its validity we substitute the assumed solution back into the differential equation and obtain

$$a_0 m^2 C \epsilon^{mt} + a_1 m C \epsilon^{mt} + a_2 C \epsilon^{mt} = 0,$$

which yields the characteristic equation that must be satisfied if Eq. (122) is to be a solution:

$$a_0 m^2 + a_1 m + a_2 = 0. \tag{123}$$

Again observe that the characteristic equation is clearly indicated by the operator form of the differential equation (121) and can be written by inspection. The characteristic equation is now quadratic and is satisfied by either of two values of m:

$$\left.\begin{aligned} m_1 &= -\frac{a_1}{2a_0} + \sqrt{\frac{a_1^2}{4a_0^2} - \frac{a_2}{a_0}} \\ m_2 &= -\frac{a_1}{2a_0} - \sqrt{\frac{a_1^2}{4a_0^2} - \frac{a_2}{a_0}} \end{aligned}\right\} \tag{124}$$

Here we have two permissible solutions: $C_1 \epsilon^{m_1 t}$ and $C_2 \epsilon^{m_2 t}$. A little thought (or trial) will show that, if either of these alone will make the left side of the differential equation (120) identically zero and thus satisfy the equation, then because the equation is linear and homogeneous the sum of the two solutions will also satisfy it. Thus the general solution with the two expected constants of integration can be written:

$$y = C_1 \epsilon^{m_1 t} + C_2 \epsilon^{m_2 t}, \tag{125}$$

where m_1 and m_2 are given by Eqs. (124) and C_1 and C_2 will be evaluated from the initial conditions of the physical system. The solution now appears as the sum of two exponential transients and will shortly be illustrated by an example.

Complex Roots; Oscillatory Systems.—In solving for the values of m from Eq. (124), it is physically quite possible for a_2 to be greater than $a_1^2/4a_0$, in which case the quantity under the radical is negative and its square root is imaginary. The two values of m can then be expressed as conjugate complex numbers of the form:[1]

$$\left. \begin{array}{l} m_1 = -\alpha + j\omega \\ m_2 = -\alpha - j\omega, \end{array} \right\} \tag{126}$$

where $j = \sqrt{-1}$ and α and ω are real numbers. We could then write the solution from Eq. (125) as

$$y = C_1 \epsilon^{(-\alpha + j\omega)t} + C_2 \epsilon^{(-\alpha - j\omega)t},$$

or, presuming that $\epsilon^{(-\alpha + j\omega)t} = \epsilon^{-\alpha t} \epsilon^{j\omega t}$ as in the case of real numbers, we can write

$$y = \epsilon^{-\alpha t}(C_1 \epsilon^{j\omega t} + C_2 \epsilon^{-j\omega t}). \tag{127}$$

To interpret the exponentials in parentheses, let us expand $\epsilon^{j\omega t}$ in a Maclaurin series, again assuming that we can manipulate the imaginary $j\omega t$ as we would a real quantity. Observing that $j = \sqrt{-1}$, so that $j^2 = -1$, $j^3 = -\sqrt{-1}$, etc., we obtain

$$\epsilon^{j\omega t} = 1 + j\omega t - \frac{(\omega t)^2}{2!} - j\frac{(\omega t)^3}{3!} + \frac{(\omega t)^4}{4!} + \cdots$$

$$= \left[1 - \frac{(\omega t)^2}{2!} + \frac{(\omega t)^4}{4!} - \cdots \right] + j\left[\omega t - \frac{(\omega t)^3}{3!} + \cdots \right].$$

[1] For a discussion of complex numbers, see Chap. VII.

However, the first bracketed series is the Maclaurin expansion of cos ωt and the second is that of sin ωt. Hence it appears that

$$\epsilon^{j\omega t} = \cos \omega t + j \sin \omega t. \qquad (128)$$

This is *Euler's formula.* Observe that by replacing ωt by $-\omega t$ we obtain $\epsilon^{-j\omega t} = \cos \omega t - j \sin \omega t$.

With the aid of these relations we can rewrite the solution (127) as

$$y = \epsilon^{-\alpha t}[(C_1 + C_2) \cos \omega t + j(C_1 - C_2) \sin \omega t],$$

or, defining new constants,

$$y = \epsilon^{-\alpha t}(A \cos \omega t + B \sin \omega t). \qquad (129)$$

This can also be written in an alternative form which is sometimes more convenient:

$$y = Y\epsilon^{-\alpha t} \cos (\omega t - \phi), \qquad (130)$$

where $Y = \sqrt{A^2 + B^2}$ and $\phi = \tan^{-1} (B/A)$.

We should now check our algebraic manipulation of complex numbers by substituting the solution back into the differential equation to see whether it is satisfied. Using the relations (124) and (126) for α and ω, this substitution will show that our solution (Eq. 129 or 130) is indeed correct.

In each of the foregoing cases the pair of complex roots carry with them two constants of integration, as of course they should. These constants are C_1 and C_2, A and B, or Y and ϕ, and they can be evaluated from the initial conditions of the physical system. When the roots of the characteristic equation are found to be complex, it is better to write the solution in the form (129) or (130) immediately rather than attempting to use the exponential form (125).

The solution (129) or (130) is of great physical significance, for it represents a damped oscillation. It has the form of a sinusoid whose amplitude $Y\epsilon^{-\alpha t}$ decreases exponentially with increasing time and eventually vanishes as shown by curve a of Fig. 46. The quantity $\epsilon^{-\alpha t}$ is called the *damping factor*, α is the *damping constant*, and ω is the *natural angular velocity*. The system will go through one cycle of oscillation when ωt increases by 2π radians, hence the natural frequency of oscillation is

$$f_n = \frac{\omega}{2\pi}.$$

For physical systems described by the second-order differential equation (120), the damping usually enters in the coefficient a_1 of the middle term.   For the hypothetical case of such a linear system without damping this coefficient vanishes, and any oscillation, once started, will continue indefinitely without decrease in magnitude.   Reference to Eqs. (124) and (126) shows that the natural angular velocity will then be given simply by $\omega = \sqrt{a_2/a_0}$. A solution for this condition is sometimes helpful in dealing with systems that are lightly damped, for the undamped solution will be approximately correct for a short time, and the simple expression for ω given above will not be appreciably in error for these systems.

Frequently it is important to know the amount of damping that will keep a system from oscillating.   Since the criterion for no oscillation is that the roots of the characteristic equation shall all be real, reference to Eqs. (124) will show that, for the second-order equation, the system will be oscillatory if $a_1{}^2 < 4a_0a_2$ and will be overdamped and nonoscillatory if $a_1{}^2 > 4a_0a_2$.

Repeated Roots; Critical Damping.—There is one more case that deserves our consideration since it forms the boundary between the overdamped and the oscillatory solutions.   This corresponds physically to what is called *critical damping* and occurs in the second-order equation when $a_1{}^2 = 4a_0a_2$.   Equations (124) show that for this condition the two values of m are equal, and we would normally try to write the solution in the form

$$y = C_1\epsilon^{-\beta t} + C_2\epsilon^{-\beta t},$$

where $-\beta$ is the numerical value of m.   However, these two terms can be combined into one because the exponents are the same, and we have left only one constant of integration $(C_1 + C_2)$ for the second-order equation.   The solution is therefore incomplete, and a second term must be added.   For this case we shall try a solution of the form

$$y = (C_1 + C_2 t)\epsilon^{-\beta t} \tag{131}$$

and attempt to check it by substitution into the original differential equation.   For this purpose the differential equation with repeated roots can be written most conveniently as

$$\frac{d^2y}{dt^2} + 2\beta \frac{dy}{dt} + \beta^2 y = 0. \tag{132}$$

Taking the first and second derivatives of Eq. (131) and substituting into Eq. (132) we obtain

$$(\beta^2 C_1 - 2\beta C_2 + \beta^2 C_2 t)\epsilon^{-\beta t} + 2\beta(C_2 - \beta C_1 - \beta C_2 t)\epsilon^{-\beta t}$$
$$+ \beta^2(C_1 + C_2 t)\epsilon^{-\beta t} = 0.$$

Since the coefficients of each of the two functions of time, $\epsilon^{-\beta t}$ and $t\epsilon^{-\beta t}$, separately cancel to zero, the relation is an identity (true for all values of time) and the differential equation is satisfied.

The form of the solution (131) for a critically damped system is shown by curve c of Fig. 46. Observe that in spite of the linear quantity in the solution, the exponential causes the solution to approach zero at large values of time, and the form of the curve does not differ markedly from the overdamped exponential case. On the other hand, the critically damped solution can be regarded as the limit of the oscillatory case as the damping is increased to make the natural frequency approach zero, and thus it forms a smooth transition between the overdamped and the oscillatory conditions.

Example.—There are a number of important physical systems, both electrical and mechanical, that can be described in terms of the second-order equation (120). One of these, shown in Fig. 46, consists of a mass M with damping D suspended from a spring K. Applied forces must be absent for the differential equation to be homogeneous, and the steady-state response will therefore be zero. However there can be transients. For example, if the mass is pulled downward and then released, it will move upward toward its equilibrium position in a manner that depends mainly on the damping in the system. This will now be investigated. The differential equation is (compare with Fig. 29 and Eqs. 61 and 62 with $F = 0$)

$$M \frac{d^2x}{dt^2} + D \frac{dx}{dt} + Kx = 0. \tag{133}$$

Write this in operator form

$$(Mp^2 + Dp + K)x = 0. \tag{134}$$

The characteristic equation can be written by inspection of this equation and is

$$Mm^2 + Dm + K = 0. \tag{135}$$

The two roots of this equation can be obtained by the quadratic formula:

$$m_1, m_2 = -\frac{D}{2M} \pm \sqrt{\frac{D^2}{4M^2} - \frac{K}{M}}. \tag{136}$$

The condition for a nonoscillatory solution is apparently

$$D^2 > 4MK.$$

Assuming that this is the case, the most convenient form of the solution will be

$$x = C_1 \epsilon^{m_1 t} + C_2 \epsilon^{m_2 t}, \tag{137}$$

where m_1 and m_2 are given by Eq. (136). The constants of integration C_1 and C_2 will be evaluated from the initial conditions, which are that at the instant the mass is released ($t = 0$) its displacement is X_0 and its velocity (dx/dt) is zero. Substituting the first condition into the solution (137) we obtain

$$X_0 = C_1 \epsilon^0 + C_2 \epsilon^0 = C_1 + C_2. \tag{138}$$

Taking the first derivative of the solution (137) and substituting the second initial condition, we have

$$\left.\frac{dx}{dt}\right|_{t=0} = 0 = m_1 C_1 + m_2 C_2. \tag{139}$$

Solving Eqs. (138) and (139) simultaneously for C_1 and C_2 and substituting these into the general solution (137), we obtain the particular solution:

$$x = \frac{X_0}{m_2 - m_1} (m_2 \epsilon^{m_1 t} - m_1 \epsilon^{m_2 t}). \tag{140}$$

To illustrate the form of the solution, let

$$W = 20 \text{ lb}, \qquad M = \frac{W}{g} = 0.621 \text{ lb-sec}^2/\text{ft (slugs)}.$$
$$K = 40 \text{ lb/ft}.$$
$$D = 25 \text{ lb-sec/ft}.$$
$$\text{Initial displacement } X_0 = 0.25 \text{ ft}.$$

The roots of the characteristic equation are, from Eq. (136), $m_1 = -38.5$ and $m_2 = -1.66$. The solution (140) then becomes

$$x = 0.261 \epsilon^{-1.66t} - 0.011 \epsilon^{-38.5t} \qquad \text{ft}. \tag{141}$$

This is plotted in curve d of Fig. 46. To obtain a rough sketch of a solution such as this, a good method is to sketch each term separately by first locating the starting point (0.261 for the first term above), and next locating a point corresponding to this coefficient divided by ϵ, which occurs at a time equal to the reciprocal of the damping constant (*e.g.*, at $t = 1/1.66 = 0.602$ sec, the first term is equal to $0.261\epsilon^{-1} = 0.261/2.718 = 0.096$ ft). A reasonably good exponential can then be drawn through these points by eye. When the component curves have been sketched,

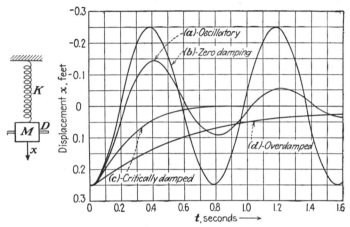

FIG. 46.—Plot of displacement vs. time, showing the effect of damping. Positive displacement is plotted downward to assist visualization of actual motion.

they can be added point by point to form a reasonably good sketch of the solution.

Observe that the solution above has been carried through in literal form. This has the advantage that the solution applies to all similar systems regardless of the values of the parameters, and also that the effect of a change in parameters is readily seen. When the equation is of higher order, it is sometimes desirable or necessary to solve the equation in numerical form, either to save time if only a particular solution is needed, or if the characteristic equation is of such high degree that its roots must be found numerically. Unfortunately a numerical solution sacrifices some of the advantage of the analytical methods.

Example Continued: Oscillatory Solution.—Assume that in the foregoing problem the damping is below the critical value

$D = 2\sqrt{MK}$ so that the roots (136) of the characteristic equation are complex.   They can then be written as

$$m_1, m_2 = -\alpha \pm j\omega, \qquad (142)$$

where
$$\alpha = \frac{D}{2M}, \qquad \omega = \sqrt{\frac{K}{M} - \frac{D^2}{4M^2}}. \qquad (143)$$

We shall then write the solution in the form (129):

$$x = \epsilon^{-\alpha t}(A \cos \omega t + B \sin \omega t). \qquad (144)$$

Use the same initial conditions as before: at $t = 0$, $x = X_0$, and velocity $= dx/dt = 0$.   Substituting the first condition into the solution we obtain

$$X_0 = \epsilon^0 \,[A \cos (0) + B \sin (0)] = A. \qquad (145)$$

For the second condition,

$$\frac{dx}{dt}\bigg|_{t=0} = 0 = -\alpha A + \omega B,$$

so $A = X_0$, $B = \alpha X_0/\omega$, and the particular solution is

$$x = X_0 \epsilon^{-\alpha t}\left(\cos \omega t + \frac{\alpha}{\omega} \sin \omega t\right). \qquad (146)$$

Assume that, in the previous problem, all conditions remain the same except that the damping is reduced to

$$D = 1.5 \text{ lb-sec/ft.}$$

From Eqs. (143), $\alpha = 1.21$ and $\omega = 7.92$ corresponding to a natural frequency of $7.92/2\pi = 1.26$ cycles per second.   For an nitial displacement of 0.25 ft the solution becomes

$$x = 0.25\epsilon^{-1.21t}(\cos 7.92t + 0.153 \sin 7.92t) \text{ ft.} \qquad (147)$$

An alternative form (as in Eq. 130) is

$$x = 0.25 \sqrt{1^2 + (0.153)^2}\; \epsilon^{-1.21t} \cos\left(7.92t - \tan^{-1}\frac{0.153}{1}\right),$$

or
$$x = 0.253\epsilon^{-1.21t} \cos (7.92t - 8.7°). \qquad (148)$$

Observe that the latter solution is inconsistent mathematically, although convenient, because the phase angle is given in degrees rather than in radians.

The solution (147) or (148) is plotted in curve a of Fig. 46. In obtaining a rough sketch of a solution such as this, Eq. (148) is the more convenient form. The cosine function has peak values of ± 1 and at these points touches the "envelope" $\pm 0.253\epsilon^{-1.21t}$. The latter can first be sketched, after which the solution can be drawn as an oscillation between the envelope curves. Calculation of the period of oscillation (reciprocal of natural frequency) will show at what intervals the solution goes through zero.

For the limiting case of zero damping, it is readily shown that the solution becomes

$$x = 0.25 \cos (8.02t),$$

and the oscillation is sustained indefinitely. This is plotted in curve b of Fig. 46, where it is seen that for the first quarter cycle the undamped solution is not greatly different from the damped solution of curve a. Furthermore, the undamped frequency of oscillation, 1.28 cycles per second, is only slightly greater than for the damped case.

Example Continued: Critical Damping.—With critical damping we have $D = 2\sqrt{MK}$, so the two roots (136) of the characteristic equation (135) are identical:

$$m_1 = m_2 = -\frac{D}{2M}. \tag{149}$$

The solution will be in the form of Eq. (131), where $\beta = D/2M$:

$$x = (C_1 + C_2 t)\epsilon^{-Dt/2M}. \tag{150}$$

Substituting the same initial conditions that at $t = 0$, $x = X_0$ and velocity $dx/dt = 0$, we obtain

$$X_0 = C_1$$

and
$$0 = -\frac{D}{2M} C_1 + C_2.$$

So the solution becomes

$$x = X_0 \left(1 + \frac{Dt}{2M}\right) \epsilon^{-Dt/2M}. \tag{151}$$

If all numerical conditions in the previous problem remain the same as before except that the damping is at the critical value, we shall have

$$D = 2\sqrt{MK} = 9.98 \text{ lb-sec/ft.}$$

For an initial displacement of 0.25 ft the solution is

$$x = 0.25(1 + 8.03t)\epsilon^{-8.03t}. \tag{152}$$

This is plotted in curve c of Fig. 46.

Observe in Fig. 46 that, when all parameters are fixed in value except the damping, the critically damped solution approaches zero faster than either the overdamped solution or the envelope of the oscillatory solution. This principle is useful in many electrical and mechanical devices, notably in instruments.

44. General Homogeneous Equation.—When the physical system has more than one degree of freedom, one usually obtains a differential equation of higher order than the second. The principles of solution are quite similar to those which we have already discussed, and their extension will be relatively simple. The general linear homogeneous equation with constant coefficients can be written in the form:

$$a_0 \frac{d^n y}{dt^n} + a_1 \frac{d^{n-1}y}{dt^{n-1}} + \cdots + a_n y = 0, \tag{153}$$

or, in operator form,

$$(a_0 p^n + a_1 p^{n-1} + \cdots + a_n)y = 0. \tag{154}$$

Assuming a solution of the form $C\epsilon^{mt}$ as before, we are led to the characteristic equation

$$a_0 m^n + a_1 m^{n-1} + \cdots + a_n = 0, \tag{155}$$

which can be written by inspection from the differential equation. This is an algebraic equation of the nth degree and will have n roots, providing us with the n constants of integration necessary for the general solution. When the characteristic equation is of high degree, and particularly when some of the roots are complex, there may be algebraic difficulties in finding the roots of the equation. However, methods have been devised for evaluating such roots numerically.[1] If the equation is cubic of the form

[1] One of the most useful of these is Graeffe's root-squaring method. See, for example, E. J. Berg, "Heaviside's Operational Calculus," Chap. XXVIII, McGraw-Hill Book Company, Inc., New York, 1936. For an approximate method that applies to highly oscillatory systems, see E. A. Guillemin, Approximate Solution for Electrical Networks, *Trans. A.I.E.E.*, Vol. 47, p. 361 (1928), or V. Bush, "Operational Circuit Analysis," p. 94, John Wiley & Sons. Inc., New York, 1937.

$a_0m^3 + a_1m^2 + a_2m + a_3 = 0$, there will be at least one real root $m = m_1$. This can be found by trial and error or by plotting $z = a_0m^3 + a_1m^2 + a_2m + a_3$ vs. m and finding the point m_1 at which the curve intersects the m-axis. The quantity $m - m_1$ will then divide into the cubic without remainder, leaving a quadratic that can be solved easily for the other two roots. If the system is highly oscillatory, a good approximation to the real root is $m_1 = -a_3/a_2$.

Having found the n roots of the characteristic equation (155), we can write n solutions of the form $C\epsilon^{mt}$. However, because the differential equation is linear and homogeneous in y, the general solution will be the sum of these solutions. For each real unrepeated root m there will be a term in the solution of the form $C\epsilon^{mt}$; for each pair of complex roots $(-\alpha \pm j\omega)$ we may use for convenience two terms of the form

$$\epsilon^{-\alpha t}(A \cos \omega t + B \sin \omega t);$$

and for a repeated root $(-\beta)$ which appears r times the corresponding terms will be

$$(C_1 + C_2t + \cdots + C_rt^{r-1})\epsilon^{-\beta t}.$$

The general solution will be the sum of all these n terms. For a particular solution our initial conditions will provide us with enough information to evaluate the n constants of integration.

45. Systems of Homogeneous Equations.—When the physical system has more than one degree of freedom there will be more than one differential equation required to describe the performance of the system. If all the driving forces or voltages are zero, the resulting system of simultaneous differential equations will be homogeneous. This means that the system must initially be in nonequilibrium in order to obtain a solution other than zero.

For example the system of Fig. 27, Chap. IV, might have a driving voltage e which is zero for all time, but might start out with the condenser C charged and perhaps with current in the inductance. In this case the equations for the system, (50) or (51), would be equal to zero on the right-hand side and would therefore be homogeneous. The second equation of (50) has an integral in one of the terms, and the corresponding operator form (51) has a p in the denominator. This can be removed by taking the first derivative of the whole equation, which amounts to multiplying the operator form through by p. Although this is not necessary, it is usually convenient.

We shall first investigate some algebraic properties of the differential operator $p \equiv d/dt$ and shall show that in a linear equation with constant coefficients the operators can be manipulated in a formal manner very much as though they were algebraic coefficients. We shall interpret the expression p^2y as meaning

$$p^2y = p(py) = \frac{d}{dt}\left(\frac{dy}{dt}\right) = \frac{d^2y}{dt^2},$$

and, similarly,
$$p^ny = \frac{d^ny}{dt^n}.$$

The law of exponents then holds, *i.e.*,

$$p^np^ry = p^{n+r}y,$$

where n and r are positive integers.

Consider next the expression $p(y + z)$ where y and z are functions of t. Then

$$p(y + z) = \frac{d}{dt}(y + z) = \frac{dy}{dt} + \frac{dz}{dt} = py + pz;$$

so the differential operator follows the distributive law of algebra. Next interpret the expression $(p - m_1)(p - m_2)y$:

$$(p - m_1)(p - m_2)y = (p - m_1)\left(\frac{dy}{dt} - m_2y\right)$$

$$= \frac{d}{dt}\left(\frac{dy}{dt} - m_2y\right) - m_1\left(\frac{dy}{dt} - m_2y\right)$$

$$= \frac{d^2y}{dt^2} - m_2\frac{dy}{dt} - m_1\frac{dy}{dt} + m_1m_2y$$

$$= [p^2 - (m_1 + m_2)p + m_1m_2]y.$$

Furthermore, the expression in reverse order $(p - m_2)(p - m_1)y$ will yield the same result. Hence the commutative law holds and

$$[p^2 - (m_1 + m_2)p + m_1m_2]y = (p - m_1)(p - m_2)y$$
$$= (p - m_2)(p - m_1)y.$$

Observe that the operators are written to the left of the variables on which they operate. We shall express the integral with respect to t as

$$\int y\, dt = \frac{1}{p}\, y,$$

so that

$$\frac{d}{dt}\int y\, dt = p\left(\frac{1}{p}\, y\right) = y,$$

and shall for the present avoid the use of $(1/p)(py)$ where we would have to consider the effect of a constant of integration. Thus armed with some of the algebraic properties of the differential operator, we shall attack the problem of simultaneous linear differential equations with constant coefficients.

Such a system of equations can be written in the general form:

$$\left.\begin{aligned}
F_{11}(p)y_1 + F_{12}(p)y_2 + \cdots + F_{1k}(p)y_k &= 0 \\
F_{21}(p)y_1 + F_{22}(p)y_2 + \cdots + F_{2k}(p)y_k &= 0 \\
\cdots\cdots\cdots\cdots\cdots\cdots\cdots\cdots\cdots\cdots\cdots\cdots\cdots \\
F_{k1}(p)y_1 + F_{k2}(p)y_2 + \cdots + F_{kk}(p)y_k &= 0,
\end{aligned}\right\} \qquad (156)$$

in which there are k unknowns $y_1, y_2, \ldots, y_k$ which may be currents, voltages, velocities, displacements, etc., and the $F(p)$'s are functions of p which operate on these variables. For specific examples of this type of system, see Eqs. (51) and (66) of Chap. IV with the driving forces and voltages set equal to zero.

We can now eliminate all the dependent variables except one in Eqs. (156), manipulating p as though it were an algebraic coefficient and employing the usual methods of algebra to effect the elimination. This will yield a derived differential equation with an order n which cannot exceed the sum of the orders of the individual equations in the system:

$$(a_0 p^n + a_1 p^{n-1} + \cdots + a_n)y_r = 0. \qquad (157)$$

In general the quantity in parentheses will be precisely the same regardless of which variable y_r we choose to retain.

The derived differential equation has the form of the general homogeneous equation (154) and will have a characteristic equation similar to (155):

$$a_0 m^n + a_1 m^{n-1} + \cdots + a_n = 0. \qquad (158)$$

From here on, the solution proceeds exactly as with the general

homogeneous equation of the preceding section: We first find the n roots of the characteristic equation (158) and then write a solution of n terms with a like number of integration constants. For the real roots we choose exponential terms of the form $C\epsilon^{mt}$; for complex roots we preferably write trigonometric terms of the form $\epsilon^{-\alpha t}(A \cos \omega t + B \sin \omega t)$ or its equivalent

$$Y\epsilon^{-\alpha t} \cos (\omega t - \phi);$$

and for a root appearing twice we would use the form

$$(C_1 + C_2 t)\epsilon^{-\beta t}.$$

For a particular solution we can evaluate the n constants of integration from the initial conditions.

Observe that since the characteristic equation (158) is in general the same regardless of the variable for which we are solving, all variables will contain similar terms with the same exponents, although with different constants of integration. Thus an oscillation arising in one part of a system will cause a similar oscillation in every other part of the system, although perhaps with somewhat smaller amplitude. This is a good rule to remember, although there are some exceptions to it.

We shall now consider a method of determining the n constants of integration from the initial conditions of the system. It will have been observed in the second-order examples of Sec. 43 that the two constants of integration were evaluated from a physical knowledge of the dependent variable and its first derivative at $t = 0$. Similarly for the nth-order equation, if we can find the initial values of the dependent variable and its first $n - 1$ derivatives, we shall be able to apply these to the solution and its corresponding derivatives, thus obtaining enough simultaneous algebraic equations to evaluate the constants. This is the method of successive initial derivatives.

Return to the original system of differential equations (156) and recall that they must be satisfied for each instant of time: for $t = 0$ as well as for other values of t. In general each individual equation is not higher than the second order, and physical knowledge will tell us the initial values of the dependent variables and their first derivatives (for example, in a mechanical system we would know the initial displacements and velocities). Hence we can place $t = 0$ in the original equations, insert all known

initial values, and solve these algebraic equations simultaneously for the initial value of the second derivatives. Returning again to the original differential equations, we can take the first derivative of each one, thus obtaining third-order equations. Again let $t = 0$, substitute the known initial values of the first and second derivatives, and solve for the third initial derivatives. This process can be continued indefinitely and will be illustrated in the example below. The method has the advantage of depending upon a simple concept and is easily remembered.

For mechanical equations written in terms of displacement and electrical equations written in terms of current, the equations

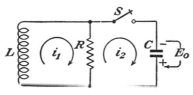

FIG. 17.—Electrical network of example.

may contain first derivatives and integrals of the variables rather than second derivatives. In this case the initial values of the variables and their integrals will be known, and the first initial derivatives rather than the second will have to be solved in the first step. Otherwise the procedure is identical with that described above.

Example: System of Homogeneous Equations.—Consider the system of Fig. 47, which is one of the simplest practical systems with two degrees of freedom. With the switch S open, the condenser C is charged to a potential E_0 volts in the direction shown. At $t = 0$ the switch is closed, and the problem is to find the resulting currents. The differential equations are found to be

$$\left. \begin{aligned} L\frac{di_1}{dt} + Ri_1 - Ri_2 &= 0 \\ -Ri_1 + Ri_2 + \frac{1}{C}\int i_2\, dt &= 0, \end{aligned} \right\} \tag{159}$$

in which, we recall, the quantity $(1/C)\int i_2\, dt$ represents the voltage across the condenser. To find the derived differential equation, write Eqs. (159) in operator form:

$$\left. \begin{aligned} (Lp + R)i_1 - Ri_2 &= 0 \\ -Ri_1 + \left(R + \frac{1}{pC}\right)i_2 &= 0. \end{aligned} \right\} \tag{160}$$

We may remove the integral in the second equation by taking the first derivative of each term (this amounts to multiplying through by p). Let us eliminate i_1 between these equations and retain i_2, which can be done in any one of several ways. For example, we can solve formally for i_1 in the first equation:

$$i_1 = \left(\frac{R}{Lp + R}\right) i_2,$$

and substitute into the second equation of (160):

$$-\left(\frac{R^2}{Lp + R}\right) i_2 + \left(R + \frac{1}{pC}\right) i_2 = 0.$$

Upon clearing of fractions this becomes

$$\left(Lp^2 + \frac{L}{RC} p + \frac{1}{C}\right) i_2 = 0. \tag{161}$$

This is the desired derived differential equation. It could also have been obtained by multiplying the first of Eqs. (160) by R and the second by $(Lp + R)$, and adding the two equations to eliminate i_1. Furthermore, if we had eliminated i_2 instead, we would have obtained a derived equation identical with Eq. (161) except that i_1 would have replaced i_2. The characteristic equation for (161) is

$$Lm^2 + \frac{L}{RC} m + \frac{1}{C} = 0, \tag{162}$$

and its roots are

$$m_1, m_2 = -\frac{1}{2RC} \pm \sqrt{\frac{1}{4R^2C^2} - \frac{1}{LC}}. \tag{163}$$

The best form for the solution will depend on whether the portion under the radical is positive, negative, or zero, *i.e.*, whether the system is overdamped, oscillatory, or critically damped. Let us assume that it is oscillatory. Following the method of Sec. 43 we shall then write the solution as

$$i_2 = \epsilon^{-t/2RC}(A \cos \omega t + B \sin \omega t), \tag{164}$$

where

$$\omega = \sqrt{\frac{1}{LC} - \frac{1}{4R^2C^2}}. \tag{165}$$

We must now evaluate the constants of integration from the initial conditions. Return to the original differential equations

as written in nonabbreviated form (159) and substitute known initial values for the quantities. Since the current through the inductance is zero initially and cannot suddenly change, $(i_1)_0 = 0$. Furthermore, the condenser is initially charged to a voltage E_0 opposite to the direction in which positive i_2 would charge it, so

$$(e_c)_0 = \left(\frac{1}{C}\int i_2\,dt\right)_0 = -E_0.$$

Therefore, just after the switch is closed $(t = 0+)$, Eqs. (159) become

$$L\left(\frac{di_1}{dt}\right)_0 + 0 - R(i_2)_0 = 0,$$
$$0 + R(i_2)_0 - E_0 = 0.$$

Solving for the unknown initial quantities we obtain

$$(i_2)_0 = \frac{E_0}{R} \tag{166}$$

and

$$\left(\frac{di_1}{dt}\right)_0 = \frac{E_0}{L}. \tag{167}$$

To obtain the required first initial derivative of i_2, take the first derivative of the original equations (159):

$$\left.\begin{aligned}
L\frac{d^2i_1}{dt^2} + R\frac{di_1}{dt} - R\frac{di_2}{dt} &= 0 \\
-R\frac{di_1}{dt} + R\frac{di_2}{dt} + \frac{1}{C}i_2 &= 0.
\end{aligned}\right\} \tag{168}$$

For $t = 0$, substitute the known initial values including those just found:

$$\left.\begin{aligned}
L\left(\frac{d^2i_1}{dt^2}\right)_0 + R\left(\frac{E_0}{L}\right) - R\left(\frac{di_2}{dt}\right)_0 &= 0 \\
-R\left(\frac{E_0}{L}\right) + R\left(\frac{di_2}{dt}\right)_0 + \frac{1}{C}\left(\frac{E_0}{R}\right) &= 0.
\end{aligned}\right\} \tag{169}$$

From this we obtain

$$\left(\frac{di_2}{dt}\right)_0 = \frac{E_0}{L}\left(1 - \frac{L}{R^2C}\right). \tag{170}$$

The second initial derivative of i_1 need not be found.

Applying the initial quantities (166) and (170) to the general solution (164) and its first derivative at $t = 0$, we find

$$(i_2)_0 = \frac{E_0}{R} = \epsilon^0[A \cos (0) + B \sin (0)],$$

$$\left(\frac{di_2}{dt}\right)_0 - \frac{E_0}{L}\left(1 - \frac{L}{R^2C}\right) = -\frac{A}{2RC} + \omega B,$$

from which A and B can be solved and the particular solution written from Eq. (164):

$$i_2 = E_0\epsilon^{-t/2RC}\left[\frac{1}{R}\cos \omega t + \frac{1}{\omega L}\left(1 - \frac{L}{2R^2C}\right)\sin \omega t\right]. \quad (171)$$

This is a damped oscillation with a natural angular velocity ω given by Eq. (165) and completes the solution.

Since i_1 will have the same characteristic equation (162) which we found for i_2, its general solution will be identical with Eq. (164), although the constants of integration will be different in value. Thus the solution for i_1 will be a damped oscillation with the same natural frequency and damping constant that we found for i_2, but the oscillation will be different in magnitude and phase.

46. The Nature of Nonhomogeneous Equations.—A nonhomogeneous linear differential equation with constant coefficients has the form:

$$a_0\frac{d^ny}{dt^n} + a_1\frac{d^{n-1}y}{dt^{n-1}} + \cdots + a_ny = f(t), \quad (172)$$

where the right side is a function of t or a constant. In operator form the equation would be written as

$$(a_0p^n + a_1p^{n-1} + \cdots + a_n)y = f(t). \quad (173)$$

A solution y is desired which, when operated upon by the portion in parentheses, will be identical with $f(t)$.

The general solution will be composed of the sum of two parts. The first of these satisfies Eq. (172) identically and is free of arbitrary constants. This part is called the *particular integral,* and in problems in dynamics where the independent variable is time, this portion of the solution is interpreted physically as the steady state. The second part of the solution makes the left side of Eq. (172) identically zero and contains the constants of integration. It is called the *complementary function* and in problems in dynamics is interpreted physically as the transient response. In nondynamic problems the terms "steady state" and "transient" lose their meaning, and the more general names "particular integral" and "complementary function" are used.

The steady-state response of a dynamic system is caused and sustained by the driving force[1] $f(t)$ and will be of the same general form as $f(t)$ for most practical driving forces. For example, if the driving force is sinusoidal, the steady-state response will be sinusoidal also.[2] The transient response is not sustained by the driving force but arises merely because of a lack of initial equilibrium. In the linear systems we are now studying, the transients are exponential exactly as in the case of the homogeneous equation in which there was no $f(t)$.

The complete solution is therefore composed of the two parts

$$y = y_{ss} + y_t, \tag{174}$$

where y_{ss} means the steady-state part of y, and y_t means the transient part of y.

Substitute the complete solution (174) into the differential equation (173),

$$(a_0 p^n + a_1 p^{n-1} + \cdots + a_n)(y_{ss} + y_t) = f(t),$$

or, recalling that the operator p follows the distributive law of algebra,

$$(a_0 p^n + a_1 p^{n-1} + \cdots + a_n)y_t + (a_0 p^n + a_1 p^{n-1} + \cdots + a_n)y_{ss} = f(t). \tag{175}$$

The various exponentials in the transient part of the solution eventually die out, leaving only the steady state, hence the steady-state solution by itself must satisfy the equation

$$(a_0 p^n + a_1 p^{n-1} + \cdots + a_n)y_{ss} = f(t). \tag{176}$$

As an example of this, see Eqs. (41) and (42) of Sec. 25. Comparison of Eqs. (175) and (176) shows that the transient part

---

[1] The term "driving force" will be used in a general sense and will include electrical voltages, electrical currents when these are used to drive a circuit, and applied mechanical displacements as well as forces.

[2] Observe that this holds only for linear systems with constant parameters.

of the solution must satisfy the corresponding homogeneous equation:

$$(a_0 p^n + a_1 p^{n-1} + \cdots + a_n)y_t = 0. \tag{177}$$

Thus the transient part of the solution, or complementary function, can be found by the methods previously described for solving homogeneous equations and contains the n constants of integration necessary in the general solution. The steady-state portion can be found by a number of methods, some of which will be described shortly.

It should be mentioned here that the initial conditions must be applied to the *total* solution $y = y_{ss} + y_t$ and never to the transient portion alone.

An interesting fact brought out by Eq. (177) is that in linear systems the transient always has the same form regardless of the conditions causing it to arise. For example, if a system is subject to oscillation at a certain natural frequency and damping constant, an oscillation with this frequency and damping constant will occur with any shock or application of driving force, independent of the steady-state response. Of course the amplitude of such oscillation or other transients will depend upon the magnitude of the shock or driving force, and consequently the constants of integration must be evaluated in the total solution. In *non-linear* systems the form of the transient may not be independent of the steady state or of the means by which it is caused. For instance in the example of Sec. 40 the natural frequency of the pendulum depends to some extent upon its initial displacement.

47. Solution of Nonhomogeneous Equations. Reduction to Homogeneous Form.—The first method to be considered is that of reducing the nonhomogeneous equation (173) to homogeneous form by differentiation, after which the methods for solving homogeneous equations can be applied. This process will yield the coefficients of the steady-state solution in the form of spurious constants of integration. These, however, can be evaluated by substituting the steady-state solution back into the original differential equation and equating coefficients of like functions of time. For this reason the process is sometimes called the *method of undetermined coefficients*. This method will not work for every conceivable form of driving force $f(t)$. However, it does apply to nearly every $f(t)$ commonly used in engineering work and is usually less laborious than the more general methods. Furthermore it will point out some short cuts that we can take for the more commonly used forms of driving force.

We shall later describe a more general method that employs a successive reduction of order of the original differential equation, which in general can be applied when the foregoing method fails.

In engineering work the form of $f(t)$ usually falls into one of the following two classes:[1]

1. It may be of a form which, if differentiated often enough, will go to zero.   Examples: $f(t) =$ a constant, $f(t) = A + Bt + Ct^2$.

2. It may be of a form which, if differentiated often enough, will come back to the original form.   In this class fall exponentials and linear combinations of exponentials, such as ϵ^{at}, $\sin \omega t$, $\cos \omega t$, and $\sinh \omega t$.

Class 1.—If $f(t)$ falls into the first class, then by differentiating it r times it goes to zero.   Differentiating Eq. (173) in this manner we get

$$p^r(a_0 p^n + a_1 p^{n-1} + \cdots + a_n)y = 0. \qquad (178)$$

This is a homogeneous equation, and the characteristic equation is

$$m^r(a_0 m^n + a_1 m^{n-1} + \cdots + a_n) = 0. \qquad (179)$$

The part in parentheses will be recognized as the characteristic equation for the transient part of the solution (compare with Eq. 177), therefore the remaining roots must indicate the form of the steady state:

$$m^r = 0, \qquad \text{or} \qquad m = 0 \qquad r \text{ times.}$$

From the discussion of repeated roots in Secs. 43 and 44, the steady-state solution must be of the form

$$y_{ss} = A_1 + A_2 t + \cdots + A_r t^{r-1}. \qquad (180)$$

Although the coefficients $A_1, A_2, \ldots, A_r$ have arisen after the fashion of constants of integration, they are not arbitrary and can be evaluated without regard to initial conditions.   The A's must have values that will make the steady-state solution

---

[1] The method is somewhat more general than this and can be shown to apply whenever $f(t)$ and its derivatives can form a set of linearly dependent functions.

satisfy the original differential equation (173) (or Eq. 176) for all values of time. Hence we can substitute the *steady-state solution by itself* back into the original differential equation (173), equate coefficients of like functions of time, and solve the resulting algebraic equations for the A's.

The transient solution y_t is obtained from the roots of

$$a_0 m^n + a_1 m^{n-1} + \cdots + a_n = 0, \tag{181}$$

by proceeding in the manner previously described for homogeneous equations. The total solution will be the sum of the steady-state and transient solutions, and the initial conditions should be applied to this total solution.

When the driving force is a constant, $f(t) = F$, a convenient short cut may be used. One differentiation will then reduce the equation to homogeneous form, giving the extra root $m = 0$, and the steady-state solution is $y = K\epsilon^0 =$ a constant (as we might expect). All derivatives of the solution will be zero, which is equivalent to placing p equal to zero in Eq. (176) and solving what remains: $y_{ss} = F/a_n$.

Example, Class 1.—As an example, consider the system of Fig. 48, which consists of a mass and damper suspended from a spring, with a force f applied to the mass. Suppose that the system is initially in static equilibrium and that a constant force $f = F$ is applied at $t = 0$. The differential equation of motion is

$$(Mp^2 + Dp + K)x = F. \tag{182}$$

One differentiation will reduce this to homogeneous form:

$$p(Mp^2 + Dp + K)x = 0. \tag{183}$$

Thus the extra root in the characteristic equation will be $m = 0$, and the steady-state solution is $x_{ss} =$ a constant. Derivatives of this will be zero, so substitution of the steady-state solution into the original equation (182) will yield

$$x_{ss} = \frac{F}{K}. \tag{184}$$

For the transient, use the homogeneous equation corresponding to (182), for which the characteristic equation is

$$Mm^2 + Dm + K = 0.$$

Assuming an oscillatory system, the two roots of this equation will be given by $m_1, m_2 = -(D/2M) \pm j\omega$ where

$$\omega = \sqrt{\frac{K}{M} - \frac{D^2}{4M^2}}. \tag{185}$$

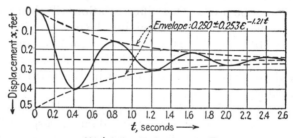

(a)-Physical system

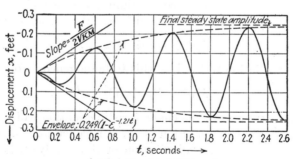

(b)-Solution for f = constant = F

(c)-Solution for $f = F \cos \omega t$,
system in resonance with applied frequency

FIG. 48.—Response of oscillatory system to two different driving forces. Positive displacement is plotted downward to assist comparison with physical system.

The transient solution can, therefore, be written in the form

$$x_t = \epsilon^{-Dt/2M}(A \cos \omega t + B \sin \omega t). \tag{186}$$

Adding the steady-state and transient portions to obtain the total solution, we obtain

$$x = x_{ss} + x_t = \frac{F}{K} + \epsilon^{-Dt/2M}(A \cos \omega t + B \sin \omega t). \quad (187)$$

To this total solution apply the initial conditions that $(x)_0 = 0$ and initial velocity $(dx/dt)_0 = 0$. From the first of these we obtain

$$0 = \frac{F}{K} + A, \quad \text{so} \quad A = -\frac{F}{K}.$$

From the second,

$$0 = -\frac{D}{2M} A + \omega B, \quad \text{so} \quad B = -\frac{DF}{2MK\omega}.$$

The general solution (187) then becomes

$$x = \frac{F}{K}\left[1 - \epsilon^{-Dt/2M}\left(\cos \omega t + \frac{D}{2\omega M} \sin \omega t\right)\right]. \quad (188)$$

Using $F = 10$ lb and the constants of the oscillatory example in Sec. 43: $W = 20$ lb, so $M = 0.621$ lb-sec²/ft, $K = 40$ lb/ft, $D = 1.5$ lb-sec/ft, the solution becomes

$$x = 0.250 - 0.253\epsilon^{-1.21t} \cos (7.92t - 8.7°).$$

This is plotted in Fig. 48b and can be compared with the oscillatory example of Sec. 43 and with curve a of Fig. 46.

Class 2.—If $f(t)$ is of the second class, sufficient differentiation will bring it back to its original form. Start with the original differential equation:

$$(a_0 p^n + a_1 p^{n-1} + \cdots + a_n) y = f(t). \quad (189)$$

Assume that r differentiations bring the right-hand side back to a constant times the original function: $Q f(t)$. Thus

$$p^r(a_0 p^n + a_1 p^{n-1} + \cdots + a_n)y = Q f(t). \quad (190)$$

Multiplying Eq. (189) by Q and subtracting Eq. (190), we obtain a homogeneous equation:

$$(p^r - Q)(a_0 p^n + a_1 p^{n-1} + \cdots + a_n)y = 0, \quad (191)$$

which can be solved by the methods described in previous sections. The roots obtained from the parenthesis on the left will yield the steady-state portion of the solution, and *this* part should be substituted back into the original equation (189) to evaluate whatever coefficients arise in the solution. The roots obtained from the right-hand parenthesis will yield the transient solution. The complete solution for y will be the sum of the steady-state and transient portions, and the initial conditions should be applied to this total solution to evaluate the constants of integration.

Many important problems involve driving forces of sinusoidal form such as $F \sin \omega t$, $F \cos \omega t$, or in more general form

$$F \cos (\omega t + \alpha),$$

where α is any phase angle. Two differentiations will then bring $f(t)$ back to its original form, yielding for the latter expression $-\omega^2 F \cos (\omega t + \alpha)$. The process described above will yield two additional roots $m = \pm j\omega$, and the corresponding steady-state solution will be of the form $A \cos \omega t + B \sin \omega t$, where ω is the angular velocity of the driving force. When a linear constant-parameter system has this type of driving force, the foregoing form of solution may be assumed immediately and the coefficients A and B evaluated by substitution in the original differential equation. The foregoing solution is said to be a *forced oscillation* as distinguished from the free transient oscillations that we have seen previously and has a frequency equal to that of the impressed driving force: $f = \omega/2\pi$. If the system is inherently oscillatory, free oscillations may initially be superimposed on the forced oscillations and, if the two are near in frequency, they may "beat" together at the beginning. Furthermore, if the system is driven at a frequency near one of its natural frequencies, the steady-state solution may have large amplitudes. This is the phenomenon of resonance and will be investigated in some detail in Chap. VII by methods more convenient for that purpose.

Example, Class 2.—To illustrate the method, assume that the system of Fig. 48a has a driving force of the form

$$f(t) = F \cos \omega t$$

suddenly applied at $t = 0$. The differential equation of motion then becomes

$$(Mp^2 + Dp + K)x = F \cos \omega t. \tag{192}$$

To reduce this to homogeneous form, take the second derivative of both sides, thus obtaining

$$p^2(Mp^2 + Dp + K)x = -\omega^2 F \cos \omega t. \tag{193}$$

Multiply the original equation by ω^2 and add the two equations:

$$(p^2 + \omega^2)(Mp^2 + Dp + K)x = 0. \tag{194}$$

This equation is homogeneous. The steady-state solution is obtained from the roots of

$$(m^2 + \omega^2) = 0,$$

which are m_1, $m_2 - \pm j\omega$. Since the roots are imaginary, the steady-state solution is oscillatory in character but with zero damping constant (forced oscillation), and the form of the solution is

$$x_{ss} = A \cos \omega t + B \sin \omega t. \tag{195}$$

This could have been assumed at the beginning from our discussion in the previous paragraph.

To evaluate the coefficients A and B, take the first and second derivatives of the steady-state solution (195) and substitute back into the original differential equation (192). Upon collection of terms this yields

$$(-\omega^2 MA + \omega DB + KA) \cos \omega t$$
$$+ (-\omega^2 MB - \omega DA + KB) \sin \omega t = F \cos \omega t.$$

This can be an identity (true for all values of time) only if

From the cosine terms, $(K - \omega^2 M)A + (\omega D)B = F$ ⎫
From the sine terms, $-(\omega D)A + (K - \omega^2 M)B = 0.$ ⎬   (196)

Solving these equations simultaneously for A and B we obtain

$$A = \frac{(K - \omega^2 M)F}{Z^2} \quad \text{and} \quad B = \frac{\omega DF}{Z^2}, \tag{197}$$

where for simplicity we have defined

$$Z^2 = (K - \omega^2 M)^2 + (\omega D)^2. \tag{198}$$

The steady-state solution is then the forced oscillation

$$x_{ss} = \frac{F}{Z^2} [(K - \omega^2 M) \cos \omega t + \omega D \sin \omega t]. \tag{199}$$

The transient portion must be added to this to form the complete solution. We shall investigate here only one special case of considerable interest: when the system is driven at a frequency such that $\omega^2 M = K$, corresponding substantially to displacement resonance if damping is not excessive (see Chap. VII). For this condition we obtain from Eq. (198), $Z = \omega D$, and the steady-state solution becomes simply $(F/\omega D) \sin \omega t$. For the transient we use the homogeneous equation corresponding to Eq. (192), for which the characteristic equation is $(Mm^2 + Dm + K) = 0$. Assuming an oscillatory transient as in the previous example, the transient solution will be of the form (186), and the total solution will be

$$x = \frac{F}{\omega D} \sin \omega t + \epsilon^{-Dt/2M}(P \cos \omega_n t + Q \sin \omega_n t), \qquad (200)$$

where we now distinguish the natural angular velocity by ω_n:

$$\omega_n = \sqrt{\frac{K}{M} - \frac{D^2}{4M^2}}. \qquad (201)$$

To the total solution apply the initial conditions $(x)_0 = 0$ and initial velocity $(dx/dt)_0 = 0$. We then obtain

$$0 = 0 + P + 0, \qquad \text{so} \qquad P = 0,$$

$$0 = \frac{F}{D} - \frac{D}{2M} P + \omega_n Q, \qquad \text{so} \qquad Q = -\frac{F}{\omega_n D},$$

and the particular solution for this special case becomes

$$x = \frac{F}{\omega D} \left(\sin \omega t - \frac{\omega}{\omega_n} \epsilon^{-Dt/2M} \sin \omega_n t \right). \qquad (202)$$

For small values of damping $\omega = \omega_n$ and Eq. (202) can be written approximately

$$x = \frac{F}{\omega D} (1 - \epsilon^{-Dt/2M}) \sin \omega t. \qquad (203)$$

Thus the sine function is contained within an exponential envelope. The form of the solution is plotted in Fig. 48c using the constants of the previous example: $M = 0.621$ lb-sec²/ft ($W = 20$ lb), $K = 40$ lb/ft, $D = 1.5$ lb-sec/ft. For the special case treated above the system is assumed to be driven at

$$\omega = \sqrt{\frac{K}{M}},$$

which for this system is 8.02 radians per second corresponding to a frequency of 1.28 cycles per second. The maximum value of the sinusoidal applied force is taken to be $F = 3.0$ lb. Observe the large amplitudes that can be obtained near resonance with a comparatively small driving force.

An important conclusion to be drawn from Eq. (203) is that, although the amplitude of oscillation may be quite high in steady-state resonance, this amplitude is not reached instantaneously but must build up from zero at a reasonable rate even when the damping is extremely small. The initial rate of build-up is obtained by taking the time derivative of the envelope indicated by Eq. (203), setting $t = 0$, and recalling that $\omega = \sqrt{K/M}$. This yields the initial rate $F/2\sqrt{KM}$ independent of damping. Thus, if we are starting a machine and wish to run it above a resonant speed, it may be possible to pass through resonance quickly enough to avoid excessive amplitudes.

49. Solution of Nonhomogeneous Equations. General Method.—In some problems a more general method than that of reduction to homogeneous form may be desirable. The method to be described employs the algebraic properties of the differential operator in reducing the order of the original differential equation. Consider the general nonhomogeneous linear equation with constant coefficients:

$$(a_0 p^n + a_1 p^{n-1} + \cdots + a_n)y = f(t). \tag{204}$$

The characteristic equation will be

$$(a_0 m^n + a_1 m^{n-1} + \cdots + a_n) = 0,$$

and we shall denote its roots, as before, by $m = m_1, m_2, \ldots, m_n$. Since these are the roots of the left-hand side of the original differential equation, we shall factor Eq. (204) into

$$a_0(p - m_1)(p - m_2) \cdots \underbrace{(p - m_n)y}_{u} = f(t). \tag{205}$$

As indicated above, denote $(p - m_2) \cdots (p - m_n)y$ by the new variable u. Then we can write

$$a_0(p - m_1)u = f(t). \tag{206}$$

Equations of this form can always be integrated by first multiplying both sides by the *integrating factor* $\epsilon^{-m_1 t}$. Then we have

$$a_0 \epsilon^{-m_1 t}(p - m_1)u = \epsilon^{-m_1 t}f(t). \tag{207}$$

The left-hand side integrates into $a_0 u \cdot \epsilon^{-m_1 t}$ as can be proved by differentiating this quantity, and the right side can be integrated when the form of $f(t)$ has been specified. Thus, integration of Eq. (207) yields

$$a_0 u \epsilon^{-m_1 t} = \int \epsilon^{-m_1 t}f(t) \, dt + \text{a constant.} \tag{208}$$

If we should retain the constants of integration throughout the process, the resulting solution would contain both transient and steady state. However, the transient is most easily found from the homogeneous equation corresponding to Eq. (204) or (205). So we shall use the present method to find only the particular integral, or steady state, and shall suppress the constants of integration. We can next solve Eq. (208) for u, which we shall designate as $u(t)$ since it will be a known function of time.

$$u(t) = \frac{\epsilon^{m_1 t}}{a_0} \int \epsilon^{-m_1 t}f(t) \, dt. \tag{209}$$

However, we have previously defined u as

$$(p - m_2) \cdot \cdot \cdot (p - m_n)y;$$

so we can now write a new differential equation from Eq. (209) which is lower in order than the original equation (204) or (205):

$$\underbrace{(p - m_2)(p - m_3) \cdot \cdot \cdot (p - m_n)y}_{v} = u(t). \tag{210}$$

Repeating the process, we denote $(p - m_3) \cdot \cdot \cdot (p - m_n)y$ by some new variable, say v, and obtain $(p - m_2)v = u(t)$. Multiply through by the integrating factor $\epsilon^{-m_2 t}$, integrate both sides (the left side integrates into $v \cdot \epsilon^{-m_2 t}$ in the same fashion as before), solve for v as a function of time, write a new differential equation from the definition of v, and repeat until the left-hand side has been integrated into y. If the constants of integration have been suppressed, this will be the desired steady-state solution. The transient portion of the solution is easily found by the methods for solving homogeneous equations, since the roots of the characteristic equation are already known.

Example.—The process will be illustrated by a simple numerical example.   Solve the differential equation

$$2\frac{d^2y}{dt^2} + 10\frac{dy}{dt} + 12y = 15t. \tag{211}$$

In operator form this is

$$(2p^2 + 10p + 12)y = 15t. \tag{212}$$

The characteristic equation is $(2m^2 + 10m + 12) = 0$, from which $m = -2$ and -3.   Therefore, the left side of Eq. (212) can be factored into

$$2(p + 2)\underbrace{(p + 3)y}_{u} = 15t. \tag{213}$$

Denoting $(p + 3)y$ by u as above we have

$$2(p + 2)u = 15t. \tag{214}$$

The integrating factor for this is ϵ^{2t}.   Therefore, write

$$2\epsilon^{2t}(p + 2)u = 15t\epsilon^{2t}.$$

This integrates into (performing the ordinary integration on the right side but suppressing the constant of integration)

$$2u\epsilon^{2t} = \tfrac{15}{4}\epsilon^{2t}(2t - 1).$$

When solved for u, this yields

$$u(t) = \tfrac{15}{8}(2t - 1). \tag{215}$$

Equating this to our previous definition of u, we get

$$(p + 3)y = \tfrac{15}{8}(2t - 1). \tag{216}$$

The new integrating factor for the left side is ϵ^{3t}.   So, multiplying through by this, integrating both sides, and solving for y, we obtain the particular integral (steady-state solution):

$$y_{ss} = \tfrac{5}{24}(6t - 5). \tag{217}$$

As the roots of the characteristic equation have been shown to be $m = -2$ and -3, the total solution can be written immediately as

$$y = \tfrac{5}{24}(6t - 5) + C_1\epsilon^{-2t} + C_2\epsilon^{-3t}, \tag{218}$$

where C_1 and C_2 are constants of integration which normally would be evaluated from the initial conditions of the system.

49. Two or More Nonhomogeneous Terms.—Equations frequently arise in which there are two or more nonhomogeneous terms of different form instead of the single $f(t)$ indicated in Eq. (172). For example, the force applied to the system of Fig. 48a might have two or more components: perhaps a steady force F_0 and a sinusoidal force $F_1 \sin \omega t$, two sinusoidal forces of different frequency $F_1 \sin \omega_1 t + F_2 \sin \omega_2 t$, or a periodic nonsinusoidal force expressible as a Fourier series $\sum_n F_n \cos (n\omega t - \alpha_n)$ as shown in Chap. X.

In the general method of solution this will offer no difficulty and we can proceed in the manner previously outlined, except that, of course, there will be two or more functions of time to be integrated on the right-hand side of the equation.

However, in the method of reduction to homogeneous form the two functions of time may not fall into the same class. For example, if the force is $F_0 + F_1 \sin \omega t$, the first term would go to zero on one differentiation, while the second would return to its original form on two differentiations. One way of handling this, useful also in other applications, is to observe that the principle of superposition will apply to these linear systems, and therefore each driving force will contribute to the response independently of other driving forces that may be present. Suppose that the differential equation is

$$(a_0 p^n + a_1 p^{n-1} + \cdots + a_n)y = f_1(t) + f_2(t) + \cdots .$$

We shall first set all the driving forces except the first equal to zero and solve for the resulting steady-state y, next set all the driving forces except the second equal to zero and again solve for the steady-state y, and so on until we have worked through all the driving forces. The total solution is then the sum of all the individual steady-state solutions plus the transient which is found once and for all from the characteristic equation

$$(a_0 m^n + a_1 m^{n-1} + \cdots + a_n) = 0.$$

50. Systems of Nonhomogeneous Equations.—We have already seen that the mathematical description of a system requires as many simultaneous equations as there are degrees of freedom.

When one or more driving forces are present in the system, certain of the individual equations will be nonhomogeneous, *i.e.*, equal to a function of time or a constant on the right. The entire system of equations must then be considered as a nonhomogeneous set, and the steady-state solution for any of the variables will in general be different from zero.

A nonhomogeneous system of differential equations can be written in a general form analogous to the homogeneous Eqs. (156):

$$\left.\begin{array}{c} F_{11}(p)y_1 + F_{12}(p)y_2 + \cdots + F_{1k}(p)y_k = f_1(t) \\ F_{21}(p)y_1 + F_{22}(p)y_2 + \cdots + F_{2k}(p)y_k = f_2(t) \\ \cdots\cdots\cdots\cdots\cdots\cdots\cdots\cdots\cdots\cdots\cdots\cdots \\ F_{k1}(p)y_1 + F_{k2}(p)y_2 + \cdots + F_{kk}(p)y_k = f_k(t) \end{array}\right\} \quad (219)$$

where y_1, y_2, etc., are the dependent variables (for example currents, velocities, or displacements), $F_{11}(p)$, $F_{12}(p)$, etc., are the functions of p which operate on these variables (each in general not higher than the second order), $f_1(t)$, $f_2(t)$, etc., are the driving forces applied to the system. All but one of these can be zero; if all are zero, the system is homogeneous.

For specific examples of systems of nonhomogeneous equations, see Eqs. (51), (54), and (66) in Chap. IV.

Because of the algebraic properties of the differential operator p, we can use algebraic methods for solving simultaneous equations to eliminate all the dependent variables in Eqs. (219) except the one in which we are interested at the moment. In this the operator p will be manipulated as though it were an algebraic quantity, except that by convention it is always written to the left of the time function on which it operates. In eliminating variables we shall find that certain functions of p will operate on various driving forces on the right-hand side (algebraically this will look like multiplication, but p is an operator, not a mere multiplier). In any particular problem we shall know the form of the driving forces, and these indicated derivatives could be performed immediately. However, in Sec. 52 we shall describe an operator method of introducing initial conditions that requires all the p's to be kept in their operator form and the indicated differentiations to be performed as late in the work as possible.

We shall thus algebraically eliminate all the dependent variables except one, which we shall denote by y_r, and obtain a derived differential equation of the form

$$D(p)y_r = M_1(p)f_1(t) + M_2(p)f_2(t) + \cdots , \quad (220)$$

where $D(p)$, $M(p)$ are polynomials in p.   The order of the derived Eq. (220) will not exceed the sum of the orders of the individual equations in the original system (219).

Disregarding for the time being the above-mentioned operator method of introducing initial conditions, we can take the derivatives indicated by $M(p)f(t)$ in Eq. (220).   The result is a nonhomogeneous differential equation with perhaps more than one $f(t)$ on the right-hand side, which can be solved by the methods described in the preceding section.   The constants of integration can be evaluated by the method of successive initial derivatives, as in the case of simultaneous homogeneous equations.   The initial derivatives can be found as in Sec. 45 by returning to the original system of Eqs. (219), substituting $t = 0$ and all known initial values into the equations, and solving the resulting simultaneous algebraic equations for the unknown initial derivatives.

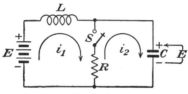

FIG. 49.—Network of example.

This can be repeated by taking the first derivative of each equation in the system, again substituting $t = 0$ and known initial values, and solving for the unknown (higher) initial derivatives.   This procedure can be continued until sufficient initial derivatives have been evaluated to permit a solution for all constants of integration.

Example: System of Nonhomogeneous Equations.—As an example, consider the system of Fig. 49, in which the switch S is initially open and the condenser is charged to the full battery voltage E in the direction shown.   The switch is closed at $t = 0$.   Find the current i_1 as a function of time.   After the switch is closed the differential equations for the system are

$$\left. \begin{aligned} L\frac{di_1}{dt} + Ri_1 - Ri_2 &= E \\ -Ri_1 + Ri_2 + \frac{1}{C}\int i_2\,dt &= 0. \end{aligned} \right\} \quad (221)$$

In operator form, these are

$$(Lp + R)i_1 - (R)i_2 = E \atop -(R)i_1 + \left(R + \frac{1}{pC}\right)i_2 = 0.} \tag{222}$$

We wish to find i_1, so eliminate i_2 algebraically. We can do this by solving the second equation for i_2 and substituting into the first, or by multiplying the first equation by $(R + 1/pC)$, the second by R, and adding. It should be realized that this "multiplication" is really a shorthand method of indicating operations by the differential operator $p \equiv d/dt$. In any case the elimination of i_2 will yield the derived differential equation:

$$\left(Lp^2 + \frac{L}{RC}p + \frac{1}{C}\right)i_1 = \left(p + \frac{1}{RC}\right)E. \tag{223}$$

This can be compared with the general form (220).

We shall not use the operator method of introducing initial conditions, so perform the derivative indicated on the right-hand side. This yields a nonhomogeneous equation of the form used in Secs. 46 and 47:

$$\left(Lp^2 + \frac{L}{RC}p + \frac{1}{C}\right)i_1 = \frac{E}{RC}. \tag{224}$$

If we solve this by reduction to homogeneous form, one differentiation will eliminate the right-hand side, giving the extra root $m = 0$ in the homogeneous equation. The steady-state solution is therefore a constant, and its derivatives are zero. If this is substituted into the differential equation (224), all terms involving derivatives will vanish (equivalent to setting $p = 0$), and we obtain simply

$$(i_1)_{ss} = \frac{E}{R}. \tag{225}$$

To find the transient portion, write the homogeneous equation corresponding to Eq. (224) and find the roots of its characteristic equation $Lm^2 + (L/RC)m + (1/C) = 0$. These roots have been found in Eq. (163). Assuming an oscillatory transient, the total solution can be written as

$$i_1 = \frac{E}{R} + \epsilon^{-t/2RC}(A \cos \omega t + B \sin \omega t), \tag{226}$$

where ω is the natural angular velocity and is given by

$$\omega = \sqrt{\frac{1}{LC} - \frac{1}{4R^2C^2}}. \tag{227}$$

Next evaluate the constants of integration A and B. Referring to Fig. 49, physical reasoning shows that the current in the inductance is initially zero since it cannot change suddenly when the switch is closed. Thus $(i_1)_0 = 0$. Furthermore the condenser is initially charged to a voltage E in the direction that positive i_2 would charge it, so that just after S is closed we must have

$$(e_c)_0 = \left(\frac{1}{C} \int i_2 \, dt\right)_0 = E.$$

Therefore, just after the switch is closed ($t = 0+$), the original differential Eqs. (221) become

$$\left. \begin{array}{c} L\left(\dfrac{di_1}{dt}\right)_0 + 0 - R(i_2)_0 = E \\ 0 + R(i_2)_0 + E = 0. \end{array} \right\} \tag{228}$$

Solving these simultaneously we obtain the desired second condition

$$\left(\frac{di_1}{dt}\right)_0 = 0.$$

Substituting this condition and also $(i_1)_0 = 0$ into the general solution (226) and its first derivative at $t = 0$, we obtain two algebraic equations that can be solved for A and B, and the particular solution for the foregoing initial conditions becomes

$$i_1 = \frac{E}{R} - \frac{E}{R} \epsilon^{-t/2RC} \left(\cos \omega t + \frac{1}{2RC\omega} \sin \omega t\right), \tag{229}$$

where the natural angular velocity ω is given by Eq. (227).

51. Change of Dependent Variable.—In some problems it may be desired to find the solution for some quantity other than, but related to, the dependent variables chosen in writing the original differential equations. For instance, in the foregoing example we might wish to find the inductor voltage or capacitor voltage as a function of time rather than one of the currents, or in a mechanical system we might wish to know the force at some point rather than the velocities or displacements. It would be possible first to solve for the original dependent variables and then use these to find the desired quantity, but this is generally more laborious than the alternative of writing the differential equation itself in terms of the desired variable. It is possible to change the variable in a simple manner, using the algebraic properties of the differential operator. The method is best shown by examples.

In the example of the previous section (Fig. 49), find the differential equation for the voltage across the inductance L. This voltage can be expressed $e_L = L(di_1/dt) = Lpi_1$. Return to the derived differential equation (223) written in terms of i_1, and solve for i_1 in a formal manner:

$$i_1 = \frac{p + \dfrac{1}{RC}}{Lp^2 + \left(\dfrac{L}{RC}\right)p + \dfrac{1}{C}} E, \qquad (230)$$

in which we follow the convention of writing all operators to the left of the time functions on which they operate. Now, however, we can write

$$e_L = Lpi_1$$

$$= \frac{Lp\left(p + \dfrac{1}{RC}\right)}{Lp^2 + \left(\dfrac{L}{RC}\right)p + \dfrac{1}{C}} E.$$

Rearranging this in the usual form we obtain the differential equation written in terms of e_L:

$$\left(Lp^2 + \frac{L}{RC}p + \frac{1}{C}\right)e_L = L\left(p^2 + \frac{1}{RC}p\right)E. \qquad (231)$$

If we do not wish to use the operator method of introducing initial conditions, we can take the derivatives indicated on the right. Since E is a constant, the right side will vanish and the equation is homogeneous as it stands. The successive initial derivatives of e_L can be found by observing that

$$(e_L)_0 = L\left(\frac{di_1}{dt}\right)_0$$

and

$$\left(\frac{de_L}{dt}\right)_0 = L\left(\frac{d^2i_1}{dt^2}\right)_0.$$

The successive initial derivatives of i_1 can be found by substituting the initial conditions into the original differential equations (221), and the above relations will then yield the initial derivatives of e_L for evaluation of the constants of integration. In a similar fashion the differential equation for condenser voltage in the circuit of Fig. 49 could be found from the relation

$$e_c = (1/pC)i_2.$$

As a second example consider the system of Fig. 50, in which it is desired to find the voltage e across the inductance and resistance as shown by the dotted line. This can be done by setting up the differential equations in the usual manner in terms of i_1 and i_2, and then solving formally for these currents after

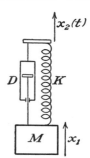

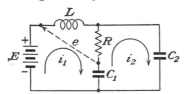

FIG. 50.—Electrical example, change of dependent variable.

FIG. 51.—Mechanical example, change of dependent variable.

the fashion of Eq. (230). The desired voltage can be written as

$$e = Lpi_1 + R(i_1 - i_2).$$

Substituting the operator expressions for i_1 and i_2 into this equation and clearing fractions will yield the desired differential equation written in terms of e.

As a mechanical example, the system of Fig. 51 consists of a mass suspended from a spring and damper whose upper ends are given a displacement $x_2(t)$ which is a known function of time. Find the differential equation for the force in the spring, neglecting the force of gravity. Summing the forces on the mass, we obtain the differential equation:

$$(Mp^2 + Dp + K)x_1 = (Dp + K)x_2(t). \qquad (232)$$

The force in the spring (tension assumed positive) is given by

$$f = K(x_2 - x_1). \qquad (233)$$

Solving Eq. (232) formally for x_1, substituting into Eq. (233), and clearing of fractions, we obtain the desired differential equation:

$$(Mp^2 + Dp + K)f = MKp^2x_2(t), \tag{234}$$

where x_2 is written $x_2(t)$ to emphasize that it is a known function of time and constitutes the driving force of the system.

52. Operator Method of Determining Initial Derivatives.— The method previously described for determining successive initial derivatives by substituting the initial conditions into the original system of differential equations is simple in principle and easily remembered. However, in systems involving several equations, the labor of solving these equations simultaneously the required number of times may be considerable. Moreover, some systems of equations when solved in this manner for $t = 0$ yield indeterminate quantities, and the method is not particularly applicable when a change of variable has been used to remove variable coefficients. We shall now describe an operator method of determining successive initial derivatives, which is easily applied and which is useful in many types of problems. Although the method uses operators, it should not be confused with operational calculus. Operational calculus is a means of determining in a rather direct manner a particular solution with the constants of integration completely evaluated, whereas we are interested here in obtaining sufficient initial derivatives to evaluate the constants of integration in the classical general solution.

The simplest and probably the most significant initial condition is that of initial equilibrium, in which the system has zero initial energy. In an electrical system this means that the inductances will initially be carrying no current and that the condensers will be initially discharged. In a mechanical system it corresponds to zero initial velocity for all masses and zero initial displacement for all springs. Such a system is said to be in an "initially relaxed condition." We shall first investigate a method for determining successive initial derivatives for initially relaxed systems and later show the means of including any initial conditions.[1]

[1] For a more rigorous discussion than that given in this chapter, see W. C. Johnson, A New Method for Introducing Relaxed Initial Conditions in Transient Problems, *Trans. A.I.E.E.*, 1941, pp. 178–181 and *Elec. Eng.*, April, 1941.

The Integral Operator.—In Sec. 45 we interpreted $(1/p)y$ to mean the time integral of y and concluded that the operations $p(1/p)y$ would result in y itself as though the p's canceled algebraically. However, we avoided the use of the operations in reverse order $(1/p)py$ because of the constant of integration that might enter. We shall now investigate this in more detail.

In order to be specific, we shall in this discussion define the integral operator $(1/p)$ as the definite integral from 0 to t, thus:

$$\frac{1}{p} y = \int_0^t y \, dt. \tag{235}$$

Consider one of the simultaneous force equations for an initially relaxed physical system, for example one of Eqs. (219), and suppose that we wish to operate on each term of this equation with the integral operator $(1/p)$. Whenever a term of the form $py = dy/dt$ appears, operation with the integral operator will yield

$$\frac{1}{p} py = \int_0^t \frac{dy}{dt} \, dt = (y)_t - (y)_0$$
$$= y - (y)_0, \tag{236}$$

since y and $(y)_t$ are identical in meaning. However, in an initially relaxed system the value of y just before the driving forces are impressed $(t = 0-)$ is zero by definition. Furthermore, when a term dy/dt is present in a force equation, the variable y is in general continuous, as otherwise the term dy/dt would be infinite at the discontinuity which would imply an infinite driving force at that time. Therefore, under these conditions y is zero just after the driving forces are impressed, and we can write from Eq. (236)

$$\frac{1}{p} py = y. \tag{237}$$

Similarly, we can show that

$$\frac{1}{p^n} p^n y = y. \tag{238}$$

Thus, *for an initially relaxed system* we can define the integral operator as in Eq. (235) and manipulate the operator p in an algebraic manner in each individual equation.

If we then divide each equation in the system (219) through by p to the highest power contained in that equation, we shall obtain equations containing only integrals with respect to time and no derivatives. Elimination of all dependent variables but one will then yield an integral equation in terms of the desired variable. However, we can obtain the same integral equation more conveniently by first finding the derived differential equation (220) in terms of the desired variable and then dividing the latter by p to the highest power contained in it. The utility of this integral equation will be seen shortly.

Consider what happens to the integral $(1/p)y$, where y is any finite function of time, as the upper limit of integration t approaches zero. This integral can be represented geometrically by the area under the graph y vs. t between the limits 0 and t, and it is evident that unless y is infinite at $t = 0$, this area will vanish as the upper limit approaches the lower. Thus we can write

$$\lim_{t \to 0} \frac{1}{p} y = \lim_{t \to 0} \int_0^t y \, dt = 0. \tag{239}$$

It should be observed that it is the quantity $(1/p)y$ and not $1/p$ itself which is zero at zero time, for $1/p$ is an operator, not merely a multiplier, and has no physical significance when considered apart from the function on which it operates. The distinction will save much confusion, since if we were to set $1/p$ itself equal to zero we should feel obliged to set p equal to infinity at $t = 0$. This, of course, is not correct and will be avoided by observing that py is not the reciprocal of $(1/p)y$, and hence is not necessarily infinite when $(1/p)y$ is equal to zero.

Initially Relaxed Systems.—Assume that the differential equations for the system have been set up in the form (219) and that from these we have obtained by algebraic methods a derived differential equation in terms of one of the variables y_r. All the derivatives and integrals in this equation should be retained in operator form. This equation can be written as

$$D(p)y_r = M_1(p)f_1(t) + M_2(p)f_2(t) + \cdots , \tag{240}$$

in which $D(p)$, $M(p)$ are polynomials in p, and the $f(t)$'s are driving forces. This equation can be put into the usual nonhomogeneous form by performing the differentiations indicated on the right and can then be solved by the methods of Sec. 47. If

$D(p)$ is of the nth degree in p, there will be n constants of integration in the general solution.

We now wish to find for an *initially relaxed system* the n initial derivatives by which the constants of integration are to be evaluated: $(y)_0$, $(dy/dt)_0 = (py)_0$, . . . , $(d^{n-1}y/dt^{n-1})_0 = (p^n y)_0$.

As indicated above, we wish to know the derivatives of y at $t = 0$, but we already know that the integrals of both y and the various $f(t)$'s are initially zero. Therefore, return to the differential equation (240) as expressed completely in operator form

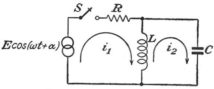

FIG. 52.—Network used in example; operator method of determining successive initial derivatives.

and put it into integral form by dividing through by p to the highest power contained in the equation.

Next set t and the various integrals $\dfrac{1}{p} y$, $\dfrac{1}{p^2} y$, $\dfrac{1}{p} f(t)$, etc, equal to zero. The initial value of y, $(y)_0$, can be solved for immediately.

Now multiply the integral equation through by p, perform the indicated differentiations on the right-hand side, and again set t and the various integrals involving $1/p$, $1/p^2$, etc., equal to zero. By substituting the known initial value $(y)_0$, the first initial derivative $(py)_0$ can be solved for immediately.

Multiply the integral equation through by p^2 and repeat the above process to obtain $(p^2 y)_0$.

The process can be continued indefinitely to obtain the necessary number of successive initial derivatives. It can be carried through in either literal or numerical form, but the literal form is preferable unless it becomes too cumbersome.

An example will serve to show the relative simplicity of the method. Consider the initially relaxed system of Fig. 52, in which the switch is closed at $t = 0$ and it is desired to find the current i_2 as a function of time. The derived differential equation for this current can be shown to be

$$\left(Lp^2 + \frac{L}{RC} p + \frac{1}{C} \right) i_2 = \frac{L}{R} p^2 E \cos (\omega t + \alpha). \qquad (241)$$

The general solution will contain two arbitrary constants of integration, hence we shall wish to know the initial values of the current and its first derivative. Physical reasoning shows that if the system is initially relaxed, $(i_2)_0 = (E \cos \alpha)/R$, but the initial value of the first derivative is difficult to find by physical reasoning and the method employed in Sec. 50 yields indeterminate quantities if used without further manipulation.

First obtain the integral equation by dividing Eq. (241) through by p^2:

$$\left(L + \frac{L}{RC}\frac{1}{p} + \frac{1}{C}\frac{1}{p^2}\right) i_2 = \frac{L}{R} E \cos (\omega t + \alpha). \qquad (242)$$

Next set t and the various integrals equal to zero:

$$L(i_2)_0 + 0 + 0 = \frac{L}{R} E \cos (\alpha).$$

The initial value of current can be solved for immediately:

$$(i_2)_0 = \frac{E \cos \alpha}{R}. \qquad (243)$$

To find the initial value of the first derivative, multiply both sides of the integral equation (242) through by p and perform the indicated differentiations:

$$\left(Lp + \frac{L}{RC} + \frac{1}{C}\frac{1}{p}\right) i_2 = -\frac{\omega L}{R} E \sin (\omega t + \alpha). \qquad (244)$$

Now set t and the integral equal to zero and obtain

$$L(pi_2)_0 + \frac{L}{RC}(i_2)_0 + 0 = -\frac{\omega L}{R} E \sin \alpha. \qquad (245)$$

However, the value of $(i_2)_0$ has been obtained in Eq. (243) and can be substituted into Eq. (245), after which we can solve for the desired initial value of the first derivative.

$$(pi_2)_0 = -\frac{E}{R}\left(\omega \sin \alpha + \frac{1}{RC} \cos \alpha\right). \qquad (246)$$

Substitution of the initial values (243) and (246) into the general solution will enable us to evaluate the two constants of integration for the condition of initial relaxation.

Nonrelaxed Initial Conditions. Superposition.—For linear systems such as those we have been discussing in this chapter, the principle of superposition can be used in extending the foregoing methods to systems that are initially in a nonrelaxed state. Observe that the principle does not in general hold for nonlinear systems, as was mentioned in Chap. II.

In using superposition in this application, the total solution is broken into two parts:

1. The solution that would be present if no physical changes such as the closing of switches or the releasing of masses occurred at $t = 0$.

2. The initially relaxed solution that would take place if there were introduced into the system at $t = 0$ such driving forces which, when added to those in solution 1, would be equal to the actual driving forces in the system after $t = 0$.

The total solution is then obtained as the sum of solutions 1 and 2. Solution 1 is easy to obtain if the system is in equilibrium previous to $t = 0$, and since solution 2 is initially relaxed, the methods given in the preceding paragraphs will apply. In general the displacements, velocities, driving forces, etc., that are present in solution 1 must be omitted in obtaining solution 2, as otherwise the sum would contain them twice.

The method is probably explained best by examples, two of which are given below. It will be seen that the method of superposition frequently points out interesting and useful relations between certain initially relaxed and initially nonrelaxed solutions.

As the first example, consider the system of Fig. 53a, which is initially in steady state with the switch S open. The condenser C is charged to an initial voltage E_0, and at $t = 0$ the switch S is closed. Find the currents in all elements as functions of time.

For the first solution, imagine the switch to remain open for all time as in Fig. 53b. In this case a current $I = E/(R_1 + R_2)$ would flow steadily through the resistances, and the condenser current would be zero. The voltage across the switch blades can be obtained by starting at one side of the switch and going around through any path in the system to the other side, algebraically adding all voltages encountered: $E_s = E_0 - IR_2$ in the direction shown in Fig. 53b. The foregoing, obtained by imagining the switch to be open for all time, is solution 1.

Actually, however, the switch is closed at $t = 0$, and the voltage across it then becomes zero. To correct solution 1, solution 2 must contain a voltage at the switch equal and opposite to that in solution 1, so that when the two are added to form the total solution the switch voltage will be zero. This is indicated in Fig. 53c by imagining a battery of voltage E_s placed across the switch blades at $t = 0$ with the reverse polarity as shown. The condenser charge and the original battery voltage were included in solution 1 and must be omitted in solution 2. Therefore, the

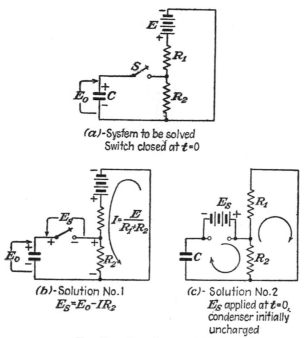

(a)-System to be solved
Switch closed at $t = 0$

(b)-Solution No.1
$E_S = E_0 - IR_2$

(c)- Solution No.2
E_S applied at $t = 0$, condenser initially uncharged

FIG. 53.—Use of superposition.

circuit of Fig. 53c is initially relaxed and the solution is easily obtained.

The net charge on the condenser at any time is equal to the charge found from solution 2 plus that present in solution 1. The switch voltage is equal to that voltage in solution 2 plus the voltage in solution 1, and the current or voltage in any part of the network is equal to the current or voltage found for that part of the system in solution 2 plus that found in solution 1. Since the first solution is almost trivial, the procedure of finding the total solution is quite simple. The method of superposition is of greatest value when the first solution is relatively easy to obtain.

It is interesting to observe that an uncharged condenser in series with a battery is equivalent to a condenser charged initially to the same voltage.

As a second example, consider the mechanical system of Fig. 54a. The weight W_1 is initially displaced upward and W_2 is displaced downward as in Fig. 54b, and at $t = 0$ the weights are released. Find the motion of the weights.

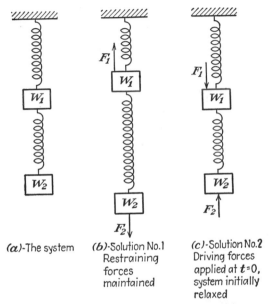

(a)-The system

(b)-Solution No.1
Restraining
forces
maintained

(c)-Solution No.2
Driving forces
applied at $t=0$,
system initially
relaxed

Fig. 54.—Mechanical example of superposition.

For solution 1, imagine that the weights are not released. The forces F_1 and F_2 will then be necessary to hold the weights in their displaced positions. Solution 1 is precisely that shown by Fig. 54b.

Actually, however, the forces F_1 and F_2 disappear after $t = 0$ since the weights are released at this time. Therefore, solution 2 will have to balance these forces with equal and opposite ones applied at $t = 0$ and thereafter. This is indicated in Fig. 54c. Furthermore, the initial displacements have already been included in solution 1 and cannot be included again in 2; so the system of Fig. 54c is initially relaxed. Solution 2 can therefore be found by the methods used for initially relaxed systems, and the superposition of displacements, velocities, forces, etc., with the corresponding ones in solution 1 will yield the true solution.

Observe that the principle of superposition shows that the transients caused in a linear system by the release of restraining forces are the same as those caused by the application of driving forces in the opposite direction.

53. Hyperbolic Functions.—In Sec. 43 we developed Euler's formula

$$\epsilon^{\pm j\theta} = \cos\theta \pm j\sin\theta, \tag{247}$$

and with its aid expressed the solution for an oscillatory system in trigonometric form. Adding and subtracting the two formulas implied in Eq. (247), we obtain expressions for the sine and cosine in terms of exponentials with imaginary exponents:

$$\left.\begin{aligned} \cos\theta &= \frac{\epsilon^{j\theta} + \epsilon^{-j\theta}}{2} \\ \sin\theta &= \frac{\epsilon^{j\theta} - \epsilon^{-j\theta}}{2j}. \end{aligned}\right\} \tag{248}$$

In physical problems, exponentials with real exponents are frequently found in combinations similar to the above, and it is found convenient to define quantities named the *hyperbolic cosine* and the *hyperbolic sine:*

$$\left.\begin{aligned} \cosh\theta &= \frac{\epsilon^{\theta} + \epsilon^{-\theta}}{2} \\ \text{and} \qquad \sinh\theta &= \frac{\epsilon^{\theta} - \epsilon^{-\theta}}{2}. \end{aligned}\right\} \tag{249}$$

Adding and subtracting Eqs. (249) we get hyperbolic relations corresponding to Eqs. (247):

$$\epsilon^{\pm\theta} = \cosh\theta \pm \sinh\theta. \tag{250}$$

These functions have the name "hyperbolic" because they can be defined in terms of the rectangular hyperbola in a manner similar to the well-known relations between the circular trigonometric functions and the circle. Thus the circle of Fig. 55 can be expressed either in the familiar form $x^2 + y^2 = a^2$, or in terms of the parametric equations

$$\left.\begin{aligned} x &= a\cos\theta \\ y &= a\sin\theta. \end{aligned}\right\} \tag{251}$$

For the hyperbolic functions we shall in an analogous manner let

$$x = a \cosh \theta \\ y = a \sinh \theta. \Big\} \qquad (252)$$

It is not hard to show from Eqs. (249) that

$$\cosh^2 \theta - \sinh^2 \theta = 1, \qquad (253)$$

whereupon substituting Eqs. (252) we obtain

$$x^2 - y^2 = a^2, \qquad (254)$$

which is the equation for the rectangular hyperbola of Fig. 56.

For the circular functions the argument θ is expressed in circular radians and may be defined either as the ratio of arc to radius s/a or, alternatively, as

$$\theta = \frac{2A}{a^2}, \qquad (255)$$

where A is the area of the shaded circular sector in Fig. 55. It can be shown that for the hyperbolic functions (249) the argument θ can also be expressed by Eq. (255), where A represents the area of the hy-

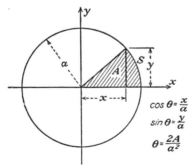

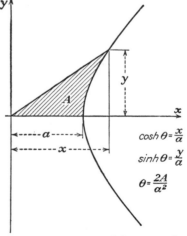

Fig. 55.—Geometrical interpretation of circular functions.

Fig. 56.—Geometrical interpretation of hyperbolic functions.

perbolic sector shown shaded in Fig. 56. Comparison of Figs. 55 and 56 will show the similarity between the geometric definitions of the two types of functions.

Other hyperbolic functions are defined in a manner similar to the circular functions, for example,

$$\tanh \theta = \frac{\sinh \theta}{\cosh \theta}. \qquad (256)$$

The hyperbolic sine, cosine, and tangent have been plotted in Fig. 57.[1]

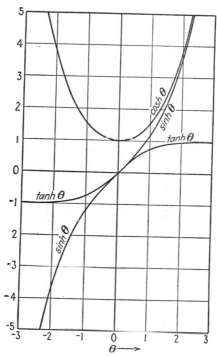

FIG. 57.—Plot of the hyperbolic functions sinh θ, cosh θ, and tanh θ.

The inverse hyperbolic functions are also defined similarly to the inverse circular functions. Thus, if

$$y = \tanh \theta, \qquad (257)$$

the inverse hyperbolic tangent of y would be written

$$\theta = \tanh^{-1} y. \qquad (258)$$

The derivatives of the hyperbolic functions are of considerable interest. It is not difficult to show from the definitions (249) that

[1] Tables of hyperbolic functions are available in various handbooks. Also see "Tables of Hyperbolic Functions," published by the Smithsonian Institution, Washington, D. C.

$$\left. \begin{aligned} \frac{d}{d\theta} \sinh \theta &= \cosh \theta \\[2mm] \frac{d}{d\theta} \cosh \theta &= \sinh \theta \\[2mm] \frac{d}{d\theta} \tanh \theta &= \operatorname{sech}^2 \theta. \end{aligned} \right\} \qquad (259)$$

Furthermore, it can be shown that

$$\sinh (\theta_1 \pm \theta_2) = \sinh \theta_1 \cosh \theta_2 \pm \cosh \theta_1 \sinh \theta_2 \qquad (260)$$

and $\quad \cosh (\theta_1 \pm \theta_2) = \cosh \theta_1 \cosh \theta_2 \pm \sinh \theta_1 \sinh \theta_2. \qquad (261)$

Comparison of Eqs. (248) and (249) shows that the hyperbolic functions of a complex argument bear a simple relation to circular functions of a real argument, *i.e.*,

$$\left. \begin{aligned} \cosh (j\theta) &= \cos \theta \\ \sinh (j\theta) &= j \sin \theta, \end{aligned} \right\} \qquad (262)$$

and similarly,

$$\left. \begin{aligned} \cos (j\theta) &= \cosh \theta \\ \sin (j\theta) &= j \sinh \theta. \end{aligned} \right\} \qquad (263)$$

Hyperbolic functions of a complex argument appear in some types of problems. These can be expressed in terms of functions of a real argument by means of Eqs. (260) and (261). If we let $\theta_1 = \alpha$, $\theta_2 = j\beta$ and employ Eqs. (262), we obtain

$$\left. \begin{aligned} \sinh (\alpha \pm j\beta) &= \sinh \alpha \cos \beta \pm j \cosh \alpha \sin \beta \\ \cosh (\alpha \pm j\beta) &= \cosh \alpha \cos \beta \pm j \sinh \alpha \sin \beta. \end{aligned} \right\} \qquad (264)$$

Let us return briefly to the examples of Sec. 43 and, with the aid of hyperbolic functions, show the close relation among the oscillatory, critically damped, and overdamped solutions developed there. In those examples a damped mass suspended from a spring was pulled downward a distance X_0 and then released. For oscillatory motion the particular solution was given by Eq. (146) and is

$$x = X_0 \epsilon^{-\alpha t} \left(\cos \omega t + \frac{\alpha}{\omega} \sin \omega t \right), \qquad (265)$$

where $\qquad \alpha = \dfrac{D}{2M}, \qquad \omega = \sqrt{\dfrac{K}{M} - \dfrac{D^2}{4M^2}}. \qquad (266)$

If the system is overdamped, $D^2 > 4KM$ and ω will become imaginary.   Therefore let $\omega = j\sigma$ where σ is a real number:

$$x = X_0\epsilon^{-\alpha t}\left[\cos(j\sigma t) + \frac{\alpha}{j\sigma}\sin(j\sigma t)\right].$$

Use Eqs. (263) to rewrite this in terms of hyperbolic functions:

$$x = X_0\epsilon^{-\alpha t}\left(\cosh\sigma t + \frac{\alpha}{\sigma}\sinh\sigma t\right). \tag{267}$$

The formal analogy between the overdamped solution (267) and the oscillatory solution (265) is now quite evident.   Furthermore, by using Eqs. (249) to expand the hyperbolic functions into exponential form, the hyperbolic solution (267) can be shown to be identical with the original exponential solution for the overdamped case [Eq. (140)].   In the latter solution note that $m_1 = -\alpha + \sigma$ and $m_2 - -\alpha - \sigma$.   It should be mentioned that in this particular type of problem the exponential solution (140) is used in computation more frequently than the hyperbolic solution (267).

Proceed next to the critically damped case, for which $D^2 = 4MK$, and both ω and σ vanish.   Evaluating the indeterminate quantity in the oscillatory solution (265) as $\omega \to 0$ we obtain

$$x = X_0\epsilon^{-\alpha t}(1 + \alpha t), \tag{268}$$

which is identical with Eq. (151) for critical damping.   Furthermore, if we similarly evaluate the overdamped solution (267) as $\sigma \to 0$, we again obtain Eq. (268).   Thus we can regard the critically damped solution as the limiting case of either the oscillatory or overdamped solutions as the damping approaches the critical value $2\sqrt{MK}$.

Problems

1. A mass weighing W lb and moving horizontally at an initial velocity V_0 ft/sec is decelerated by means of a damper with a damping constant D lb-sec/ft.

a. Find an expression for velocity as a function of time.

b. At what value of time will the transient be reduced to $1/\epsilon = 0.368$ of its initial value?

c. Sketch the solution roughly to scale for $W = 25$ lb, $D = 5$ lb-sec/ft, $V_0 = 12$ ft/sec.

d. Find the distance required to stop the weight, using the data in (c).

2. A condenser with a capacitance of C farads is charged to a potential difference of E_0 volts and is then discharged through a resistance of R ohms.

a. Find the condenser voltage as a function of time.

b. What is the time constant of the RC series circuit?

c. Sketch the condenser voltage vs. time roughly to scale for $C = 200$ μf, $R = 1,000$ ohms, and $E_0 = 100$ volts.

3. A condenser with a capacitance of C farads is discharged through an inductance L henrys and a resistance R ohms in series. Find an expression for the resistance required to suppress oscillation, and evaluate the critical resistance for (*a*) $L = 4$ henrys, $C = 100$ μf, (*b*) $L = 4$ henrys, $C = 1.0$ μf, (*c*) $L = 0.04$ henry, $C = 1.0$ μf.

4. A mass M and damper D are suspended from a spring K as in Fig. 46. With the system at rest, the mass is struck sharply so as to give it an initial vertical velocity V_0.

a. Solve for the displacement as a function of time, assuming the system to be oscillatory.

b. Sketch the solution roughly to scale for $W = 15$ lb, $K = 30$ lb/ft, $D = 1.0$ lb-sec/ft, $V_0 = 2.0$ ft/sec. State the frequency of oscillation.

5. A pendulum is suspended from a torsional spring with a spring constant of K lb-ft/radian. The length of the pendulum is L ft and the bob weighs W lb. Set up the differential equation of motion assuming small displacements so that $\sin \theta \approx \theta$, and find an expression for the period of oscillation.

6. The d-c shunt motor shown schematically in Fig. P6 is running without shaft load and is to be stopped quickly by dynamic braking. The line

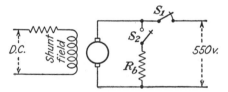

Fig. P6.—Dynamic braking.

switch S_1 is opened and switch S_2 is closed to connect the braking resistor across the armature. Calculate the speed as a function of time after switching and determine the time required to reach a speed of 200 rpm. Neglect mechanical losses and assume that the motor draws negligible line current at no load.

Data: Motor rating: 8 pole, 1,000 hp, 700 rpm, 550 volts.
　　　　Armature resistance, $R_a = 0.0086$ ohm.
　　　　Braking resistance, $R_b = 0.305$ ohm.
　　　　WR^2 of armature $= 23,000$ lb-ft^2.
　　　　Initial speed of the motor $= 700$ rpm.

The counter emf of the motor is proportional to speed at constant field flux: $E_c = K_1\omega$, where ω is the angular velocity in radians per second.

The electrical torque of the motor is proportional to armature current at constant field flux: $T_e = K_2 i_a$. For this motor, $K_2 = 5.52$ lb-ft/amp.

7. Find the roots of the cubic equations:

a. $2m^3 + 470m^2 + 3.18 \times 10^5 m + 3.63 \times 10^7 = 0$.

b. $2.7m^3 + 446m^2 + 5,950m + 12,180 = 0$.

8. A resistance R ohms, an inductance L henrys, and a capacitance C farads are to be connected in parallel and used in the grid circuit of a Thyratron tube. Set up the differential equations for the parallel RLC combination and determine an expression for the resistance required to prevent oscillation. Should the resistance be higher or lower than the critical value to overdamp this circuit?

9. A series combination of R ohms resistance and L henrys inductance is connected across a battery voltage E at $t = 0$.

a. Find the current as a function of time.

b. Sketch the solution roughly to scale for $R = 5$ ohms, $L = 0.125$ henry, $E = 10$ volts.

10. The circuit shown in Fig. P10 is to be used to measure the deionization time of a Thyratron tube. The condenser C is precharged to the battery voltage E in the direction shown, and at $t = 0$ the switch is closed.

a. Set up the differential equation for the condenser charge (or the condenser voltage). Find the condenser voltage as a function of time.

b. Using $E = 250$ volts, $R = 167$ ohms, $C = 5$ μf, sketch the condenser voltage vs. time.

c. Using the data in (*b*), find the time required for the voltage from a to b to rise to $+10$ volts.

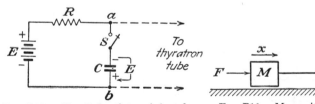

Fig. P10.—Circuit for determining de-   Fig. P11.—Mass with damper.
ionization time of Thyratron tube.

11. The mass M shown in Fig. P11 is attached to a damper D and has a constant force F acting upon it. The mass starts with zero initial velocity and displacement.

a. Find an expression for the displacement of the mass at any time.

b. Sketch displacement vs. time for $W = 50$ lb., $D = 10$ lb-sec/ft, and $F = 20$ lb. Find the approximate time required to travel 0.6 ft.

12. In the system shown in Fig. P12, $W = 2.0$ lb, $K = 0.8$ lb/in., and $D = 0.25$ lb-sec/in. With the weight initially at rest in the equilibrium position, a constant force $F = 1.6$ lb is suddenly applied at $t = 0$.

a. Is the system overdamped or oscillatory?

b. Find an expression for displacement as a function of time.

c. If the damping were reduced to a very small value, what would be the natural frequency of oscillation?

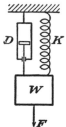

FIG. P12.— Mass suspended from spring and damper.

13. For purposes of testing, it is desired to obtain a constant current for a brief time through a resistance R and capacitance C connected in series. For this purpose a linearly varying voltage of the form $e = At$ is applied to the circuit at $t = 0$.

a. Find the current as a function of time.

b. Sketch current vs. time to scale for $R = 250$ ohms and $C = 200$ μf, if $e = 500t$ volts for $0 < t < 0.5$ sec.

14. A voltage $E\epsilon^{-\alpha t}$ is applied at $t = 0$ to a circuit consisting of a resistance R and an inductance L connected in series.

a. Solve for the current as a function of time.

b. Sketch the solution to scale for $E = 12$ volts, $R = 5$ ohms, $L = 0.05$ henry, and $\alpha = 50$ sec^{-1}, between the limits $0 < t < 0.06$ sec.

c. Using the data in (b), find the maximum current and the time at which it occurs.

15. A resistance R and capacitance C are connected in series and a voltage $E\epsilon^{-\alpha t}$ is applied at $t = 0$. If α is numerically equal to $1/RC$, find the resulting current as a function of time. Sketch the solution to scale for $E = 100$ volts, $R = 500$ ohms, $\alpha = 10$ sec^{-1}.

16. The illustration shows an inductive circuit which is to be opened by the relay contact S. To minimize sparking a condenser is connected across the contacts.

The circuit is in steady state with S closed, and at $t = 0$ S is suddenly opened. Set up the differential equation for condenser charge (or condenser voltage) and solve for condenser voltage as a function of time. Determine approximately the maximum switch voltage and the time at which it occurs. How could the operation be improved?

Data: $E = 10$ volts, $R = 8$ ohms, $L = 0.25$ henry, $C = 0.1$ μf.

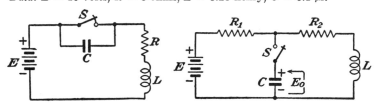

FIG. P16.—Inductive circuit to be opened by relay.   FIG. P17.—Circuit to reverse current in R_1.

17. The circuit shown in the diagram is in steady state with the switch S open. It is desired to reverse the direction of the current in R_1 momentarily without reversing the current in R_2. To accomplish this the condenser C is charged in the direction shown to a voltage higher than the battery voltage, and at $t = 0$ the switch S is closed.

Set up the differential equations and solve for the current in R_1. Sketch the form of this current for the interval $-0.001 < t < 0.015$ sec.

Data: $E = 120$ volts, $R_1 = 20$ ohms, $R_2 = 300$ ohms, $L = 0.5$ henry, $C = 200 \ \mu f$.   Initial condenser voltage $E_0 = 140$ volts.

18. A train consisting of a locomotive coupled to a single car is standing at rest, when a comparatively steady driving force is suddenly applied by the wheels of the locomotive.   Assume a linear spring action and linear damping in the coupling.

a. Using the nomenclature indicated below, find the differential equation for the motion of the car.

W_1 = weight of locomotive.
W_2 = weight of car.
K = spring constant of coupling.
D = damping constant of coupling.
F = driving force applied by wheels.

b. If $W_1 = 65,000$ lb, $W_2 = 30,000$ lb, and $K = 9,000$ lb/in., find the value of D that will just suppress oscillations.

c. Using the data given for part (*b*) and with $D = 1,800$ lb-sec/ft, $F = 6,000$ lb, solve for the acceleration of the car as a function of time and plot roughly to scale for the first 2 sec of motion.

19. The two-wheeled vehicle shown in the illustration has a spring and shock absorber.   It will be assumed that the only relative motion is vertical.   The wheel is rather suddenly moved upward a distance A by striking an obstruction in the road.   Find the vertical motion of the body if $W = 1,400$ lb, $K = 900$ lb/ft, $D = 500$ lb-sec/ft, $A = 0.2$ ft, and sketch the form of the motion vs. time.

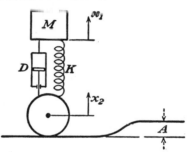

Fig. P19.—A problem in springing.

Note: The sudden upward displacement of the wheel will cause the shock absorber to transmit a large force to the mass and will give it an initial upward velocity at the top of the bump.   If the bump is abrupt so that the mass will not displace appreciably while the wheel is coming up, the operator method can be used to find the initial velocity.   As an alternate method, the spring force can be neglected in comparison with the damper force during the transition period, so that

$$D \frac{dx_2}{dt} = M \frac{dv_1}{dt}.$$

Integration of this between proper limits will give the velocity of the mass at the top of the bump.

20. In the operation of tandem rolling mills, the transient variation in motor speed as a bar comes under the rolls is of considerable importance. When a bar enters the rolls, it suddenly impresses a torque on the driving motor, and because of the electromechanical coupling, the transient drop in speed may be considerable.

The sketch shows schematically a d-c shunt motor driving a pair of rolls. Set up the differential equations for the system and solve for the motor speed, using the data below. Assume that before the bar enters the rolls, the motor is running with negligible torque and armature current. Sketch a curve of speed vs. time roughly to scale.

Data: T = torque suddenly applied to motor = 17,500 lb-ft.

J = moment of inertia of motor = 970 lb-ft-sec^2 including the rolls.

E = terminal voltage of motor = 600 volts.

R = resistance of armature = 0.115 ohm.

L = inductance of armature = 0.0279 henry.

The counter emf of the motor is proportional to speed for constant field flux: $E_c = K_1\omega$ where ω is the speed in radians per second. For this motor $K_1 = 36.2$ volt-sec/radian.

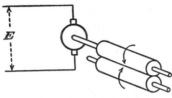

The electrical torque of the motor is proportional to armature current at constant field flux: $t_e = K_2 i$. For this motor $K_2 = 29.1$ lb-ft/amp.

Fig. P20.—Rolling-mill operation.

21. Show by the exponential definitions of cosh θ and sinh θ that

$$\cosh^2 \theta - \sinh^2 \theta = 1.$$

22. Prove the following differentiation formulas:

$$\frac{d}{d\theta} \sinh \theta = \cosh \theta.$$

$$\frac{d}{d\theta} \cosh \theta = \sinh \theta.$$

$$\frac{d}{d\theta} \tanh \theta = \operatorname{sech}^2 \theta.$$

23. Prove that $\sinh (\theta_1 + \theta_2) = \sinh \theta_1 \cosh \theta_2 + \cosh \theta_1 \sinh \theta_2$.

24. *a.* Show that

$$\sinh^{-1} u = \log_\epsilon (u + \sqrt{u^2 + 1}).$$
$$\cosh^{-1} u = \log_\epsilon (u + \sqrt{u^2 - 1}).$$
$$\tanh^{-1} u = \frac{1}{2} \log_\epsilon \left(\frac{1 + u}{1 - u} \right).$$

Note that $\epsilon^{a \log_\epsilon b} = b^a$.

b. Using these formulas and a table of natural logarithms, find $\sinh^{-1} (2)$ $\cosh^{-1} (2)$, and $\tanh^{-1} (\frac{1}{2})$.

25. Using Eqs. (250) and (252), show that $\theta = \log_\epsilon (x + y)/a$. Then show that the hyperbolic angle θ is given by $\theta = 2A/a^2$ where A is the area of the shaded hyperbolic sector in Fig. 56.

26. A mass M is repelled from the origin along the x-axis by a force that varies linearly with the distance from the origin: $f = kx$. If the mass starts from rest at $x = x_0$, find x as a function of time, using a hyperbolic solution. Sketch the form of x vs. time.

Compare with the solution obtained if the force is one of attraction toward the origin, as it would be if the force were caused by a spring with its equilibrium position at $x = 0$.

B. MISCELLANEOUS EQUATIONS

A great many physical problems can be expressed with reasonable accuracy in terms of linear constant-coefficient differential equations, and this, combined with their relative ease of solution, has made these equations of great practical importance. However, it should not be implied that this is the only type of equation that is of interest in physical problems. Indeed, most systems are linear only by assumption. In some phenomena the nonlinear effects are all-important, for example in relaxation oscillations and subharmonic resonance. Unfortunately, the equations that arise in the study of practical nonlinear and variable-parameter systems are frequently difficult to solve. This has undoubtedly retarded the understanding and development of such systems and has restricted the employment of the useful characteristics that they may possess. An extended study of these problems is beyond the scope of this text, but we shall consider some equations that are of particular interest either because they are relatively easy to solve or because, like Bessel's equation, they appear so frequently in physical problems.[1]

54. Equations with Variables Separable.—Certain equations of the first order and first degree can be placed in the form

$$f_1(x) \, dx + f_2(y) \, dy = 0. \tag{269}$$

The variables are then said to be separated, and the solution can be obtained immediately by integrating.

$$\int f_1(x) \, dx + \int f_2(y) \, dy = c, \tag{270}$$

where c is the constant of integration.

Example.—As an example, calculate the velocity of a body falling vertically through the air from an initial condition of rest, assuming that the

---

[1] For a more extended treatment of certain types of differential equations, see, for example, H. T. H. Piaggio, "Differential Equations," George Bell & Sons, Ltd., London, 1939.

An excellent discussion of some nonlinear problems, together with an extensive bibliography, will be found in a paper by Th. von Kármán, The Engineer Grapples with Nonlinear Problems, *Bull. Amer. Math. Soc.*, Vol. 46, pp. 615–683 (August, 1940).

air resistance is proportional to the square of the velocity.[1] The resisting force can be expressed as Kv^2 where K is a constant depending upon the shape and size of the body.   The differential equation can then be written as

$$\frac{W}{g}\frac{dv}{dt} + Kv^2 = W. \tag{271}$$

This can be rearranged into

$$\frac{dv}{W - Kv^2} - \frac{g}{W}dt = 0, \tag{272}$$

and the variables are separated.   Integrating, we obtain the general solution

$$\frac{1}{\sqrt{WK}}\tanh^{-1}v\sqrt{\frac{K}{W}} - \frac{g}{W}t = c. \tag{273}$$

The body is initially at rest, so at $t = 0$, $v = 0$. Substituting this condition into Eq. (273) and observing that $\tanh^{-1}(0) = 0$, we obtain $c = 0$. So solving for v we obtain the particular solution

$$v = \sqrt{\frac{W}{K}}\tanh\sqrt{\frac{K}{W}}\,gt. \tag{274}$$

As t becomes large, the hyperbolic tangent approaches unity; so the terminal velocity is $v_t = \sqrt{W/K}$.   The general shape of the velocity vs. time curve will be that of the hyperbolic tangent shown in Fig. 57.   The distance traveled as a function of time can be found by integrating Eq. (274).

Exercises

Solve the following differential equations:

1. $\dfrac{dy}{dx} + \dfrac{1}{1 - x^2}y = 0.$

2. $\dfrac{dy}{dt} + (a + b\sin\omega t)y = 0.$

3. $\dfrac{dy}{dx} + \dfrac{a + y}{(b + x)^2} = 0.$

4. $\dfrac{dy}{dx} - ax(b^2 + y^2) = 0.$

5. $\dfrac{dy}{dx} = \dfrac{y}{x}(1 - ax).$

6. $\dfrac{dy}{dt} + Ay^2 = B.$

7. $\dfrac{1}{x}\dfrac{dy}{dx} + 2y = 0.$

8. $\dfrac{dy}{dx} - A\dfrac{x}{y} = 0.$

[1] This is a reasonable approximation for velocities considerably smaller than that of sound if the Reynolds number is not too small (see Chap. IX, Sec. 83).

9. $\dfrac{dy}{dx} + \epsilon^{-(y+x)} = 0.$

10. $\dfrac{dy}{dx} - y \cos ax = 0.$

11. $x\dfrac{dy}{dx} - y = 1.$

12. $\dfrac{dy}{dx} + \dfrac{\sec^2 x}{2(1+y)} = 0.$

55. Homogeneous Equation of First Order.—A function $f(x, y)$ is said to be homogeneous of the nth degree in x and y if, when these variables are replaced respectively by kx and ky where k is any number, the k's can be factored out of the function so that

$$f(kx, ky) = k^n f(x, y).$$

For example, if we apply this test to

$$f(x, y) = x^2 + 3xy + 2y^2,$$

we see that

$$f(kx, ky) = (kx)^2 + 3(kx)(ky) + 2(ky)^2$$
$$= k^2(x^2 + 3xy + y^2),$$

and the function is homogeneous of degree two.

A differential equation of the form

$$f_1(x, y)\, dx + f_2(x, y)\, dy = 0 \qquad (275)$$

is said to be homogeneous if the two functions $f_1(x, y)$ and $f_2(x, y)$ are homogeneous and of the same degree. This type of homogeneous equation should not be confused with the homogeneous linear differential equation introduced in Sec. 42. which was homogeneous in the dependent variable y only.

The quotient f_1/f_2 will be homogeneous of degree zero and can be expressed as a function of the ratio y/x:

$$\frac{dy}{dx} = -\frac{f_1(x, y)}{f_2(x, y)} = F\left(\frac{y}{x}\right). \qquad (276)$$

This suggests the change of variable

$$y = vx, \qquad (277)$$

the derivative of which with respect to x is

$$\frac{dy}{dx} = \frac{dv}{dx}x + v. \qquad (278)$$

Substituting Eqs. (277) and (278) into Eq. (276) we obtain

$$\frac{dv}{dx} x + v = F(v),$$

or, rearranging,

$$\frac{dv}{F(v) - v} = \frac{dx}{x}, \tag{279}$$

and the variables are separated so the methods of the preceding section will apply.

Example.—For example, consider the first-order equation

$$x^2 \frac{dy}{dx} + y^2 = xy, \tag{280}$$

which can be put into the form of Eq. (275): $(x^2) \, dy + (y^2 - xy) \, dx = 0$ and is seen to be homogeneous. Solving Eq. (280) for dy/dx we obtain

$$\frac{dy}{dx} = \frac{xy - y^2}{x^2}.$$

The change of variable $y = vx$, $dy/dx = x \, dv/dx + v$, reduces this to

$$x \frac{dv}{dx} = -v^2,$$

or, separating the variables,

$$\frac{dv}{v^2} = -\frac{dx}{x}.$$

Integration then yields

$$-\frac{1}{v} + \log_\epsilon x = c,$$

and upon changing back to the original variables by $v = y/x$ we obtain

$$\log_\epsilon x - \frac{x}{y} = c. \tag{281}$$

This is the desired general solution of the differential equation (280). If desired, we can solve for y:

$$y = \frac{x}{\log_\epsilon x - c}. \tag{282}$$

Let us check the solution by differentiation of Eq. (281). This yields

$$\frac{1}{x} - \frac{y - x \dfrac{dy}{dx}}{y^2} = 0,$$

which upon clearing of fractions becomes

$$y^2 - xy + x^2 \frac{dy}{dx} = 0,$$

which is identical with the original differential equation.

Exercises

Solve the following differential equations:

1. $x \dfrac{dy}{dx} = x + 2y.$

2. $x^2 \dfrac{dy}{dx} + xy + y^2 = 0.$

3. $xy \dfrac{dy}{dx} - \dfrac{x^2}{2} - y^2 = 0.$

4. $y \dfrac{dy}{dx} = x + 2 \dfrac{y^2}{x}.$

5. $(x^2 + 2xy) \dfrac{dy}{dx} - (x^2 + xy + 2y^2) = 0.$

6. $x \dfrac{dy}{dx} - x \sqrt{\dfrac{x}{ax + by}} - y = 0.$

56. Exact Differential Equations.—Suppose that we have a function of the two variables x and y:

$$F(x, y) = c. \qquad (283)$$

Since this function is equal to a constant, its total differential is zero; so from elementary calculus we can write

$$dF = \frac{\partial F}{\partial x} dx + \frac{\partial F}{\partial y} dy = 0. \qquad (284)$$

However, since the partial derivatives will also be functions of x and y in general, we can express Eq. (284) as

$$P(x, y) \, dx + Q(x, y) \, dy = 0. \qquad (285)$$

This is a differential equation whose general solution is Eq. (283), and is said to be "exact" since the left side can be obtained from the function F by differentiation only, without any other operations. We desire (1) a means of testing whether a given differential equation of the form (285) is exact and (2) a method for determining its general solution (283).

First, observe that

$$\frac{\partial P}{\partial y} = \frac{\partial}{\partial y}\left(\frac{\partial F}{\partial x}\right) = \frac{\partial^2 F}{\partial y \, \partial x},$$

and that

$$\frac{\partial Q}{\partial x} = \frac{\partial}{\partial x}\left(\frac{\partial F}{\partial y}\right) = \frac{\partial^2 F}{\partial x \, \partial y},$$

and, since the order of differentiation is immaterial, we see that

$$\frac{\partial P}{\partial y} = \frac{\partial Q}{\partial x}. \qquad (286)$$

The condition (286) is both necessary and sufficient for the Eq. (285) to be an exact differential of some function $F(x, y)$.

To obtain the solution $F(x, y) = c$ of the differential Eq. (285), recall that $P = \partial F/\partial x$. Therefore, by integrating $P\,dx$ as if y were constant, we shall obtain all the terms in F that originally contained x. This will not give us the terms that involved only y, but these can be obtained by integrating $Q\,dy$ as though x were constant, disregarding all terms that duplicate those already obtained. The sum of these integrals, equated to a constant, is the desired solution.

Example.—As an example, solve the equation

$$(4x^3 + 6xy + y^2)\,dx + (3x^2 + 2xy + 2)\,dy = 0. \qquad (287)$$

First, check the equation to see whether it is exact.

$$\frac{\partial}{\partial y}(4x^3 + 6xy + y^2) = 6x + 2y.$$

$$\frac{\partial}{\partial x}(3x^2 + 2xy + 2) = 6x + 2y.$$

Thus the condition (286) is satisfied and the equation is exact. Therefore, the terms in the solution containing x are

$$\int P\,dx = \int(4x^3 + 6xy + y^2)\,dx = x^4 + 3x^2y + y^2x. \qquad (288)$$

Furthermore, we obtain

$$\int Q\,dy = \int(3x^2 + 2xy + 2)\,dy = 3x^2y + xy^2 + 2y. \qquad (289)$$

The only nonduplicate term in Eq. (289) is $2y$, so adding Eq. (288) to the nonduplicate term of Eq. (289) we obtain the solution

$$x^4 + 3x^2y + y^2x + 2y = c. \qquad (290)$$

This can be checked by differentiation, which will yield the original differential equation (287) immediately.

If the exact differential equation (287) is divided through by y, we obtain an equation that cannot be derived from the solution (290) by differentiation only, since it also involves an algebraic manipulation:

$$\left(4\frac{x^3}{y} + 6x + y\right)dx + \left(3\frac{x^2}{y} + 2x + \frac{2}{y}\right)dy = 0. \qquad (291)$$

This equation is not exact, for

$$\frac{\partial P}{\partial y} = -4\frac{x^3}{y^2} + 1 \quad \text{and} \quad \frac{\partial Q}{\partial x} = 6\frac{x}{y} + 2.$$

It is evident, however, that if we multiply Eq. (291) through by y it will be exact, and for this equation the quantity y is said to be an integrating factor. It can be shown that for an equation of the form $P\,dx + Q\,dy = 0$ the number of integrating factors is infinite, although even one may be difficult to find in some problems. They are, however, known for some cases.

Exercises

Test the following differential equations for exactness and solve those which are exact:

1. $(ax + 2y)\dfrac{dy}{dx} + (ay + 2bx) = 0.$

2. $(x^2 + 2xy + 1)\dfrac{dy}{dx} + (2y^2 + xy) = 0.$

3. $2xy\dfrac{dy}{dx} + y^2 = a + 2bx.$

4. $2y(a + \sin bx)\dfrac{dy}{dx} + by^2 \cos bx = x^2.$

5. $(ax + b + \epsilon^{ax})\dfrac{dy}{dx} + a(y - 2x + y\epsilon^{ax}) = 0.$

6. $(ax^2 - by^2)\dfrac{dy}{dx} = y^2 + 2axy.$

7. $\left(a\dfrac{x^2}{y^2} - b\right)\dfrac{dy}{dx} = 1 + \dfrac{2ax}{y}.$

57. General Linear Equation of First Order.—The linear equation of the first order is of the general form [compare Eq. (108), Sec. 41]:

$$a_0(t)\frac{dy}{dt} + a_1(t)y = f(t),\qquad (292)$$

where the a's can be functions of t or constants. The solution of this equation with constant coefficients has already been discussed in Secs. 42 and 47, and we shall here extend the method of solution to variable coefficients. If we divide each term by $a_0(t)$, we obtain the standard form

$$\frac{dy}{dt} + Py = Q,\qquad (293)$$

where P and Q are, in general, functions of t: $P = a_1(t)/a_0(t)$ and $Q = f(t)/a_0(t)$. If this equation is multiplied by the integrating factor $\epsilon^{\int P\,dt}$, it becomes exact:

$$\epsilon^{\int P\,dt}\left(\frac{dy}{dx} + Py\right) = \epsilon^{\int P\,dt}\,Q.\qquad (294)$$

The left side of this integrates into $y\epsilon^{\int P\,dt}$, as can be proved by differentiation; so by integrating both sides we obtain the solution

$$y\epsilon^{\int P\,dt} = \int \epsilon^{\int P\,dt}\, Q\, dt + c, \tag{295}$$

which can be solved for y. This should be compared with the means employed in the general method of solving linear constant-coefficient differential equations (Sec. 48). The portion of the solution given by $\epsilon^{-\int P\,dt} \int \epsilon^{\int P\,dt}\, Q\, dt$ is the particular integral, and $c\epsilon^{-\int P\,dt}$ is the complementary function.

Example: Electrical System with Variable Parameter.—The circuit of Fig. 58a consists of a battery in series with a resistance and a variable inductance. The parameters are assumed not to depend on the current, and hence the system is linear.

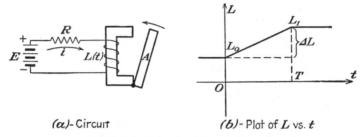

(a)- Circuit   (b)- Plot of L vs. t

Fig. 58.—Electrical circuit with variable parameter.

and hence the system is linear. With the system in steady state at $t = 0$, the armature A is closed in a time T so that the inductance varies linearly as shown in Fig. 58b:

$$L = L_0 + \frac{\Delta L}{T} t \qquad \text{for } 0 < t < T. \tag{296}$$

The problem is to find the current as a function of time. The voltage equation is

$$\frac{d\psi}{dt} + Ri = E, \tag{297}$$

in which, for this linear system, the flux linkages are given by

$$\psi = Li = \left(L_0 + \frac{\Delta L}{T} t\right) i. \tag{298}$$

Taking the derivative of Eq. (298) and substituting into Eq. (297) we obtain a differential equation expressed in terms of current:

$$\left(L_0 + \frac{\Delta L}{T} t\right)\frac{di}{dt} + \left(R + \frac{\Delta L}{T}\right) i = E. \tag{299}$$

This can be put in the standard form:

$$\frac{di}{dt} + \left(\frac{\Delta L + RT}{L_0 T + \Delta L t}\right) i = \frac{ET}{L_0 T + \Delta L t}. \tag{300}$$

The integrating factor is $\epsilon^{\int P \, dt}$, and its exponent will be

$$\int P \, dt = \int \frac{\Delta L + RT}{L_0 T + \Delta L t} \, dt = \left(1 + \frac{RT}{\Delta L}\right) \log_\epsilon (L_0 T + \Delta L t).$$

Because, in general, $\epsilon^{a \log b} = (\epsilon^{\log b})^a = b^a$, the integrating factor reduces to merely

$$\epsilon^{\int P \, dt} = (L_0 T + \Delta L \, t)^{1+RT/\Delta L}.$$

Multiplying both sides of the differential equation (300) by this factor, it becomes exact and can be integrated immediately into

$$i(L_0 T + \Delta L \, t)^{1+RT/\Delta L} = \frac{ET}{RT + \Delta L} (L_0 T + \Delta L \, t)^{1+RT/\Delta L} + c. \quad (301)$$

This is the general solution. The initial condition is $(i)_{t=0} = E/R$; so by substituting this into Eq. (301) we can evaluate c and write the particular solution as

$$i = \frac{E}{R + \dfrac{\Delta L}{T}} \left[1 + \frac{\Delta L}{RT} \cdot \frac{1}{\left(1 + \dfrac{\Delta L \, t}{L_0 T}\right)^{1+RT/\Delta L}} \right]. \quad (302)$$

The two terms in brackets represent, respectively, the particular integral and complementary function. The foregoing solution holds, of course,

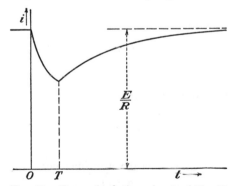

Fig. 59.—Form of solution, circuit of Fig. 58.

only for $0 < t < T$, after which the coefficients are constant and the current builds exponentially toward the original steady state value of E/R. The general form of the solution is shown in Fig. 59.

It will be interesting to find the value of the current just after the change is complete ($t = T$) as the time of the change becomes quite small. For the condition $T \ll \Delta L/R$, Eq. (302) yields $(L_0 + \Delta L)(i)_T \approx L_0(i)_0$ which is precisely what we would calculate by the constant-flux-linkage theorem of Chap. II, Sec. 21. Furthermore, we can now estimate the accuracy of this theorem for a larger time of change T, limited, of course, by our assumption of a linear change of inductance. For the case when the inductance is doubled ($\Delta L = L_0$), the following ratios of final current to initial current can be computed from Eq. (302) for various values of $RT/\Delta L$:

$\dfrac{\text{Time of change}}{\text{Time constant } \dfrac{\Delta L}{R}} = \dfrac{RT}{\Delta L}$	$(i)_T/(i)_0$
0	0.500
0.1	0.514
0.2	0.529
0.5	0.569
1.0	0.625

The ratio of currents as computed for this case by the constant-flux-linkage theorem is 0.500, which checks exactly with the foregoing equation as the time of change approaches zero. When the time of change is numerically equal to $\Delta L/R$, the results of the constant-flux-linkage theorem are 20 per cent low.

Exercises

Solve the following differential equations:

1. $\dfrac{dy}{dt} + (\cos \omega t)y = A \sin \omega t \cos \omega t.$

Note that $\left(\dfrac{1}{\omega} \epsilon^{(1/\omega) \sin \omega t} \sin \omega t \cos \omega t \, dt \right)$ is of the form $(\epsilon^u \, u \, du)$.

2. $\dfrac{dy}{dt} + \dfrac{a}{t} y = B.$

Note that $\epsilon^{a \log_\epsilon b} = b^a.$

3. $\dfrac{dy}{dt} + (\tanh t)y = A.$

4. $\dfrac{dy}{dt} + ty = t.$

Note that $\epsilon^{t^2/2} t \, dt$ is of the form $\epsilon^u \, du.$

5. $\cos t \dfrac{dy}{dt} + y \csc t = \cos^2 t.$

6. $\dfrac{dy}{dt} - 2ty = A.$

Express the solution in terms of the error function:

$$\text{erf } t = \frac{2}{\sqrt{\pi}} \int_0^t \epsilon^{-t^2} \, dt.$$

58. Certain Equations of Second Order.—In some equations of the second order, one or both of the variables x and y may not appear explicitly. These equations can be reduced to the first order by a change of variable.

Equations with y Missing.—These equations are of the form

$$\frac{d^2y}{dx^2} = f\left(\frac{dy}{dx}, x\right). \tag{303}$$

Change variable: let

$$v = \frac{dy}{dx}. \qquad (304)$$

The differential equation can then be written as

$$\frac{dv}{dx} = f(v, x), \qquad (305)$$

which is of the first order and perhaps can be solved for v by the methods previously described. Integration of Eq. (304) will then yield y as a function of x.

Example.—For example, solve

$$\frac{d^2y}{dx^2} + x \left(\frac{dy}{dx}\right)^2 = 0. \qquad (306)$$

Substituting $v = dy/dx$, this reduces to the first-order equation

$$\frac{dv}{dx} + xv^2 = 0. \qquad (307)$$

Separating the variables, we obtain

$$\frac{dv}{v^2} + x \, dx = 0,$$

which integrates into

$$-\frac{1}{v} + \frac{x^2}{2} = \text{constant} = -\frac{c_1{}^2}{2}.$$

Solve this for $v = dy/dx$:

$$\frac{dy}{dx} = v = \frac{2}{x^2 + c_1{}^2}.$$

By integration we then obtain the desired solution:

$$y = \frac{2}{c_1} \tan^{-1} \frac{x}{c_1} + c_2. \qquad (308)$$

Equations with x Missing.—These equations have the form

$$\frac{d^2y}{dx^2} = f\left(\frac{dy}{dx}, y\right). \qquad (309)$$

Make the change of variable

$$\frac{dy}{dx} = v. \qquad (310)$$

The original equation can then be written as

$$\frac{dv}{dx} = f(v, y). \qquad (311)$$

Now divide Eq. (311) by Eq. (310) to eliminate dx:

$$\frac{dv}{dy} = \frac{f(v, y)}{v}. \tag{312}$$

This is a first-order equation which perhaps can be solved for v as a function of y. Inversion and integration of Eq. (310) will then yield x as a function of y.

Example.—As an example, solve

$$y \frac{d^2y}{dx^2} + \left(\frac{dy}{dx}\right)^2 = 0. \tag{313}$$

Change variable:

$$\frac{dy}{dx} = v, \tag{314}$$

and write Eq. (313) as

$$y \frac{dv}{dx} = -v^2. \tag{315}$$

Divide Eq. (315) by Eq. (314) and obtain the first-order equation

$$y \frac{dv}{dy} = -v. \tag{316}$$

Separation of variables yields

$$\frac{dv}{v} = -\frac{dy}{y}.$$

Integrating this we obtain

$$v = \frac{c}{y}. \tag{317}$$

Substitute this expression into Eq. (314), invert, and integrate.

$$x = \int \frac{y}{c} dy + c_2 = \frac{y^2}{2c} + c_2,$$

or

$$y = c_1 \sqrt{x - c_2}, \tag{318}$$

where we have defined the new constant of integration $c_1 = \sqrt{2c}$ for convenience.

Exercises

Solve the following differential equations:

1. $\dfrac{d^2y}{dx^2} = \sqrt{1 + \left(\dfrac{dy}{dx}\right)^2}$.

2. $\dfrac{d^2y}{dx^2} - \dfrac{x}{x^2 + 1} \dfrac{dy}{dx} = 0$.

3. $\dfrac{d^2y}{dx^2} + y \left(\dfrac{dy}{dx}\right)^3 = 0$.

4. $y \dfrac{d^2y}{dx^2} - \left(\dfrac{dy}{dx}\right)^2 = a \dfrac{dy}{dx}$.

5. $x \dfrac{d^2y}{dx^2} - \dfrac{dy}{dx} = A.$

6. $\dfrac{d^2y}{dx^2} + \dfrac{A}{y^3} = 0.$

59. Euler's Equation.—Euler's equation, also sometimes called *Cauchy's equation* or the homogeneous linear equation, is of considerable physical importance and occurs, for example, in the analysis of stresses in thick-walled tubes and in curved beams. Its general form is

$$x^n \frac{d^n y}{dx^n} + a_1 x^{n-1} \frac{d^{n-1} y}{dx^{n-1}} + \cdots + a_{n-1} x \frac{dy}{dx} + a_n y = f(x), \quad (319)$$

where the a's are constants.

This equation is linear with variable coefficients and can be reduced to a linear equation with constant coefficients by the change of variable $x = \epsilon^z$, after which the methods of Sec. 47 will apply.

Example.—To illustrate the method, solve

$$x^2 \frac{d^2 y}{dx^2} + x \frac{dy}{dx} - y = \log_\epsilon x. \qquad (320)$$

Change variable: let

$$x = \epsilon^z, \qquad (321)$$

from which $\qquad \dfrac{dx}{dz} = \epsilon^z, \qquad$ so $\qquad \dfrac{dz}{dx} = \epsilon^{-z}.$

Then $\qquad \dfrac{dy}{dx} = \dfrac{dy}{dz} \cdot \dfrac{dz}{dx} = \dfrac{dy}{dz} \epsilon^{-z}$

and $\qquad \dfrac{d^2 y}{dx^2} = \dfrac{d}{dx}\left(\dfrac{dy}{dx}\right) = \dfrac{dz}{dx} \cdot \dfrac{d}{dz}\left(\dfrac{dy}{dz} \epsilon^{-z}\right) = \epsilon^{-2z}\left(\dfrac{d^2 y}{dz^2} - \dfrac{dy}{dz}\right).$

Upon substituting these relations into Eq. (320) we obtain the linear constant-coefficient equation

$$\frac{d^2 y}{dz^2} - y = z. \qquad (322)$$

Using the methods of Sec. 47, we write this in operator form ($p \equiv d/dz$):

$$(p^2 - 1)y = z. \qquad (323)$$

Two differentiations reduce this to an equation homogeneous in y: $p^2(p^2 - 1)y = 0$, for which the characteristic equation is $m^2(m^2 - 1) = 0$. The repeated root $m = 0$ shows that the particular integral is of the form $A + Bz$, and substitution into Eq. (322) shows that $A = 0$, $B = -1$.

The roots $m = \pm 1$ yield the complementary function, and the general solution is

$$y = -z + C_1\epsilon^z + C_2\epsilon^{-z}.$$

Changing variable back to x by means of Eq. (321) we obtain the desired solution of Eq. (320):

$$y = -\log_\epsilon x + C_1 x + \frac{C_2}{x}. \tag{324}$$

Exercises

Find the general solution of

1. $4x^2 \dfrac{d^2y}{dx^2} - 3y = 6$.

2. $x^2 \dfrac{d^2y}{dx^2} + 4x \dfrac{dy}{dx} + 2y = 0$.

3. $x^2 \dfrac{d^2y}{dx^2} + 5x \dfrac{dy}{dx} + 3y = x$.

4. $x^2 \dfrac{d^2y}{dx^2} + 4x \dfrac{dy}{dx} + 2y = \log_\epsilon x^a$.

5. $\dfrac{d^2y}{dx^2} + \dfrac{1}{x}\dfrac{dy}{dx} - \dfrac{y}{x^2} = 1$.

6. $x^2 \dfrac{d^2y}{dx^2} + (2a + 1)x \dfrac{dy}{dx} + a^2y = 0$.

60. Bessel's Equation and Bessel Functions.—In the first part of this chapter we developed comparatively simple methods for solving linear constant-coefficient differential equations of any order. Later sections showed a few of the special methods that are necessary in solving even comparatively simple looking differential equations of other types. Indeed the solutions of linear variable-coefficient equations of higher order than the first cannot, in general, be expressed in terms of the so-called "elementary functions." Some of these equations lead to new functions which are generally defined by infinite series or by definite integrals and, if they are of sufficient importance, their values may be tabulated after the fashion of trigonometric or logarithmic tables. The definition of new functions by infinite series corresponds to the definition of the elementary sine function by a series and, although there may be no simple geometric interpretation as in the case of the trigonometric functions, it is possible to plot them graphically. Thus, although they are not so commonly used as the elementary functions, they are not greatly different in nature and can be used just as readily when the tabulated values are at hand.

A differential equation of great importance which gives rise to a new set of functions is Bessel's equation, named after the

German astronomer and mathematician. It is encountered in many problems, including heat flow, vibration of thin diaphragms, transients on electrical transmission lines, and eddy currents in cylindrical conductors, to name but a few, and occurs most frequently in problems involving cylindrical coordinates. The equation has the form

$$\frac{d^2y}{dx^2} + \frac{1}{x}\frac{dy}{dx} + \left(1 - \frac{n^2}{x^2}\right)y = 0, \qquad (325)$$

where n is a constant. This is a differential equation of the second order, and its general solution must have two constants of integration. This solution can be written as the sum of two linearly independent solutions, each multiplied by a constant of integration, just as the solution of the familiar linear constant-coefficient equation

$$\frac{d^2y}{dt^2} + \omega^2 y = 0$$

is $y = A \cos \omega t + B \sin \omega t$, where $\cos \omega t$ and $\sin \omega t$ themselves are linearly independent solutions. The two solutions of Bessel's equation are called *Bessel functions* of the first and second kinds, respectively. The functions depend on the value of n in Eq. (325) and for any given value of n are said to be of the nth order.

Bessel Functions of Zero Order.—We shall first examine the particular case of Bessel's equation (325) when $n = 0$. The differential equation is then

$$\frac{d^2y}{dx^2} + \frac{1}{x}\frac{dy}{dx} + y = 0. \qquad (326)$$

To obtain one of the solutions of Eq. (326), assume that it can be written in the form of a series:

$$y = a_0 + a_1 x + a_2 x^2 + a_3 x^3 + \cdots. \qquad (327)$$

Taking derivatives for substitution into Eq. (326), we obtain

$$\frac{1}{x}\frac{dy}{dx} = a_1 x^{-1} + 2a_2 + 3a_3 x + \cdots,$$

$$\frac{d^2y}{dx^2} = 2a_2 + 6a_3 x + \cdots.$$

Substituting into the differential equation (326), we then have

$$(a_1)x^{-1} + (a_0 + 2^2 a_2) + (a_1 + 3^2 a_3)x + (a_2 + 4^2 a_4)x^2 + \cdots$$
$$= 0.$$

This equation can be satisfied identically only if the coefficient of each power of x is separately equal to zero, *i.e.*, if

$$(a_1) = 0,$$

$$(a_0 + 2^2 a_2) = 0, \text{ from which } a_2 = -\frac{a_0}{2^2},$$

$$(a_1 + 3^2 a_3) = 0, \text{ from which } a_3 = 0,$$

$$(a_2 + 4^2 a_4) = 0, \text{ from which } a_4 = -\frac{a_2}{4^2} = \frac{a_0}{2^2 \cdot 4^2},$$

and so on. Evidently, the value of a_0 is arbitrary; so we shall choose $a_0 = 1$ for convenience. Substitution of the foregoing

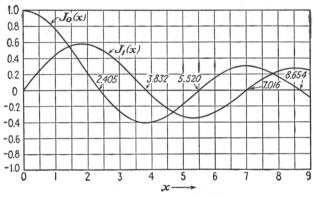

Fig. 60.—Bessel functions of the first kind.

values for the coefficients into the series (327) then yields a solution of the differential equation (326) which is designated by the symbol $J_0(x)$:

$$J_0(x) = 1 - \frac{x^2}{2^2} + \frac{x^4}{2^2 \cdot 4^2} - \frac{x^6}{2^2 \cdot 4^2 \cdot 6^2} + \cdots, \quad (328)$$

or, more compactly,
$$J_0(x) = \sum_{k=0}^{\infty} (-1)^k \frac{(\tfrac{1}{2}x)^{2k}}{(k!)^2}. \quad (329)$$

This is known as the Bessel function of the first kind of zero order. Tables of its values are available,[1] and it has been plotted in Fig. 60. It will be seen that the graph of $J_0(x)$

[1] Comprehensive tables of Bessel functions will be found in Jahnke and Emde, "Tables of Functions," Dover Publications, New York, 1943, and in G. N. Watson, "Theory of Bessel Functions," Cambridge University Press, London, 1922. Smaller tables will be found in many textbooks.

somewhat resembles a damped cosine wave, although the period is slightly variable. As a matter of fact, the defining series bears some resemblance to the infinite series for the trigonometric cosine function.

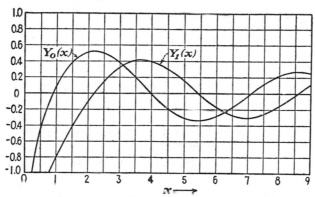

Fig. 61.—Bessel functions of the second kind.

We next need a second solution for the differential Eq. (326), linearly independent of the first. This can be found by assuming a solution of the form[1]

$$y = CJ_0(x) \log x + b_0 + b_1x + b_2x^2 + \cdots .$$

Weber's form of this solution has been found to be particularly convenient for large values of x and is

$$Y_0(x) = \frac{2}{\pi} \left[\left(\log \frac{x}{2} + \gamma \right) J_0(x) \right.$$
$$\left. - \sum_{k=1}^{\infty} (-1)^k \frac{(\frac{1}{2}x)^{2k}}{(k!)^2} \left(1 + \frac{1}{2} + \frac{1}{3} + \cdots + \frac{1}{k} \right) \right], \quad (330)$$

where γ is Euler's constant, 0.5772 . . . . Values of this function are plotted in Fig. 61. It will be observed that as $x \to 0$, $Y_0(x) \to -\infty$.

We can now write the general solution of the differential equation (326) as

$$y = C_1J_0(x) + C_2Y_0(x), \quad (331)$$

where C_1 and C_2 are arbitrary constants.

[1] The considerations leading to this solution will not be given here. For a more extensive treatment of this and of the many other aspects of Bessel functions not treated here, see, for example, N. W. McLachlan, "Bessel Functions for Engineers," Oxford University Press, New York, 1934.

In most practical problems the differential equation will not be in the standard form (326) but will involve some additional constant k:

$$\frac{d^2y}{dx^2} + \frac{1}{x}\frac{dy}{dx} + k^2y = 0. \tag{332}$$

By the change of variable $z = kx$, the foregoing equation reduces to standard form and the solution of Eq. (332) is found to be

$$y = C_1 J_0(kx) + C_2 Y_0(kx). \tag{333}$$

Bessel Functions of Positive Integral Order.—For the more general Bessel equation

$$\frac{d^2y}{dx^2} + \frac{1}{x}\frac{dy}{dx} + \left(1 - \frac{n^2}{x^2}\right)y = 0, \tag{334}$$

we can obtain a first solution by assuming an infinite series of the form

$$y = x^m(a_0 + a_1x + a_2x^2 + \cdots). \tag{335}$$

Substituting this into Eq. (334) and setting the coefficients of the various powers of x equal to zero as before, we obtain the relations

$$(m^2 - n^2)a_0 = 0,$$
$$[(m + 1)^2 - n^2]a_1 = 0, \qquad [(m + 2)^2 - n^2]a_2 + a_0 = 0,$$

or in general,

$$[(m + k)^2 - n^2]a_k + a_{k-2} = 0.$$

The latter gives a recursion formula which expresses each coefficient in terms of a preceding one:

$$a_k = -\frac{a_{k-2}}{(m + k)^2 - n^2}.$$

The first relation shows that for $a_0 \neq 0$ we must have $m = \pm n$. If we consider for the time being the case when n is a positive integer or zero, the value $m = -n$ will cause certain of the coefficients to become infinite, so let $m = n$. The second relation shows that $a_1 = 0$, and the recursion formula then indicates that all coefficients with odd subscripts will vanish. For the others we shall let $a_0 = 1/(2^n n!)$ which is consistent with our previous choice of unity when $n = 0$ (note that $0! = 1$), and use the recursion formula with $m = n$ and $k = 2, 4, 6, \cdots$. This yields the first solution of Eq. (334), designated $J_n(x)$ and called the *Bessel function* of the first kind and order n:

$$J_n(x) = \left(\frac{1}{2}x\right)^n \left[\frac{1}{n!} - \frac{(\frac{1}{2}x)^2}{1!(n+1)!} + \frac{(\frac{1}{2}x)^4}{2!(n+2)!} - \cdots \right] \quad (336)$$

or
$$J_n(x) = \sum_{k=0}^{\infty} (-1)^k \frac{(\frac{1}{2}x)^{n+2k}}{k!(n+k)!}, \quad (337)$$

which holds when n is a positive integer or zero. Observe that when $n = 0$ this reduces to Eq. (329) for $J_0(x)$. Values of $J_1(x)$ are plotted in Fig. 60.

Weber's second independent solution of Eq. (334) is designated by $Y_n(x)$[1] and is called the Bessel function of the second kind and order n. Values of $Y_1(x)$ are plotted in Fig. 61.

The complete solution of Eq. (334) can now be written as

$$y = C_1 J_n(x) + C_2 Y_n(x). \quad (338)$$

In practical problems Bessel's equation frequently has the form

$$\frac{d^2y}{dx^2} + \frac{1}{x}\frac{dy}{dx} + \left(k^2 - \frac{n^2}{x^2}\right)y = 0, \quad (339)$$

where k is a constant. This can be put into standard form by the change of variable $z = kx$, and the solution of Eq. (339) is then found to be

$$y = C_1 J_n(kx) + C_2 Y_n(kx). \quad (340)$$

The derivatives of Bessel functions are important, for example in the introduction of boundary conditions. From the series expansions we can show that

$$\frac{d}{dx} J_0(x) = -J_1(x) \qquad \text{or} \qquad \frac{d}{dx} J_0(kx) = -kJ_1(kx) \quad (341)$$

and $\dfrac{d}{dx} Y_0(x) = -Y_1(x)$ \qquad or \qquad $\dfrac{d}{dx} Y_0(kx) = -kY_1(kx).$ \quad (342)

Furthermore, \qquad $\dfrac{d}{dx}[x^{-n}J_n(x)] = -x^{-n}J_{n+1}(x)$ \quad (343)

and \qquad $\dfrac{d}{dx}[x^n J_n(x)] = x^n J_{n-1}(x).$ \quad (344)

Also \qquad $\dfrac{d}{dx} J_n(x) = \dfrac{n}{x} J_n(x) - J_{n+1}(x)$ \quad (345)

$$= -\frac{n}{x} J_n(x) + J_{n-1}(x). \quad (346)$$

[1] The Jahnke-Emde tables use the symbol $N_\nu(x)$.

Some of these formulas may lead to functions of negative order. These and functions of nonintegral order will be considered in the next section.

Bessel Functions of Other Orders. Gamma Functions.—It will be recalled that the assumed solution (335) led to the alternatives $m = n$ and $m = -n$. For positive integral values of n we discarded the latter to avoid trouble with the coefficients and had to find a second independent solution of different form. However, if n is not zero or an integer, there is no difficulty with the coefficients, and we can use both values $m = \pm n$ to obtain two independent solutions which we shall denote by $J_n(x)$ and $J_{-n}(x)$. These solutions can be expressed in a form corresponding to Eq. (337) provided that we generalize the idea of a factorial by use of the so-called "gamma function." The gamma function of n is symbolized by $\Gamma(n)$ and is defined for positive n by the integral

$$\Gamma(n) = \int_0^\infty x^{n-1}\epsilon^{-x}\,dx. \tag{347}$$

If we replace n by $n + 1$ and integrate by parts, it is easy to show that

$$\Gamma(n + 1) = n\Gamma(n) = n(n - 1)\Gamma(n - 1), \text{ etc.} \tag{348}$$

This is similar to the recursion law of the factorial, for example, $6\,! = 6 \cdot 5! = 6 \cdot 5 \cdot 4!$, etc. Furthermore, integration of Eq. (347) shows that $\Gamma(2) = \Gamma(1) = 1$, so that for positive integral values of n we can write from Eq. (348):

$$\Gamma(n + 1) = n(n - 1)(n - 2) \cdots 1,$$

which is the elementary definition of factorial n, and therefore $\Gamma(n + 1) = n!$ Moreover, the gamma function defined by the integral (347) can be used for all positive values of n, whether integral or nonintegral, and provides a useful extension of the factorial. The recursion formula $\Gamma(n + 1) = n\Gamma(n)$ can be used to define the gamma function for negative values of n. Tables of values are available over a limited range of n,[1] and with the aid of the recursion formula they can be extended to any real value of n. The function $\Gamma(n + 1)$ is plotted in Fig. 62.

---

[1] See PIERCE, B. O., "A Short Table of Integrals," p. 140, also the Jahnke-Emde tables, Sec. II.

If we now return to Eq. (337) for $J_n(x)$ and replace $(n + k)!$ by $\Gamma(n + k + 1)$, we obtain a generalized formula that will apply to all values of n including fractions.   Then for n not zero or an integer we can write the general solution of Eq. (334) as

$$y = C_1 J_n(x) + C_2 J_{-n}(x). \tag{349}$$

It is also possible to investigate the Bessel functions of negative integral order with the aid of the generalized form of Eq. (337). This leads to the formulas

$$J_{-n}(x) = (-1)^n J_n(x) \tag{350}$$
$$= J_n(-x), \tag{351}$$

in which n is a positive integer.

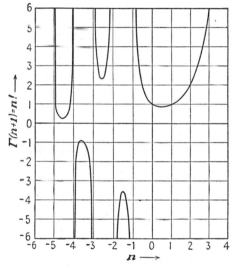

Fig. 62.—The gamma function $\Gamma(n + 1) = n!$

Modified Functions.—If in the general Bessel equation (334) we exchange jx for x where $j = \sqrt{-1}$, the equation becomes

$$\frac{d^2y}{dx^2} + \frac{1}{x}\frac{dy}{dx} - \left(1 + \frac{n^2}{x^2}\right)y = 0. \tag{352}$$

A solution will be obtained by replacing x by jx in the series (337), thus obtaining $J_n(jx)$.   This is standardized by defining

$$I_n(x) = j^{-n}J_n(jx),$$

which is known as the modified Bessel function of the first kind of order n. Another solution is known as the modified Bessel function of the second kind and is symbolized by $K_n(x)$.[1] The general solution of Eq. (352) is then

$$y = C_1 I_n(x) + C_2 K_n(x). \tag{353}$$

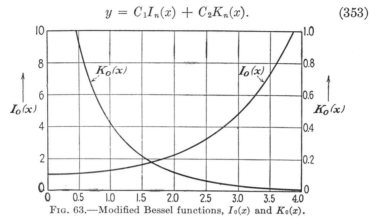

FIG. 63.—Modified Bessel functions, $I_0(x)$ and $K_0(x)$.

The functions $I_0(x)$ and $K_0(x)$ are plotted in Fig. 63. It is not difficult to show that

$$\frac{d}{dx} I_0(x) = I_1(x). \tag{354}$$

In certain eddy current problems the function

$$J_0(\sqrt{-j}\, x) = J_0(j^{\frac{3}{2}} x)$$

arises. The real and imaginary parts of this are tabulated as the *ber* and *bei* functions:

$$J_0(j^{\frac{3}{2}} x) = \text{ber } x + j \text{ bei } x. \tag{355}$$

Example: Application of Bessel Functions.—As one of many possible examples, calculate the temperature distribution within a cylinder when the rate of heat production in the cylinder varies linearly with the temperature and the outside surface is kept at a uniform temperature θ_R.[2] We shall assume that the material of the cylinder is homogeneous and isotropic (*i.e.*, has the same properties in all directions), that all the heat produced is being conducted in steady state to the outside surface, and that the axial tempera-

[1] The nomenclature is not well standardized, and several different sets of symbols for some of the Bessel functions are in use.

[2] For an application of this, see R. H. Wilhelm, W. C. Johnson, and F. S. Acton, Conduction, Convection, and Heat Release in Catalytic Converters, *Ind. Eng. Chem., Ind. Ed.*, Vol. 35, pp. 562–575 (May, 1943).

ture gradient is negligible so that all the heat flows outward radially. Figure 64a shows a cross section of the cylinder. The rate of heat production per unit volume at any point is linearly related to the temperature:

$$q = q_0 + m\theta, \quad \text{(example of units: Btu/hr-ft}^3\text{)} \quad (356)$$

where θ is the temperature and q_0 and m are constants.

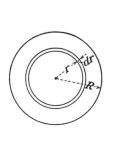 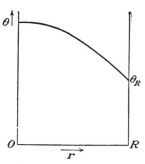

(a)-Cross section of cylinder   (b)-General form of solution

Fig. 64.—Temperature distribution in cylinder, rate of heat release varying linearly with temperature.

Consider an axial length L. The heat produced within a cylindrical volume of radius r (Fig. 64a) is found by integrating the rate of heat production (356) over the volume of this cylinder:

$$Q = \int_0^r (q_0 + m\theta)2\pi r L \, dr. \quad (357)$$

This heat must escape through the surface of the cylinder of radius r, and from the fundamental law of heat conduction, $Q = -kA \, d\theta/dr$ where k is the conductivity, A is the area, and $d\theta/dr$ is the temperature gradient. From this,

$$Q = -k(2\pi r L)\frac{d\theta}{dr}. \quad (358)$$

Equating the heat produced (357) to the heat conducted (358), taking the derivative of both sides to remove the integral sign, and rearranging, we obtain the desired differential equation:

$$\frac{d^2\theta}{dr^2} + \frac{1}{r}\frac{d\theta}{dr} + \frac{m}{k}\theta = -\frac{q_0}{k}. \quad (359)$$

This is a linear differential equation (with a variable coefficient), and since the right side is not zero its solution will have both a particular integral and a complementary function. The right side is a constant; so for the particular integral assume $\theta = $ constant, substitute into Eq. (359), and obtain $\theta = -q_0/m$. The complementary function is obtained by setting the right side equal to zero, which yields Bessel's equation in the form (332), for which the solution has the form (333). The complete solution is the sum of these and is, therefore,

$$\theta = -\frac{q_0}{m} + C_1 J_0\left(r \sqrt{\frac{m}{k}}\right) + C_2 Y_0\left(r \sqrt{\frac{m}{k}}\right). \tag{360}$$

The boundary conditions are that $\theta = \theta_R$ at $r = R$, and since by symmetry no heat flows across the axis of the cylinder, $d\theta/dr = 0$ at $r = 0$. Applying the latter condition first, we obtain

$$\left(\frac{d\theta}{dr}\right)_{r=0} = 0 = -\sqrt{\frac{m}{k}} C_1 J_1(0) - \sqrt{\frac{m}{k}} C_2 Y_1(0).$$

However, $J_1(0) = 0$ and $Y_1(0) = -\infty$; so the last term is unsuitable and $C_2 = 0$. For the other boundary condition, Eq. (360) then becomes

$$\theta_R = -\frac{q_0}{m} + C_1 J_0\left(R \sqrt{\frac{m}{k}}\right),$$

from which we can solve for C_1 and write the particular solution as

$$\theta = \left(\theta_R + \frac{q_0}{m}\right) \frac{J_0\left(r \sqrt{\frac{m}{k}}\right)}{J_0\left(R \sqrt{\frac{m}{k}}\right)} - \frac{q_0}{m}. \tag{361}$$

A plot of the temperature vs. r shows that it starts at the value θ_R at the surface of the cylinder, increases toward the center, and finally approaches the center with zero slope as indicated in Fig. 64b. However, if the quantity $R \sqrt{m/k}$ approaches 2.405 (the first zero of J_0), the temperature increases without limit and the assumptions break down.

If the slope of the heat release vs. temperature curve is negative, we can exchange $-m$ for m in all the equations, and the solution is then expressed by the modified Bessel function:

$$\theta = \left(\theta_R - \frac{q_0}{m}\right) \frac{I_0\left(r \sqrt{\frac{m}{k}}\right)}{I_0\left(R \sqrt{\frac{m}{k}}\right)} + \frac{q_0}{m}. \tag{362}$$

As the slope m approaches zero, the solutions (361) and (362) approach a parabolic form (which is obtained most easily by going back to the original equations):

$$\theta = \theta_R + \frac{q_0}{4k} (R^2 - r^2). \tag{363}$$

It is interesting to observe that the corresponding problem for a flat slab produces the differential equation

$$\frac{d^2\theta}{dx^2} + \frac{m}{k}\theta = -\frac{q_0}{k}. \tag{364}$$

This is a linear equation with constant coefficients and should be compared with Eq. (359). The solution corresponding to Eq. (361) is

$$\theta = \left(\theta_B + \frac{q_0}{m}\right)\frac{\cos\left(x\sqrt{\frac{m}{k}}\right)}{\cos\left(B\sqrt{\frac{m}{k}}\right)} - \frac{q_0}{m}, \tag{365}$$

where B is the thickness from the center line to the outside surface and x is the variable distance from the center line toward that surface. If the slope of the heat-release-vs.-temperature curve is negative and we replace m by $-m$, the solution corresponding to Eq. (362) is

$$\theta = \left(\theta_B - \frac{q_0}{m}\right)\frac{\cosh\left(x\sqrt{\frac{m}{k}}\right)}{\cosh\left(B\sqrt{\frac{m}{k}}\right)} + \frac{q_0}{m}. \tag{366}$$

As the slope m approaches zero, both the above solutions approach the parabolic equation

$$\theta = \theta_B + \frac{q_0}{2k}\,(B^2 - x^2). \tag{367}$$

Comparison of Eq. (365) with Eq. (361), Eq. (366) with Eq. (362), and Eq. (367) with Eq. (363) shows an interesting similarity between the solutions for cylindrical and flat bodies.

Exercises

1. Using the defining series, show that

(a) $\dfrac{d}{dx}\,J_0(x) = -J_1(x)$.

(b) $\dfrac{d}{dx}\,[xJ_1(x)] = xJ_0(x)$.

2. Compute the numerical values of $J_0(1)$ and $J_1(2)$ to three decimal places.

3. Evaluate $\displaystyle\int_0^R rJ_0(kr)\,dr$.

4. Solve

$$\frac{d^2y}{dx^2} + \frac{1}{x}\frac{dy}{dx} + k^2y = k^2A$$

with the boundary conditions $y = 0$ at $x = L$ and $dy/dx = 0$ at $x = 0$.

5. By use of the defining integral, show that

$$0! = \Gamma(1) = 1.$$

6. Integrate Eq. (347) by parts to show that $\Gamma(n + 1) = n\Gamma(n)$.

7. Given that $\Gamma(2) = 1$, use the recursion formula to show that

$$\Gamma(6) = 5!$$

8. Given the definition $(\frac{1}{2})! = \Gamma(\frac{3}{2}) = \sqrt{\pi}/2$, find $(-\frac{1}{2})!$ and $(\frac{3}{2})!$

9. Evaluate $\Gamma(3.71)$, given that $\Gamma(1.71) = 0.9105$.

10. By the change of variable $y = \epsilon^{-x}$, show that

$$\Gamma(n) = \int_0^1 \left(\log_\epsilon \frac{1}{y}\right)^{n-1} dy.$$

Problems

1. A boat with mass M is moving at a velocity v_0 when the propulsive force is stopped. The resisting force of the water is approximated by the relation $f = K_1 v + K_2 v^2$. Find an expression for the velocity of the boat as a function of time.

Sketch velocity vs. time roughly to scale for $W = 3,000$ lb, $v_0 = 10$ ft/sec, $K_1 = 4$ lb-sec/ft, and $K_2 = 0.8$ lb-sec²/ft².

2. A vertical cylindrical water tank is discharging through an orifice in its side. The velocity of the water in the orifice is given by $\sqrt{2gh}$ where h is the height of the surface of the water above the orifice. The cross-sectional area of the tank is A_t, the effective area of the orifice is A_0, and the water surface is initially at a height h_0 above the orifice.

a. Find an expression for the height h as a function of time.

b. If the tank is 4 ft in diameter and the effective area of the orifice is 0.75 in.², find the time required for the water level to fall from a height of 10 ft to 4 ft.

3. A mass M is moving with an initial velocity v_0 and is decelerated with a damper whose damping coefficient varies linearly with time: $D = D_0 + \alpha t$. Find the resulting velocity as a function of time.

4. A certain nonlinear inductor has a saturation curve which can be expressed approximately as $i = C_1\psi + C_3\psi^3$, where i is in amperes and ψ is

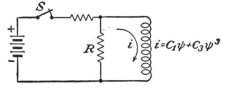

Fig. P4.—Circuit with nonlinear inductor.

in weber-turns. It is connected in the circuit shown in the illustration. With the switch S closed, the current is allowed to build up until the flux linkages of the inductor are ψ_0. At this instant the switch is opened. Set up the differential equation in terms of flux linkages, and solve for the flux linkages as a function of time after the switch is opened. What does the solution reduce to if $C_3 = 0$?

5. Two chemicals, a and b, combine to form a compound c. The law of combination is that the rate of increase of c at any instant is proportional to the product of the amounts of a and b remaining:

$$\frac{dc}{dt} = k(a_0 - c)(b_0 - c),$$

where a_0 and b_0 are the initial amounts of a and b, respectively.

a. If $c = 0$ at $t = 0$, find c as a function of time.

b. What does this solution reduce to if $a_0 = b_0$?

6. A battery with voltage E is connected to a series circuit consisting of an inductance of L henrys and a time-varying resistance which increases according to the equation $R = R_0/(1 - \alpha t)$ for $0 < t < 1/\alpha$.

a. Set up the differential equation for the circuit and solve for the initial condition $i = E/R_0$ at $t = 0$.

b. Sketch the current to scale as a function of time between the time limits indicated above if $E = 10$ volts, $R_0 = 5$ ohms, $L = 0.25$ henry, $1/\alpha = 0.10$ sec.

7. The differential equation for free sinusoidal vibrations of a circular membrane with clamped edges can be shown to be

$$\frac{d^2y}{dr^2} + \frac{1}{r}\frac{dy}{dr} + \frac{\rho\omega^2}{T} y = 0,$$

where y = displacement normal to the plane of the membrane.

r = radius.

T = tension per unit length at clamped edge.

ρ = mass per unit area.

ω = angular velocity of vibration = $2\pi f$.

a. Solve this equation, using the boundary conditions $y = Y$ at $r = 0$, $y = 0$ at $r = R$, and show how the natural frequencies of vibration are determined by the roots of $J_0(x)$. The first three roots are given in Fig. 60.

b. Compute the first three natural frequencies of a stretched circular membrane if $R = 7$ in., $T = 1.5$ lb/in., and the weight per unit area is 3×10^{-4} lb/in.^{2} Sketch the form of y vs. r for each.

8. A mass M is initially at rest at $x = a$ and is attracted to the origin with a force that varies inversely with the distance: $f = k/x$. Find the time required to reach the origin.

Note: First reduce the differential equation to one of first order and show that

$$\frac{dx}{dt} = - \sqrt{2 \frac{k}{M} \log_\epsilon \frac{a}{x}}.$$

Invert this equation and integrate, using the relation given in Ex. 10 at the end of Sec. 60.

CHAPTER VII

VECTOR REPRESENTATION OF SINUSOIDS

61. Introduction.—The usefulness of complex numbers and plane vectors in the steady-state solution of linear a-c circuits is well known. However, their usefulness is not confined to this field but can be extended to any type of linear system with sinusoidal applied voltages or driving forces. Thus the calculation of charges and voltages as well as currents in electrical systems, and of forced vibrations and oscillations in mechanical systems, are all calculated with relative ease by vector methods. Furthermore, by means of the Fourier series and superposition, these methods can be extended to the steady-state solution of linear systems with nonsinusoidal periodic driving forces and to the solution of transients by use of the Fourier integral (see Chap. X).

If the voltage or driving force in a *linear* system is of sinusoidal form, the response will also be sinusoidal in steady state. If we are interested only in the steady-state (forced) response and not in the transients that precede it, we need not obtain the complete solution of the differential equations but can solve for the steady state by short-cut vector methods. These methods also present another possibility in determining the complete solution of nonhomogeneous differential equations when the driving forces are sinusoidal, alternative to the methods of Chap. VI: we can first find the steady state by vector methods, next determine the form of the transients from the corresponding homogeneous equation, and finally combine the two to form the complete solution.

The section that follows assumes a previous acquaintance with complex numbers, and is given mainly for review and reference.

62. Complex Numbers.—All "real" numbers, whether positive or negative, integral, fractional, or irrational (as $\sqrt{2}$), can be represented by points on a line indicated as the axis of reals in Fig. 65. The concept of adding and subtracting real numbers by the addition of directed line segments (*i.e.*, plane vectors) along the real axis is a familiar one. Furthermore, the result of adding, subtracting, multiplying, or dividing real numbers is always another real number which also can be represented by a point on this axis. However, there is no place on this axis for the square roots of negative numbers such as $\sqrt{-4}$, for there is no real number whose square is negative. This has given rise to the name *imaginary* for such numbers.

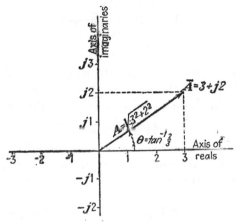

FIG. 65.—The complex plane.

We now observe that the multiplication of either a positive or a negative number by -1 can be regarded as a 180° rotation (about the origin) of the point representing this number. Since this amounts algebraically to two multiplications by $\sqrt{-1}$, we might expect that we could represent multiplication by $\sqrt{-1}$ as a rotation of the point through 90°. Since any imaginary number can be expressed as $\sqrt{-1}$ times a real number, for example $\sqrt{-4} = 2\sqrt{-1}$, we thus find that we can represent imaginary numbers by points located on an axis at right angles to the axis of reals. This is shown in Fig. 65, where positive rotation has been taken to be counterclockwise as usual, and $\sqrt{-1}$ has been indicated by the symbol j.

Having visualized real and imaginary numbers as points on two mutually perpendicular axes (or as plane vectors joining the origin and these points), the next step is to represent the sum of a real and an imaginary number. This is the so-called "complex number" and is of the form $a + jb$ where a and b are real numbers.   We might expect that this addition would logically follow the law for addition of plane vectors (as for two forces at right angles), and could be represented by a point with coordinates a and jb or by the associated vector $\bar{A}$ on the complex plane, as illustrated for the complex number $3 + j2$ in Fig. 65.

If we denote the length or *absolute value* of the vector $\bar{A}$ by A or $[\bar{A}]$, and the angle that it makes with the positive real axis by θ, we see that

$$\bar{A} = a + jb; \tag{368}$$

so

$$A = |\bar{A}| = \sqrt{a^2 + b^2} \tag{369}$$

and

$$\theta = \tan^{-1}\frac{b}{a}. \tag{370}$$

These relations are shown for the complex number $3 + j2$ in Fig. 65.   It is evident that in general the complex number $\bar{A}$ can be expressed in terms of its absolute value and angle by

$$\bar{A} = A(\cos \theta + j \sin \theta). \tag{371}$$

Continuing to algebraic operations on complex numbers, we can let these follow the usual laws of algebra, whereupon addition will yield results corresponding to the parallelogram law for plane vectors:

$$(a + jb) + (c + jd) = (a + c) + j(b + d). \tag{372}$$

This is illustrated in Fig. 66 for the complex numbers $\bar{A} = 3 + j2$ and $\bar{B} = 1 + j2$.

By observing that $j^2 = -1$, we obtain for multiplication:

$$(a + jb) \cdot (c + jd) = (ac - bd) + j(ad + bc). \tag{373}$$

A quotient of two complex numbers can be expressed as another complex number by rationalization, *i.e.*, by multiplying both numerator and denominator by the conjugate of the denominator:

$$\frac{a + jb}{c + jd} = \frac{a + jb}{c + jd} \cdot \frac{c - jd}{c - jd} = \frac{(ac + bd) + j(bc - ad)}{c^2 + d^2}. \tag{374}$$

The results of these operations are shown in Fig. 66 for the complex numbers $\bar{A} = 3 + j2$ and $\bar{B} = 1 + j2$.   Other rules for multiplication and division will be developed shortly.

The exponential form of a complex number will next be shown. Euler's formula, developed in Sec. 43, Chap. VI, states that

$$\epsilon^{j\theta} = \cos \theta + j \sin \theta. \tag{375}$$

Comparison of Eqs. (375) and (371) indicates that the quantity $\epsilon^{j\theta}$ can be represented by a plane vector having an absolute value of unity and located at an angle θ counterclockwise from the real axis. Furthermore, substituting Eq. (375) into Eq. (371), we obtain a compact exponential form for the complex number $\bar{A}$:

$$\bar{A} = A\epsilon^{j\theta}. \tag{376}$$

This is also sometimes written in the symbolic polar form:

$$\bar{A} = A\underline{/\theta}. \tag{377}$$

The fundamentally correct unit for θ is the radian, although degrees are sometimes used for convenience.

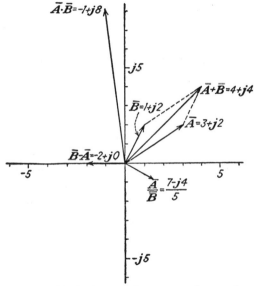

Fig. 66.—Algebraic operations on complex numbers.

Given the two complex quantities $\bar{A} = A\epsilon^{j\theta}$ and $\bar{B} = B\epsilon^{j\phi}$, their product can now be expressed as

$$\bar{A}\bar{B} = AB\epsilon^{j(\theta+\phi)} = AB\underline{/\theta + \phi}. \tag{378}$$

Evidently the absolute value of the product can be obtained simply by multiplying together the absolute values of the two factors, while the angle of the product is the sum of the angles of the two factors.   Similarly, in division the magnitudes are divided and the angles are subtracted:

$$\frac{\bar{A}}{\bar{B}} = \frac{A}{B}\, \epsilon^{j(\theta-\phi)} = \frac{A}{B}\, \underline{/\theta - \phi}. \tag{379}$$

Frequently the procedure indicated by Eqs. (378) and (379) is more convenient than that shown by Eqs. (373) and (374).

Reference to Eq. (376) shows that a complex number raised to the power n can be expressed by

$$(\bar{A})^n = A^n\epsilon^{jn\theta} = A^n(\cos n\theta + j \sin n\theta). \tag{380}$$

This is known as *De Moivre's theorem.*

63. Representation of Sinusoids.—If we refer to Euler's formula (375) and let $\theta = \omega t$ where t is time, we see that the angle θ of the unit vector $\epsilon^{j\theta}$ increases linearly with t, *i.e.*, the tip of the vector rotates uniformly about the origin as a center.   The projection of the tip of this vector on the real axis evidently will have simple harmonic motion with a frequency equal to the speed of rotation, $f = \omega/2\pi$; for example, this is the principle of the Scotch yoke for generating such motion mechanically.   The foregoing is another way of saying that the *real part* of $\epsilon^{j\omega t}$ varies in a sinusoidal manner with t.   This is justified mathematically by Eq. (375), which shows that the real part of $\epsilon^{j\omega t}$ is merely $\cos \omega t$.   Evidently we could use the imaginary part ($\sin \omega t$) just as well, but we shall here use the real part consistently.   Using the abbreviation $\Re_e$ to indicate "the real part of," we can write from Eq. (375):

$$\cos \omega t = \Re_e[\epsilon^{j\omega t}]. \tag{381}$$

Since $\sin \omega t = \cos (\omega t - \pi/2)$, we can replace θ in Eq. (375) by $\omega t - (\pi/2)$ and write

$$\begin{aligned} \sin \omega t &= \Re_e[\epsilon^{j(\omega t-\pi/2)}] \\ &= \Re_e[\epsilon^{j\omega t}\epsilon^{-j\pi/2}]. \end{aligned}$$

Similarly, the general sinusoid can be written as

$$\left. \begin{aligned} \cos (\omega t + \alpha) &= \Re_e[\epsilon^{j(\omega t+\alpha)}] \\ \cos (\omega t + \alpha) &= \Re_e[\epsilon^{j\omega t}\epsilon^{j\alpha}]. \end{aligned} \right\} \tag{382}$$

or

The advantage of rewriting a sinusoid as the real part of an exponential is that the latter is a particularly simple function to manipulate mathematically, and also that in a linear system of equations the real and imaginary parts automatically keep themselves separated, so that in the solution one can return to the sinusoids again. Furthermore, in many problems we shall be able to interpret the solution in its vector form without attempting to return to trigonometric functions.

The quantity $A\epsilon^{j(\omega t+\alpha)} = (A\epsilon^{j\alpha})\epsilon^{j\omega t} = \bar{A}\epsilon^{j\omega t}$ can be regarded as a vector rotating at a frequency $f = \omega/2\pi$ on the complex plane as shown in Fig. 67a. The length of the vector is A. At $t = 0$ it makes an angle α with the real axis and can be repre-

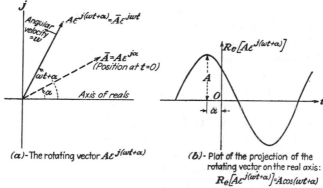

(a)-The rotating vector $A\epsilon^{j(\omega t+\alpha)}$

(b)- Plot of the projection of the rotating vector on the real axis:
$$Re[A\epsilon^{j(\omega t+\alpha)}]=A\cos(\omega t+\alpha)$$

Fig. 67.—Generation of a sinusoid by a rotating vector.

sented by the complex number $\bar{A} = A\epsilon^{j\alpha}$. Furthermore, it rotates uniformly counterclockwise with an angular velocity of ω radians per unit time. The projection of the vector on the real axis is equal at any instant to $A\cos(\omega t + \alpha)$, as shown in Fig. 67b. Although α is expressed fundamentally in radians, degrees are sometimes used for convenience.

It should be remarked at this point that complex numbers and their associated plane vectors as used in these applications are not equivalent to the space vectors used in vector analysis and do not follow the same rules for manipulation except in certain special instances, for example, the addition of space vectors lying in one plane. In general, the rules of vector analysis will not apply to the complex numbers and plane vectors that we are considering here.

64. Derivatives and Integrals.—Let us now examine the derivative of the rotating plane vector $\bar{A}\epsilon^{j\omega t}$ where $\bar{A}$ is a complex number. Denoting the differential operator d/dt by p and differentiating in the usual manner, we obtain

$$\frac{d}{dt}(\bar{A}\epsilon^{j\omega t}) = p(\bar{A}\epsilon^{j\omega t}) = j\omega(\bar{A}\epsilon^{j\omega t}), \qquad (383)$$

and we see that the differential operator p is merely replaced by $j\omega$.

The second derivative turns out to be

$$\begin{aligned} p^2(\bar{A}\epsilon^{j\omega t}) &= (j\omega)^2(\bar{A}\epsilon^{j\omega t}) \\ &= -\omega^2(\bar{A}\epsilon^{j\omega t}), \end{aligned} \qquad (384)$$

and again the differentiation merely replaces p by $j\omega$.

The integral with respect to time will contain no constant of integration since a constant term cannot be present in a steady-state sinusoidal response:

$$\int (\bar{A}\epsilon^{j\omega t})\, dt = \frac{1}{p}(\bar{A}\epsilon^{j\omega t}) = \frac{1}{j\omega}(\bar{A}\epsilon^{j\omega t}), \qquad (385)$$

in which we see the same replacement as before.

This demonstrates an important characteristic of these operations: when the differentiation or integration of the rotating vector is indicated by the operator p, the performance of the indicated operation results in the algebraic quantity $j\omega$ replacing the differential operator p. This is an important feature of the method, for, when we are solving for the steady-state sinusoidal response of a system, it permits us to reduce the differential equations to algebraic equations in a simple manner.

65. Application to Steady-state Sinusoidal Response.—We shall suppose that the system of differential equations has been set up and all the dependent variables eliminated except the one in which we are interested at the moment. If there is a single sinusoidal driving force, the differential equation for a linear system can be written in the form:

$$D(p)y = M(p)F \cos (\omega t + \alpha), \qquad (386)$$

where $D(p)$ and $M(p)$ are polynomials in p. For a specific example of this type of equation, see Eq. (241) of Sec. 52, Chap. VI. The angle α takes care of any possible phase position of the driving force; for example, if the driving force is $F \sin \omega t$, the angle α will be $-\pi/2$. If there is more than one driving force, there will be additional terms on the right side of Eq. (386). If there are driving forces of different frequencies, the principle of super-position should be used: the solution for each frequency can be found separately as though the others were not present, and the separate solutions later combined to form the total solution. This will be shown in more detail in Chap. X.

Suppose that, instead of solving Eq. (386) directly, we digress for a moment and examine the solution of the equation

$$D(p)\bar{y} = M(p)Fe^{j(\omega t+\alpha)}, \tag{387}$$

where $\bar{y}$ is not identical with the old variable y in Eq. (386) but possibly bears some relation to it which we shall now try to discover.

By Euler's formula, our new Eq. (387) can be written as

$$D(p)\bar{y} = M(p)F[\cos(\omega t + \alpha) + j\sin(\omega t + \alpha)]. \tag{388}$$

We shall now apply the reasoning of superposition to the two terms inside the brackets. The first term taken alone produces an equation identical with Eq. (386); it is the part in which we are interested, and we know by physical reasoning that the corresponding solution will be a real quantity. The second term in brackets is purely imaginary, and we would expect that its corresponding solution would be purely imaginary also. Thus the solution $\bar{y}$ of Eq. (387) will be a complex number containing a real part corresponding to the desired solution y of Eq. (386), and an imaginary part in which we are not particularly interested at the moment. Hence we can write

$$y = \mathcal{R}_e[\bar{y}]. \tag{389}$$

In Eq. (387) the driving force is exponential and, since the system is linear, we can assume that the steady-state response will be exponential also, of the form:

$$\bar{y} = \bar{Y}e^{j\omega t}, \tag{390}$$

where $\bar{Y}$ is a complex number. Making this substitution in Eq. (387), there results

$$D(p)\bar{Y}e^{j\omega t} = M(p)Fe^{j(\omega t+\alpha)}. \tag{391}$$

However, in taking the derivatives of $e^{j\omega t}$ the quantity $j\omega$ merely replaces the p, and therefore the differential equation (391) can be reduced immediately to the algebraic equation

$$D(j\omega)\bar{Y}\epsilon^{j\omega t} = M(j\omega)F\epsilon^{j\alpha}\epsilon^{j\omega t}$$

or
$$D(j\omega) \cdot \bar{Y} = M(j\omega) \cdot F\epsilon^{j\alpha}. \qquad (392)$$

This equation relates the vector driving force at $t = 0$ ($F\epsilon^{j\alpha}$) with the vector response at $t = 0$ ($\bar{Y}$) and can be solved immediately for the response. Observe that the equation can be written directly from the differential Eq. (386) by replacing the instantaneous driving force $F\cos(\omega t + \alpha)$ by the vector driving force $F\epsilon^{j\alpha}$, the instantaneous response y by the vector response $\bar{Y}$, and p by $j\omega$. Solving for $\bar{Y}$ we obtain the complex number

$$\bar{Y} = \frac{M(j\omega)}{D(j\omega)} F\epsilon^{j\alpha}. \qquad (393)$$

This complex number represents the position at $t = 0$ of the vector which, rotating at an angular velocity ω, generates the instantaneous sinusoidal solution by its projection on the real axis.

The notation is somewhat simplified by defining the ratio $D(j\omega)/M(j\omega)$ as $\bar{Z}$, with an absolute value Z and a phase angle ϕ:

$$\frac{D(j\omega)}{M(j\omega)} = \bar{Z} = Z\epsilon^{j\phi}. \qquad (394)$$

Then from Eq. (393):

$$\bar{Y} = \frac{F\epsilon^{j\alpha}}{Z\epsilon^{j\phi}} = \frac{F}{Z} \epsilon^{j(\alpha-\phi)}. \qquad (395)$$

The relationship between these vector quantities and the instantaneous values of driving force and response are shown in Fig. 68.

From here there are at least two alternate methods of completing the solution, depending on the information we desire.

1. *Maximum Value and Phase Angle.*—We may wish to find only the maximum value of the response y and perhaps its phase angle with respect to the driving force. Referring to Eqs. (389) and (390) we see that the maximum value of y is equal to the absolute value of the vector $\bar{Y}$, since the absolute value of $\epsilon^{j\omega t}$ is always unity. This is what we would expect, of course, from our concept of y as the projection on the real axis of the rotating vector $\bar{Y}\epsilon^{j\omega t}$. Thus from Eq. (395) we can write

$$y_{\text{max.}} = |\bar{Y}| = \frac{F}{Z}, \qquad (396)$$

where F is the maximum value of the driving force and Z is the absolute value of the vector ratio $\bar{Z}$ given by Eq. (394).

The phase angle by which the solution y lags the driving force is obtained from Eq. (395) as the angle ϕ. This was defined in Eq. (394), and reference to the general formula of Eq. (370) shows that

$$\phi = \tan^{-1} \frac{\text{imaginary part of } \bar{Z}}{\text{real part of } \bar{Z}}. \tag{397}$$

If $\bar{Z}$ as given by Eq. (394) is a complex fraction, it can be rationalized to find its real and imaginary parts.

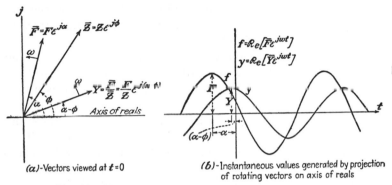

(*a*)-Vectors viewed at $t=0$

(*b*)-Instantaneous values generated by projection of rotating vectors on axis of reals

Fig. 68.—Vector representation and instantaneous values.

In electrical calculations the driving force $\bar{F}$ is frequently a voltage and the response $\bar{Y}$ a current, and the vector ratio $\bar{Z}$ is then called the *impedance*. When the current to be found is that flowing through the source of voltage, the ratio $\bar{Z}$ is said to be the *driving point impedance*, and when the current is to be found in another part of the network the corresponding ratio $\bar{Z}$ is called the *transfer impedance*. The reciprocal of $\bar{Z}$ is called the *admittance*. It should be observed, however, that the general relations (386) to (397) hold regardless of whether the driving force is a voltage or a current (as is sometimes the case), or whether the differential equation (386) is set up in terms of current, charge, or voltage in any part of the network.

When the driving force is a voltage and the response is a current, the impedance $\bar{Z}$ is commonly found by combining individual branch impedances in series and parallel. In using this method the impedances $j\omega L$ and $1/j\omega C$ are used instead of the operational pL and $1/pC$.   Observe that this is the same replacement of p by $j\omega$ that has been used above.   Fundamentally, the vector method is based on the properties of linear differential equations mentioned in the previous sections.   There are many cases when impedances cannot conveniently be combined in series and parallel, and the more fundamental method of writing the differential equations and replacing p by $j\omega$ should be followed.

Effective values are generally used for voltage and current, and, since for a sine wave the effective value is equal to the maximum value divided by $\sqrt{2}$, both sides of Eq. (395) can be divided by this quantity to express both current and voltage in effective or root-mean-square values.   It should be remembered, however, that the process of using maximum values in vector equations is the fundamental one.

In mechanical systems the vector ratio $\bar{Z}$ between force and velocity or displacement is frequently called the *velocity impedance* or *displacement impedance*, depending on whether the equation is written in terms of v or x.   In mechanical systems it is sometimes difficult to combine mechanical impedances in series and parallel, mainly because the relations are more difficult to visualize.   However, the fundamental method based on the differential equations of the system can be used without difficulty.

2. *Instantaneous Values.*—We may wish to find the trigonometric expression for the instantaneous response y.   To do this we shall merely find the projection of the rotating vector $\bar{Y}\epsilon^{j\omega t}$ on the real axis.   Thus by Eqs. (389) and (390) we have

$$\text{Instantaneous } y = \mathfrak{R}_e[\bar{Y}\epsilon^{j\omega t}]. \tag{398}$$

Substituting from Eq. (395) we obtain

$$y = \mathfrak{R}_e\left[\frac{F}{Z}\,\epsilon^{j(\omega t+\alpha-\phi)}\right].$$

Expressing the exponential by Euler's formula (375) and taking the real part of the bracketed quantity, we obtain the desired result:

$$y = \frac{F}{Z}\cos(\omega t + \alpha - \phi), \tag{399}$$

where Z and ϕ are defined in Eqs. (394) and (397).

66. Summary of the Method.—The method will now be summarized for convenience.

1. Write the differential equation in terms of the desired variable y. This will take the form:

$$D(p)y = M(p)F \cos (\omega t + \alpha).$$

2. Replace the driving force $F \cos (\omega t + \alpha)$ by the vector $F\epsilon^{j\alpha}$, the variable y by the vector $\bar{Y}$, and p by $j\omega$. Solve the resulting algebraic equation for $\bar{Y}$, which is the rotating vector solution as viewed at $t = 0$:

$$\bar{Y} = \frac{M(j\omega)}{D(j\omega)} F\epsilon^{j\alpha}$$

This complex number can be evaluated and interpreted immediately; however, for convenience, define

$$\bar{Z} = Z\epsilon^{j\phi} = \frac{D(j\omega)}{M(j\omega)}.$$

The vector solution can then be written as

$$\bar{Y} = \frac{F}{Z} \epsilon^{j(\alpha - \phi)}$$

where Z is the absolute value of $\bar{Z}$. From Eq. (397) the phase angle ϕ is

$$\phi = \tan^{-1} \frac{\text{imaginary part of } \bar{Z}}{\text{real part of } \bar{Z}}.$$

3. The maximum value of the instantaneous response y is equal to the absolute value of the rotating vector $\bar{Y}\epsilon^{j\omega t}$ and is

$$y_{\text{max.}} = |\bar{Y}| = \frac{F}{Z}.$$

The angle by which the response lags the driving force is ϕ, given above.

4. If, on the other hand, it is desired to obtain an expression for instantaneous values of y, we can project the rotating vector $\bar{Y}\epsilon^{j\omega t}$ on the real axis ($y = \Re_e[\bar{Y}\epsilon^{j\omega t}]$) and obtain as in Eq. (399):

$$y = \frac{F}{Z} \cos (\omega t + \alpha - \phi).$$

67. Electrical Example.—Consider first a simple example for which we already know the answer. A capacitance C and resistance R are connected in series across a voltage $E \cos \omega t$. Find the steady-state current. The differential equation is

$$\left(R + \frac{1}{pC}\right) i = E \cos \omega t. \tag{400}$$

Replace $E \cos \omega t$ by the vector $E \epsilon^{j0} = E$, i by the vector $\bar{I}$, and p by $j\omega$. Solving for $\bar{I}$ we obtain

$$\bar{I} = \frac{E}{R + \dfrac{1}{j\omega C}} = \frac{E}{R - j\dfrac{1}{\omega C}}. \tag{401}$$

The vector impedance is evidently

$$\bar{Z} = R - j\frac{1}{\omega C} = \sqrt{R^2 + \left(\frac{1}{\omega C}\right)^2}\, \epsilon^{j\phi}, \tag{402}$$

where $\qquad \phi = \tan^{-1} \dfrac{-1/\omega C}{R} = -\tan^{-1} \dfrac{1}{R\omega C}. \tag{403}$

Thus ϕ is negative and the current leads the voltage. The vector expression for current (401) can now be written as

$$I = \frac{E}{Z}\, \epsilon^{j(0-\phi)} = \frac{E}{\sqrt{R^2 + \left(\dfrac{1}{\omega C}\right)^2}}\, \epsilon^{\tan^{-1}(1/R\omega C)} \tag{404}$$

The maximum value of instantaneous current is therefore given by

$$i_{\text{max.}} = |\bar{I}| = \frac{E}{\sqrt{R^2 + \left(\dfrac{1}{\omega C}\right)^2}}, \tag{405}$$

and its phase angle is given by Eq. (403).

If the trigonometric form of the instantaneous current is desired, we can write

$$i = \frac{E}{\sqrt{R^2 + \left(\dfrac{1}{\omega C}\right)^2}} \cos\left(\omega t + \tan^{-1} \frac{1}{R\omega C}\right). \tag{406}$$

Observe that the quantity $(1/\omega C)$ is the reactance of the condenser, usually denoted by X_c. The vector and instantaneous relations are shown in Fig. 69.

Using the trigonometric formula for the cosine of the sum of two angles, Eq. (406) can be expanded into an alternative form:

$$i = \frac{E\left[R\, \cos \omega t - \left(\frac{1}{\omega C}\right) \sin \omega t \right]}{R^2 + \left(\frac{1}{\omega C}\right)^2}. \qquad (407)$$

Continuation of the Example.—Suppose that in the previous example the voltage $E \cos \omega t$ were switched into the initially

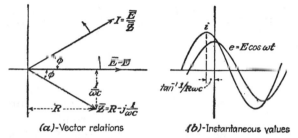

(a)-Vector relations   *(b)*-Instantaneous values

FIG. 69.—Solution of RC series circuit with sinusoidal voltage applied.

relaxed circuit at $t = 0$ and it was desired to find the total response, including transients. Instead of using the classical methods of Chap. VI for solving the nonhomogeneous differential equation (400), we could obtain the steady-state solution more easily by vector methods as above, and use the homogeneous equation corresponding to Eq. (400) to find the transients. Referring to Eq. (400), the homogeneous equation would be

$$\left(R + \frac{1}{pC} \right) i = 0,$$

for which the characteristic equation is

$$R + \frac{1}{mC} = 0,$$

which yields the root: $m = -1/RC$. The transient part of the solution is, therefore,

$$i_t = K\epsilon^{-t/RC}, \qquad (408)$$

where K is the constant of integration. The steady-state solution is given by Eq. (406), and the total solution will be the sum of Eqs. (406) and (408). The initial condition is found to be that at $t = 0$, $i = E/R$, so apply this to the total solution:

$$\frac{E}{R} = K\epsilon^0 + \frac{E}{\sqrt{R^2 + \left(\frac{1}{\omega C}\right)^2}} \cos\left(\tan^{-1}\frac{1}{R\omega C}\right),$$

from which

$$K = \frac{E}{R[(R\omega C)^2 + 1]}.$$

The total solution is then

$$i = \frac{E\epsilon^{-t/RC}}{R[(R\omega C)^2 + 1]} + \frac{E}{\sqrt{R^2 + \left(\frac{1}{\omega C}\right)^2}} \cos\left(\omega t + \tan^{-1}\frac{1}{R\omega C}\right).$$

(409)

Thus the instantaneous current consists of an exponentially decaying transient superimposed upon the sinusoidal steady-state current.

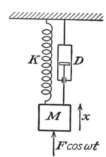

Fig. 70.—Example of forced oscillation.

68. Mechanical Example Showing Resonance.—A mass M with damping D is suspended from a spring K, as in Fig. 70, and a force $F \cos \omega t$ is applied to the mass. Find the steady-state motion (forced oscillation) of the mass. The differential equation is

$$(Mp^2 + Dp + K)x = F \cos \omega t. \quad (410)$$

Replace $F \cos \omega t$ by the vector $F\epsilon^{j0} = F$, x by the vector $\bar{X}$, and p by $j\omega$. Solving for the vector displacement $\bar{X}$ we obtain

$$\bar{X} = \frac{F}{(K - \omega^2 M) + j\omega D}. \quad (411)$$

The displacement impedance is seen to be

$$\bar{Z} = (K - \omega^2 M) + j\omega D$$

or

$$\bar{Z} = \sqrt{(K - \omega^2 M)^2 + (\omega D)^2} \cdot \epsilon^{j\phi}, \quad (412)$$

where

$$\phi = \tan^{-1}\frac{\omega D}{K - \omega^2 M}. \quad (413)$$

The vector expression for displacement (411) can be written as

$$\bar{X} = \frac{F}{\sqrt{(K - \omega^2 M)^2 + (\omega D)^2}} \epsilon^{-i\phi}, \tag{414}$$

and the motion lags the force by the angle given in Eq. (413). The amplitude of the motion is given by the absolute value of $\bar{X}$:

$$x_{max.} = \frac{F}{\sqrt{(K - \omega^2 M)^2 + (\omega D)^2}}. \tag{415}$$

Usually we are interested mainly in the amplitude of the motion and perhaps its phase angle, as given above. However, we can write the expression for instantaneous steady-state displacement x quite simply as

$$x = x_{max.} \cos{(\omega t - \phi)}, \tag{416}$$

where ϕ and $x_{max.}$ are given by Eqs. (413) and (415), respectively.

When this system does not have excessive damping, it can exhibit the important phenomenon of *resonance:* if we apply a driving force of constant amplitude and vary the frequency, there will be a certain frequency at which the motion becomes greatest, and either higher or lower frequencies will produce smaller amplitudes. Resonance will occur when the mechanical impedance Z is a minimum, a condition that we can calculate most easily by minimizing $Z^2 = (K - \omega^2 M)^2 + (\omega D)^2$. Taking the derivative of Z^2 with respect to ω and placing it equal to zero, we obtain for the resonant angular velocity

$$\omega_r = \sqrt{\frac{K}{M} - \frac{D^2}{2M^2}}. \tag{417}$$

The resonant frequency is given by $f_r = \omega_r/2\pi$. Substituting the above value of ω_r into Eq. (415), we find for the amplitude of motion at resonance:

$$\text{Resonant } x_{max.} = \frac{F}{D}\sqrt{\frac{M}{K}}\left(\frac{1}{\sqrt{1 - \frac{D^2}{4MK}}}\right). \tag{418}$$

When the damping is so great that $D^2 > 2KM$, the resonant frequency in Eq. (417) becomes imaginary and resonance can no longer exist. Under these conditions the maximum amplitude will take place at frequencies approaching zero, and Eq. (418) will have no physical meaning.

The phenomenon of resonance is of greatest interest when the damping in the system is quite small, for the amplitude of motion may then become comparatively great. For the condition $D^2 << 4KM$ (*i.e.*, when the damping is much less than the

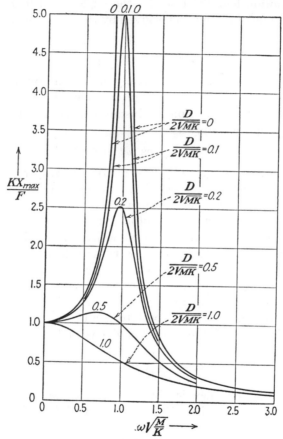

Fig. 71.—Maximum displacement vs. frequency for various amounts of damping —system of Fig. 70.   Plotted in terms of dimensionless groups.

critical value for free vibrations), the resonant angular velocity and amplitude of motion become more simply

$$\omega_r \approx \sqrt{\frac{K}{M}} \tag{419}$$

and   Resonant $x_{max.} \approx \dfrac{F}{\omega D} \cdot$ (420)

The amplitude of motion at resonance is then limited by the damping in the system.

The amplitude of vibration for various amounts of damping is plotted against frequency in Fig. 71, in terms of the dimensionless groups $Kx_{max.}/F$, $\omega \sqrt{M/K}$, and $D/2 \sqrt{MK}$.

The phase relation between driving force and resulting motion is particularly interesting. Equation (413) shows that for frequencies approaching zero the motion is in phase with the driving force. This is what we would expect from physical reasoning, since the spring then offers the main resisting force.

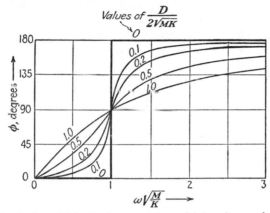

FIG. 72.—Angle by which displacement lags driving force, plotted against frequency for various amounts of damping—system of Fig. 70.

At higher frequencies the motion lags the driving force: in the vicinity of resonance the motion lags by 90°, while at very high frequencies it lags by nearly 180°, *i.e.*, the motion and force are nearly in phase opposition. This is caused by the predominance of inertia force at frequencies far above resonance and is similar to the result obtained with mass and driving force alone. The shift in phase with frequency is quite slow for systems with large damping but is rather abrupt when the damping is small, as shown by Fig. 72. When the damping approaches zero, Eq. (413) shows that the shift from in-phase to out-of-phase motion occurs rapidly at the point of resonance.

If the differential equation (410) had been written in terms of the velocity of the mass instead of displacement, it would have been found that the resonant velocity for this system occurs when $K = \omega^2 M$ regardless of damping and is given simply by F/D. The velocity in simple harmonic motion depends upon both displacement and frequency, and hence its resonant point occurs at a slightly higher frequency than that of displacement. The resonant velocity of this system is precisely analogous to current resonance in a series RLC electrical circuit. The electrical phenomenon analogous to displacement resonance might be called *charge resonance*, although the term is rarely used, and would correspond to the greatest voltage across the condenser.

There is a close correspondence between the resonant frequencies of a system and its natural frequencies in free oscillation, although the two are not identical in value when damping is present. The natural frequency of the foregoing system is obtained by first writing the characteristic equation from the differential equation (410):

$$Mm^2 + Dm + K = 0.$$

This has the roots

$$m = -\frac{D}{2M} \pm \sqrt{\frac{D^2}{4M^2} - \frac{K}{M}}.$$

If the damping is small enough so that $D^2 < 4MK$, the radical will become imaginary, and if the system is shocked it will have a transient oscillation with a natural frequency corresponding to

$$\omega_n = 2\pi f_n = \sqrt{\frac{K}{M} - \frac{D^2}{4M^2}}.$$

This is quite similar to Eq. (417) for the resonant angular velocity, and in fact becomes approximately equal to it for small values of damping [see Eq. (419)]. This is what we might expect from physical reasoning, for at resonance we are driving the system most nearly in accord with its natural tendencies.

More complicated systems have differential equations of higher order than the above, and hence they have the possibility of a number of different natural frequencies of oscillation, which in general would be present simultaneously in a transient condition. Corresponding to these they will have a number of different resonant frequencies for forced oscillation. In general the resonant frequencies, amplitudes, and other characteristics of these systems can be found by the methods illustrated for the simple system above.

When the damping is not great, it has comparatively little effect except in the region of resonance, where it prevents the amplitude from becoming infinite. The solution of resonant frequencies and of forced oscillations in complicated lightly damped systems can sometimes be simplified by neglecting damping entirely, although the results must then be interpreted with care, especially in the regions of resonance.

69. Conclusion.—Vector methods have long been applied with profit to the solution of electrical systems and probably are of equal importance in the investigation of forced vibrations and oscillations in mechanical systems. In electrical systems some short cuts are possible in setting up the equations, but in mechanical systems the more general procedure starting with the differential equations is almost necessary. In electrical systems involving a bridge-type network the differential-equation procedure may be shorter than the alternative wye-delta transformation which would permit a combination of impedances in series and parallel. When mutual inductance is present or when it is desired to find the current in one part of a network caused by voltage applied to another part, the differential-equation method may again be preferable.

In obtaining the complete solution, both transient and steady state, of differential equations when the driving forces are sinusoidal, the steady state can be found by short-cut vector methods, and the transient can be found from the corresponding homogeneous equation. This is usually shorter than the classical methods for solving nonhomogeneous equations described in Chap. VI.

Problems

The following complex numbers will be used in the problems below:

$$\bar{A}_1 = 4 + j3. \qquad \bar{A}_3 = 5\underline{/60°}.$$
$$\bar{A}_2 = -6 + j8. \qquad \bar{A}_4 = 6\epsilon^{-j120°}.$$

1. Draw vectors on the complex plane representing the complex numbers above.

2. Express $\bar{A}_1$ and $\bar{A}_2$ in polar form, and $\bar{A}_3$ and $\bar{A}_4$ in rectangular form.

3. Find $\bar{A}_1 + \bar{A}_2$ and $\bar{A}_1 - \bar{A}_2$ and express the results in both rectangular and polar form.

4. *a.* Find $\bar{A}_1\bar{A}_2$ and $\bar{A}_1/\bar{A}_2$ in rectangular form.

b. Repeat part (a) using the polar form of the complex numbers, and express the results in polar form.

5. Find $\bar{A}_3\bar{A}_4$ and $\bar{A}_3/\bar{A}_4$ in polar form.

6. Evaluate $\epsilon^{\bar{A}_1}$ and express in rectangular form.

7. Find $(\bar{A}_3)^2$ and $\sqrt{\bar{A}_3}$ in polar form.

8. Find the magnitude of $\dfrac{100 - j54}{45 + j65}$ in the simplest possible manner.

9. Evaluate $\mathfrak{R}_e[4\epsilon^{j4\pi t}]$ for $t = 0$, 0.0625, 0.125, 0.25, 0.375, and 0.5 sec. (The argument is given in radians.) Plot the result vs. time. What is the frequency of the function? What is its maximum value?

10. a. The function $y = 5 \cos (\omega t + 30°)$ is to be represented by a rotating vector. Draw this vector for $t = 0$ and give its complex number representation.

b. Repeat for $y = 8 \sin \omega t$.

11. The following complex numbers represent the positions at $t = 0$ of vectors that are rotating with an angular velocity of ω radians per second. Write the corresponding functions of time in trigonometric form:

$\qquad$ (a) $\bar{Y} = Y\epsilon^{j50°}$, $\qquad$ (b) $\bar{E} = E\underline{/-20°}$, $\qquad$ (c) $\bar{I} = -3 + j4$.

12. a. Evaluate $x = \dfrac{dy}{dt} + 2y$ if $y = 3 \cos (2t - 30°)$, and express in the form $X_{max.} \cos (\omega t + \phi)$.

b. Evaluate $\bar{x} = \dfrac{d\bar{y}}{dt} + 2\bar{y}$ if $\bar{y} = 3\epsilon^{j(2t-30°)}$, express in exponential form, and compare with the results of part (a).

13. A voltage $E \cos \omega t$ is applied to a resistance R and an inductance L connected in series.

a. Set up the differential equation for the system and solve vectorially for the amplitude and phase angle of the steady-state current.

b. If $E = 162.7$ volts amplitude (115 volts rms), $R = 40$ ohms, $L = 0.070$ henry, and the frequency is 60 cycles per second, find the vectors representing current $\bar{I}$, resistance voltage $\bar{E}_R$, inductance voltage $\bar{E}_L$, the sum $\bar{E}_R + \bar{E}_L$, and applied voltage $\bar{E}$. Draw these vectors at $t = 0$ on the complex plane.

14. A voltage $E \sin \omega t$ is suddenly applied at $t = 0$ to a series circuit made up of a resistance of R ohms and an inductance of L henrys.

a. If $E = 155.5$ volts amplitude, $L = 0.10$ henry, $R = 6.0$ ohms, and $\omega = 377$ radians per second (60 cycles), find the steady-state vector current in polar form. Write the expression for the steady-state instantaneous current in trigonometric form.

b. Find the form of the transient current from the corresponding homogeneous differential equation and write the complete solution for the current as a function of time after the switch is closed. Sketch the form of this current vs. time roughly to scale for the duration of the transient.

15. a. Solve the system shown in Fig. P15 for the amplitude and phase position of the velocity v, if $W = 3.86$ lb, $D = 1.2$ lb-sec/in., $F = 10$ lb, $\alpha = 60°$, and $\omega = 500$ radians per second.

b. Draw the vectors representing the velocity, the applied force, the inertia force, and the damper force, and show that the vector sum of damper and inertia forces is equal to the applied force.

c. If the force is suddenly applied at $t = 0$ and the mass initially has zero velocity, find the complete solution for velocity, including the transient, as a function of time. Sketch the solution roughly to scale.

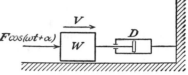

FIG. P15.—Vibrating mechanical system.

16. A galvanometer is placed on a heavy iron plate which is in turn supported on springs. The floor vibrates vertically with a motion $x_f = X_f \cos \omega t$. The mass of the galvanometer and plate is M, and the total spring constant of the springs is K.

a. Neglecting damping, find an expression for the amplitude of vibration of the galvanometer, X_g, using vectorial methods.

b. If the galvanometer and plate together weigh 15 lb and are supported on springs with a total spring constant of 30 lb/in., plot the ratio X_g/X_f over the frequency range $0 < f < 20$ cycles per second. Over what frequency range will the mounting be effective in reducing the vibration of the galvanometer?

17. A voltage $E \cos \omega t$ is applied to a series circuit composed of a resistance of R ohms, an inductance of L henrys, and a capacitance of C farads.

a. Find an expression for the steady-state instantaneous current, in the form $I \cos (\omega t - \phi)$.

b. Discuss the variation in amplitude and phase angle of this current as the frequency is varied, assuming all other quantities kept constant.

18. For the circuit and data shown in Fig. P18, set up the differential equations in terms of charge, and solve directly for the steady-state vector charge on the condenser, $\bar{Q}_2$, in coulombs. Express the result in polar form.

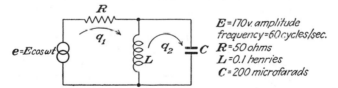

$E = 170v.\ amplitude$
$frequency = 60\ cycles/sec.$
$R = 50\ ohms$
$L = 0.1\ henries$
$C = 200\ microfarads$

FIG. P18.—Electrical network with a-c voltage applied.

19. Figure P19 shows schematically a form of vibration instrument. The vibrating body moves vertically with a displacement $x_2 = X_2 \cos \omega t$. The force transmitted through the spring to the mass causes it to vibrate with the displacement x_1, and the amplitude of the difference between these two displacements, $x_1 - x_2$, is read on the scale.

a. Set up the differential equation for x_1 in terms of x_2, and find an expression for the amplitude read on the scale.

b. What should be the relation among ω, M, and K if the scale is to read the amplitude of vibration of the body, X_2?

c. What should be the relation among ω, M, and K if the scale is to read an amount proportional to the maximum acceleration of the body, $\omega^2 X_2$?

20. Machines that operate with considerable vibration are frequently mounted on flexible supports (spring, rubber, felt, etc.) to isolate the vibration, but the constants of this support must be chosen correctly in order to obtain the desired result. Figure P20 shows a flexibly mounted motor with a periodic force applied from unbalance in the rotor.

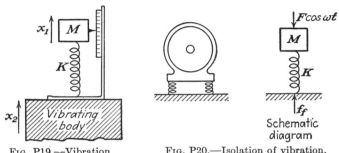

Fig. P19.—Vibration instrument.

Fig. P20.—Isolation of vibration.

a. Using vector methods, solve for the force transmitted to the floor. Neglect damping.

b. Define the ratios:

$$\text{Transmissibility} = \epsilon = \frac{\text{force transmitted to floor}}{\text{applied force}}$$

and

$$\frac{\text{Resonant frequency}}{\text{Applied frequency}} = \frac{\omega_r}{\omega} = \frac{1}{\omega}\sqrt{\frac{K}{M}}.$$

Manipulate the result obtained in (*a*) so as to express ϵ as a function of ω_r/ω and plot ϵ over the range $0 < \omega_r/\omega < 2$. What conclusions can be drawn from this curve regarding the effectiveness of elastic mounting in isolating vibration?

c. At a given frequency, the transmissibility can be shown to depend only on the static deflection of the weight on the spring, δ_{st}. Arrange the results of (*a*) to express $\delta_{st} = W/K$ as a function of ϵ and f. Plot δ_{st} (inches) vs. frequency (cycles per second) for $\epsilon = -0.10$ and $\epsilon = -0.05$. What conclusions can be drawn from these curves?

d. A 12-lb motor which runs at 1,145 rpm is to be mounted so that $\epsilon = 0.05$. From the results of (*b*) find the proper spring constant. From the results of (*c*) find the required static deflection and check the two results.

21. A certain type of reciprocating refrigeration compressor, belt-driven from an electric motor, produces a pulsating torque and causes objectionable variations of current in the lines supplying the motor. It is suggested that the angular pulsations of the shaft can be reduced by making the cooling fan rather heavy and mounting it elastically on the motor shaft so that it will act as a dynamic vibration absorber, or "tuned flywheel." The system is shown schematically in Fig. P21. Since the constant torques balance out, both the constant torque and the normal steady rotation of the shaft can be ignored.   Thus the analysis will consider only the angular motion caused by the pulsating component of force.

a. Assuming a sinusoidal torque of the form $T \cos \omega t$ and neglecting damping, find an expression for the amplitude of motion of the motor shaft.

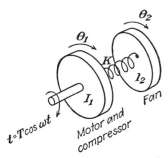

FIG. P21.—Schematic diagram of refrigeration motor, compressor, and spring-mounted fan used as vibration absorber.

b. For the data given below, find the WR^2 of the fan that will make the motion of the motor shaft very small.   Also find the resonant frequency at which the motion of the motor shaft will be very great.   Discuss the effect of damping in the elastic mounting.

Data: Frequency of pulsation = 10.2 cycles per second.
Spring constant of mounting, K = 5.27 lb-ft/radian.
WR^2 of motor and compressor referred to motor shaft = 0.0713 lb-ft².

CHAPTER VIII

THE CHECKING OF EQUATIONS

70. Introduction.—The result is the important thing and, if it is to be of any value, it must be free from essential errors of any kind. An engineer who permits essential errors to slip by him is likely to be more of a liability than an asset. Not only must the method be correct, but the whole work from beginning to end, down to the last decimal place, must be correct also. Since everyone is likely to make mistakes, the only way in which one can be reasonably sure of accuracy is to check his results before passing them on. The purpose of this chapter is to present some methods by which errors in equations can be discovered and eliminated.

71. Some Methods of Checking.—Probably the most fundamental method of checking physical calculations is to compare some calculated results with the results of physical experiment. This is particularly necessary when the analysis is along entirely new lines. It checks everything from the formulation of the problem, through the assumptions and analysis, down to the final decimal point. It has the obvious disadvantage of requiring the time and equipment to perform the experiments.

Another method of checking is to work the problem through by an entirely different method. This may double the amount of work involved, but it provides an excellent check on the mathematics.

One can also check his calculations, both literal and numerical, by comparing them with the results obtained by others. For this method of checking to be at all reliable it is necessary that the work be entirely independent. When examining the work of others it is extremely easy to be led into the same mistakes that they made, and one must always be on guard against this possibility.

Probably the most obvious method of checking (and used surprisingly little) is to examine the results in the light of experience and to satisfy oneself that they are really reasonable in magnitude.

Except for the last method, those described above require considerable extra work and are not always suitable. It is therefore convenient, and indeed almost necessary, to use the two methods that will be described in some detail: the dimensional check and the limiting case check.

72. Nature of Dimensional Checking.—The student is probably already familiar with some of the features of dimensional checking. It is based on the fact that nearly all physical equations are dimensionally homogeneous, *i.e.*, each of the various terms in an equation must be expressed in terms of the same combination of fundamental units. The equations fall into two general classifications: (1) those containing quantities of the same general type; for example, those containing only electrical or only mechanical quantities, and (2) equations that contain a mixture of two or more types of quantities; for example, both mechanical and electrical or both mechanical and thermal quantities. The two types will be considered separately.

73. Equations Containing One Type of Quantity.—If one confines his attention to one type of physical system, three fundamental quantities are sufficient to describe all possible quantities in the system. In mechanics the three fundamental quantities are often taken to be mass, length, and time, but, since we can measure force more directly than we can measure mass, it is more convenient in engineering work to use force, length, and time as fundamental dimensions. Any other mechanical quantity can be expressed in terms of these three. For example, velocity has the dimensions of length per unit time: feet per second or inches per second; and mass is expressed as weight (or force) divided by the acceleration of gravity: in foot-pound-second units it is lb-sec^2/ft.

After choosing the three fundamental dimensions, it is possible to express each quantity in an equation in terms of these three by writing in place of each symbol the names or symbols of its dimensions. By canceling names (or symbols) in numerator and denominator, it can be determined whether all terms of the equation have the same dimensions.

There is some advantage in using the names of the dimensional quantities rather than their symbols, as this permits one to check on his use of feet and inches, seconds and hours, etc. For example, it might turn out that the acceleration of gravity should be expressed in a certain equation as in./sec^2 rather than as the more usual ft/sec^2, and the use of the names rather than the symbols of length and time would point this out. However, this will not be convenient when quantities of two or more types are mixed together.

In a purely electrical system it is convenient to take the volt, ampere, and second to be fundamental dimensions. Any impedance would then have the dimensions of volts per ampere, and from the fundamental formula $e = -L\,di/dt$ we see that inductance would have the dimensions volt-sec/amp. Power would be volt-amperes and energy would be volt-ampere-seconds. Now check the expression for energy stored in the magnetic field of an inductance: $\varepsilon = LI^2/2$. Observe that the factor $\frac{1}{2}$ is purely numerical (has no dimensions) and that[1]

$$[\varepsilon] = EIT.$$

Also
$$[L] = \frac{ET}{I}.$$

Then from the formula $\varepsilon = LI^2/2$:

$$[EIT] = \left[\frac{ET}{I}\,I^2\right],$$
$$[EIT] = [EIT],$$

and the expression is dimensionally correct.

Similarly, in purely thermal equations one could choose three convenient thermal units as fundamental: perhaps quantity of heat (Btu), temperature (degrees F), and time (seconds).

Observe that the dimensional check will not check purely numerical factors, signs, or missing terms. However, it will disclose many common errors and has the advantage of being easy to use. The method can be used to check the original equations, the solution, or any step between. It is evident, however, that the equations must be kept in purely literal form, for in a numerical equation the dimensions of the quantities are obscured.

[1] In this discussion, brackets will be taken to mean "the dimensions of." Thus $[v] = $ ft/sec would be read "The dimensions of velocity are feet per second."

Example 1.—Check the differential equation (derived in Sec. 31):

$$(Mp^2 + Dp + K)y = F. \tag{421}$$

Observe first that

$$[M] = \text{lb-sec}^2/\text{ft}.$$
$$[K] = \text{lb/ft}.$$
$$[D] = \text{lb-sec/ft (force per unit velocity)}.$$
$$[p] = 1/\text{sec}.$$
$$[y] = \text{ft}.$$
$$[F] = \text{lb}.$$

Substituting these dimensions into Eq. (421),

$$\left\{ \left[\frac{\text{lb-sec}^2}{\text{ft}} \cdot \frac{1}{\text{sec}^2} \right] + \left[\frac{\text{lb}}{\text{ft}} \right] + \left[\frac{\text{lb-sec}}{\text{ft}} \cdot \frac{1}{\text{sec}} \right] \right\} \text{ft} \stackrel{?}{=} [\text{lb}].$$

By cancellation, [lb] + [lb] + [lb] = [lb], which shows that the equation is dimensionally homogeneous.

Next check the solution obtained with relaxed initial conditions:

$$y = \frac{F}{K} - \epsilon^{-Dt/2M} \left(\frac{DF}{2MK\omega} \sin \omega t + \frac{F}{K} \cos \omega t \right), \tag{422}$$

where

$$\omega = \sqrt{\frac{K}{M} - \frac{D^2}{4M^2}}.$$

The dimensions of ω are

$$[\omega] = \sqrt{\left[\frac{\text{lb}}{\text{ft}} \cdot \frac{\text{ft}}{\text{lb-sec}^2} \right] - \left[\frac{\text{lb}^2\text{-sec}^2}{\text{ft}^2} \cdot \frac{\text{ft}^2}{\text{lb}^2\text{-sec}^4} \right]}$$

$$= \sqrt{\frac{1}{\text{sec}^2}} = \frac{1}{\text{sec}}.$$

This is correct, since ω is expressed in radians per second, and radians are the ratio of arc to radius and are dimensionless.

Next check the arguments of the exponential and the sine and cosine.

$$[\omega t] = \frac{1}{\text{sec}} \cdot \text{sec} = \text{dimensionless}.$$

$$\left[\frac{Dt}{2M} \right] = \frac{\text{lb-sec}}{\text{ft}} \cdot \text{sec} \cdot \frac{\text{ft}}{\text{lb-sec}^2} = \text{dimensionless}.$$

This is correct, since the arguments of all exponentials and trigonometric functions must be dimensionless, and these functions themselves are dimensionless. Complete the check of Eq. (422):

$$[\text{ft}] = \left[\text{lb} \cdot \frac{\text{ft}}{\text{lb}} \right] + \left[\frac{\text{lb-sec}}{\text{ft}} \cdot \text{lb} \cdot \frac{\text{ft}}{\text{lb-sec}^2} \cdot \frac{\text{ft}}{\text{lb}} \cdot \text{sec} \right] + \left[\text{lb} \cdot \frac{\text{ft}}{\text{lb}} \right].$$

By cancellation we find [ft] = [ft] + [ft] + [ft], which shows that the solution is dimensionally homogeneous.

Example 2.—In a certain electrical problem the following differential equation was obtained:

$$\left(p^2RL + p\frac{L}{C} + \frac{R}{C}\right)i = (pR + p^2L)e. \tag{423}$$

Choosing the fundamental dimensions to be volts, amperes, and seconds, we see that

Since $Ri = E$, $[R] = \dfrac{\text{volts}}{\text{amp}}\left(\text{or }\dfrac{E}{I}\right).$

Since $-L\dfrac{di}{dt} = e$, $[L] = \dfrac{\text{volt-sec}}{\text{amp}}\left(\text{or }\dfrac{ET}{I}\right).$

Since $\dfrac{1}{C}\displaystyle\int i\,dt = e$, $[C] = \dfrac{\text{amp-sec}}{\text{volts}}\left(\text{or }\dfrac{IT}{E}\right).$

And as usual, $[p] = \dfrac{1}{\text{sec}}\left(\text{or }\dfrac{1}{T}\right).$

Then the equation is, dimensionally,

$$\left\{\left[\frac{1}{\text{sec}^2}\cdot\frac{\text{volts}}{\text{amp}}\cdot\frac{\text{volt-sec}}{\text{amp}}\right] + \left[\frac{1}{\text{sec}}\cdot\frac{\text{volt-sec}}{\text{amp}}\cdot\frac{\text{volts}}{\text{amp-sec}}\right]\right.$$
$$\left. + \left[\frac{\text{volts}}{\text{amp}}\cdot\frac{\text{volts}}{\text{amp-sec}}\right]\right\}\text{amp} \overset{?}{=} \left\{\left[\frac{1}{\text{sec}}\cdot\frac{\text{volts}}{\text{amp}}\right] + \left[\frac{1}{\text{sec}^2}\cdot\frac{\text{volt-sec}}{\text{amp}}\right]\right\}\text{volts}.$$

Cancellation shows that each of the terms has the dimensions of volts²/amp-sec, and the equation is dimensionally correct.

74. Example of Tracing an Error.—The problem will be to find the value of resistance which, when connected in parallel with an inductance and condenser, will suppress oscillation. Neglecting driving voltages, the differential equation for resistor current is found to be

$$\left[\left(R + \frac{1}{pC}\right)\left(pL + \frac{1}{pC}\right) - \frac{1}{p^2C^2}\right]i = 0. \tag{424}$$

Expand, $$\left(pRL + \frac{1}{LC} + \frac{R}{pC}\right)i = 0. \tag{425}$$

The characteristic equation is

$$RLm^2 + \frac{1}{LC}m + \frac{R}{C} = 0. \tag{426}$$

Solving for m,

$$m = -\frac{1}{2L^2CR} \pm \frac{1}{2LR}\sqrt{\frac{1}{L^2C^2} - \frac{4R^2L}{C}}. \tag{427}$$

The value of R that will suppress oscillation is that value which will make the quantity under the radical real:

$$R > \frac{1}{2\sqrt{L^3C}}.$$
(428)

Now check this equation dimensionally, using dimensional symbols for convenience:

$$\left[\frac{E}{I}\right] \neq \left[\frac{I}{ET^2}\right],$$

and the equation is not dimensionally homogeneous.

Trace this error back and check Eq. (426). Observe that m would enter the solution as ϵ^{mt}, so mt must be dimensionless, and m has the dimensions of (time)$^{-1}$. Equation (426) yields

$$\left[\frac{E}{I} \cdot \frac{ET}{I} \cdot \frac{1}{T^2}\right] + \left[\frac{I}{ET} \cdot \frac{E}{IT} \cdot \frac{1}{T}\right] + \left[\frac{E}{I} \cdot \frac{E}{IT}\right] \overset{?}{=} 0.$$

(Zero can have any dimensions.)

This reduces to

$$\frac{E^2}{I^2T} + \frac{1}{T^3} + \frac{E^2}{I^2T} \overset{?}{=} 0,$$

and the middle term is seen to be wrong. We might obtain a clue to where the error lies by observing that, if we invert the dimensional formula for inductance (the first factor in the middle term), the equation becomes homogeneous. If Eq. (426) is wrong, we see that Eq. (425) must be wrong also, so the error must have come in expanding Eq. (424). To check our deductions we expand Eq. (424) more carefully and find that the middle term of Eq. (425) should be written L/C instead of $1/LC$. This is a simple and fast method for tracing errors.

75. Equations Containing More Than One Type of Quantity.— If one confines his attention to one type of physical system, three fundamental dimensions are sufficient to express all quantities in that system. However, if another type of system is brought into the equations, another fundamental dimension chosen from the new system is necessary to relate completely all quantities in the two systems. We shall retain force, length, and time as fundamental mechanical dimensions and shall add temperature for thermal equations (written θ to distinguish it from time) and charge Q for electrical equations.

TABLE OF DIMENSIONAL FORMULAS
Technical System, Based on Force, Length, Time, Charge, and Temperature

Symbol	Quantity	Dimensions
	Mechanical	
F	Force	$[F]$
L	Length	$[L]$
t	Time	$[T]$
M	Mass	$[FT^2L^{-1}]$
ε	Energy	$[FL]$
P	Power	$[FLT^{-1}]$
v	Velocity	$[LT^{-1}]$
a	Acceleration	$[LT^{-2}]$
K	Spring constant	$[FL^{-1}]$
D	Damping coefficient	$[FTL^{-1}]$
T	Torque	$[FL]$
I	Moment of inertia	$[FLT^2]$ (as used in dynamics)
ω	Angular velocity	$[T^{-1}]$
α	Angular acceleration	$[T^{-2}]$
ρ	Mass density	$[FT^2L^{-4}]$
μ	Viscosity	$[FTL^{-2}]$
	Electrical (power and energy same as in mechanical system)	
Q	Charge	$[Q]$
I	Current	$[QT^{-1}]$
V	Voltage	$[FLQ^{-1}]$
$R, X,$ or Z	Impedance	$[FLTQ^{-2}]$
L	Inductance	$[FLT^2Q^{-2}]$
C	Capacitance	$[Q^2L^{-1}F^{-1}]$
ϕ	Magnetic flux	$[FLTQ^{-1}]$
ρ	Resistivity	$[FTL^2Q^{-2}]$
μ	Absolute permeability	$[FT^2Q^{-2}]$
ϵ	Absolute dielectric constant (permittivity)	$[Q^2F^{-1}L^{-2}]$
F	Magnetomotive force	$[QT^{-1}]$
	Thermal	
θ	Temperature	$[\theta]$
Q	Quantity of heat	$[FL]$
k	Conductivity	$[FT^{-1}\theta^{-1}]$
S	Entropy	$[FL\theta^{-1}]$

Dimensional formulas for electrical quantities will be built up in the following manner. Choose force, length, time, and charge as fundamental dimensions, and denote them, respectively, by F, L, T, and Q. Since current is the rate of passage of charge, $i = dq/dt$, we must have

$$[I] = [QT^{-1}].$$

Electric power has the dimensions of voltage times current and would be expressed in mechanical units as force times length divided by time. Therefore, $[VI] = FL/T$, and by substituting from the above expression for I, we have

$$\text{Voltage } [V] = [FLQ^{-1}].$$

Resistance (and impedance in general) has the dimensions of voltage divided by current:

$$[R] \text{ or } [Z] = [FLTQ^{-2}].$$

Induced voltage is proportional to the number of turns times the rate of change of magnetic flux. As the number of turns is purely numerical, magnetic flux is expressed by

$$[\phi] = [FLTQ^{-1}].$$

By continuing in this manner one can build up a complete set of dimensional formulas. The table on page 212 gives dimensional formulas for some commonly used physical quantities.

Example: Mixed Quantities.—An expression for the power absorbed by an eddy-current brake has been derived under certain assumptions as

$$W = 1.4 \times 10^{-4} \frac{(p^5 N \rho \mu)^{\frac{1}{2}} z F^2}{D} \quad \text{watts per disk side,}$$

where p = number of poles per disk side.
N = revolutions per second.
ρ = resistivity of disk.
μ = permeability of disk.
z = radial length of pole.
F = ampere-turns per pole.
D = effective diameter of disk.

Note that the number of poles is purely numerical, the speed N has the dimensions of (time)$^{-1}$, and the ampere-turns per pole has the dimensions of current since the number of turns is purely numerical. Referring to the table and writing in place of each symbol its dimensional formula, we have

$$[FLT^{-1}] \stackrel{?}{=} \frac{[T^{-1} \cdot FTL^2Q^{-2} \cdot FT^2Q^{-2}]^{\frac{1}{2}}[L][QT^{-1}]^2}{[L]}$$
$$= [FLT^{-1}],$$

which proves that the equation is dimensionally homogeneous.

76. Limiting Case Method.—The limiting case check can be applied to original equations, solutions, or steps between. The principle is to simplify the equation by the removal of enough quantities so that the correctness of those remaining can be easily determined. The method consists essentially of the following two steps:

1. Simplify the equation to be checked by setting one or more quantities equal to zero or infinity as a limit.

2. Determine what the equation should actually be under these conditions, either by physical reasoning or by rewriting the original equations under the simplified conditions and solving these.

Since it is evident that this method does not check those quantities removed in the simplification, one should apply the check several times, removing different quantities each time. This method of checking will usually determine missing or extra terms, is a good check on the form of the remaining terms, and often indicates incorrect signs. Its combination with a dimensional check will indicate a great majority of errors.

Example 1: *Limiting Case Checking.*—A resistance R and inductance L are connected in series and a voltage $E \cos \omega t$ applied to the combination. Check the calculated steady-state current:

$$i_{ss} = \frac{E(R \cos \omega t - \omega L \sin \omega t)}{R^2 + \omega^2 L^2}.$$

First set L equal to zero. The equation then yields

$$i_{ss} = \frac{E}{R} \cos \omega t \qquad (L = 0).$$

This is evidently correct, since we now have only a pure resistance connected across a voltage $E \cos \omega t$.

As the next limiting case set $R = 0$ in the original solution. Then

$$i_{ss} = - \frac{E}{\omega L} \sin \omega t \qquad (R = 0).$$

The maximum value is right, for it is the peak voltage divided by the inductive reactance. However, the current should lag the voltage, and a sketch will show that the negative sine leads (comes up through zero before) the cosine. Therefore the sign must be wrong. If one is not sure of his reasoning, he can return to the original differential equation:

$$Ri + L \, di/dt = E \cos \omega t,$$

set $R = 0$, and integrate both sides, obtaining

$$\text{Correct } i_{ss} = \frac{E}{\omega L} \sin \omega t \qquad (R = 0),$$

thus showing that the sign in the original equation is wrong. Observe that each term in the original equation has now been checked once and that the only error has been discovered.

Example 2: *Limiting Case Checking.*—The mechanical system of Fig. 73 consists of two identical cylinders joined by a third coaxial cylinder around which is wrapped a thin cord. The cylinders rest on a horizontal plane surface and are assumed to roll without slipping. A horizontal force f is applied to the cord. Check the differential equation for motion of the axis of the cylinders:

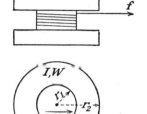

FIG. 73.—Mechanical system of Example 2.

$$\left(\frac{I}{r_2} + r_2 \frac{W}{g}\right) \frac{d^2x}{dt^2} = f(r_2 - r_1). \quad (429)$$

1. The acceleration is seen to be directly proportional to f. This is the expected result for a linear system.

2. Let $r_2 - r_1 = 0$. From Eq. (429) the acceleration is zero. By physical reasoning this is correct, for if $r_1 = r_2$ the force will be applied at the line of contact with the plane and, since slippage is assumed to be zero, there will be no motion. This checks the presence of the right-hand factor $(r_2 - r_1)$ and also its internal algebraic sign.

3. Let $r_1 = 0$ and $I = 0$. Equation (429) then becomes

$$\frac{W}{g} \frac{d^2x}{dt^2} = f.$$

This is correct, for the force is now applied to the center of gravity and there can be no rotational reaction, so the problem becomes equivalent to the rectilinear translation of a mass. This checks the mass term on the left and the sign of the right side of Eq. (429).

4. Let $r_1 = 0$ and $W = 0$ but leave I in the equation (this is physically impossible but convenient for purposes of checking). Observing that the angular rotation of the cylinder is given by $\theta = x/r_2$, Eq. (429) becomes

$$I \frac{d^2\theta}{dt^2} = fr_2.$$

This is also correct, for the only reaction can be that of rotation, and the applied torque is fr_2. This checks the remaining quantities in Eq. (429).

Problems

1. Given the equation for the viscous force exerted on two sliding parallel plates with a viscous medium between them:

$$F = \mu \frac{Av}{d},$$

where μ is the viscosity of the medium, A is the plate area, d is the spacing between the plates, and v is the relative velocity. Find the dimensional formula for μ in terms of F, L, and T.

2. Show that the quantity $1/\sqrt{\mu\epsilon}$ has the dimensions of a velocity, where μ is absolute permeability and ϵ is absolute dielectric constant.

3. Find the dimensions of flux linkage in terms of E, I, and T.

4. The differential equation for the acceleration of weight W_2 in Fig. P4 has been derived as

$$\left[\frac{W_1 W_2}{g^2} p^2 + \frac{(W_1 + W_2)}{g} Dp + K \frac{(W_1 + W_2)}{g} \right] a_2 = (Dp + K)f.$$

a. Check this equation dimensionally and indicate errors if any.

b. If W and f are expressed in pounds, K in pounds per inch, and D in lb-sec/in., what will be the proper units and magnitude of g and what will be the dimensions of a_2?

5. Check the differential equation given in Prob. 4 (see Fig. P4) by the limiting case method and indicate errors if any.

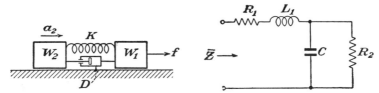

FIG. P4.—Mechanical system for exercise in checking.   FIG. P6.—Electrical system for exercise in checking.

6. The vector expression for the input impedance of the network of Fig. P6 has been derived as

$$\bar{Z} = \frac{R_1 R_2 + \dfrac{L}{C} + j\omega \left(R_2 L - \dfrac{R_1 + R_2}{\omega^2 C} \right)}{R_2 - j\dfrac{1}{\omega C}}.$$

Check this equation dimensionally (using E, I, and T as fundamental dimensions) and also by the limiting case method. Indicate errors if any.

7. Check the equation below by the dimensional and limiting case methods, and indicate errors if any. Two solid spheres of the same material, with diameters d_1 and d_2, are pressed together with a force P. The radius of the area of contact has been derived as

$$r = \sqrt[3]{PE\left(\frac{d_1{}^2}{d_1 + d_2}\right)} \quad \text{in.,}$$

where P is in pounds, d_1 and d_2 are in inches, and E is the modulus of elasticity in pounds per square inch.

8. Check the formula below by the dimensional and limiting case methods, and indicate errors if any.   The time required for a cylinder to roll without slippage from the top to the bottom of an inclined plane has been derived as

$$T = \frac{1}{r \cos \theta} \sqrt{\frac{2h(Mr + I)}{Mg}} \quad \text{sec,}$$

where M = mass of cylinder.
    I = moment of inertia of cylinder.
    r = radius of cylinder.
    h = height of plane.
    θ = angle of inclination of plane measured from the horizontal.
    g = acceleration of gravity.

CHAPTER IX

DIMENSIONAL ANALYSIS

77. Introduction.—In determining the characteristics of a physical system by analytical means, one usually expresses in equation form the relations that must be satisfied by the system, and then solves these equations by mathematical means to obtain the relation between a dependent variable in which he is interested and the various independent variables and parameters of the system. It is possible, however, to deduce something of the relations that must be satisfied by the system from a consideration of the dimensions of the various quantities that are used to formulate the problem.

Consider first a very simple example: Suppose that we wish to find the time t required for an object traveling at a uniform velocity v to traverse a distance d, and cannot remember offhand whether the suitable formula is $t = vd$, $t = d/v$, or $t = v/d$. Using the dimensions

$$[t] = \text{sec},$$
$$[v] = \text{ft/sec},$$
$$[d] = \text{ft},$$

it is easy to see that the only possible combination of v and d that will make a dimensionally homogeneous equation is

$$\text{sec} = \frac{\text{ft}}{\text{ft/sec}}$$

or
$$t = \frac{d}{v}.$$

Two useful applications of dimensional analysis are the changing of units and the derivation of formulas. These will now be considered in some detail.

78. Changing Units.—A frequently occurring problem is the changing of units of a quantity, for example, changing a certain number of inches per second into miles per hour, or changing joules per meter into pounds. With the ordinary hit-and-miss method one must decide whether the second units are larger or

218

smaller than the first, and then determine whether to multiply or divide by the conversion factors.   This sometimes becomes a complicated and hazardous process.   It can be done quite easily, however, by the following dimensional analysis:

1. After the magnitude of the quantity write the names of the units in which it is measured.

2. Replace each name by its equivalent in the new units, and arithmetically combine all numbers in the new expression.

Example 1.—Find the equivalent in miles per hour of 947 in./sec.   First observe that

$$12 \text{ inches} = 1 \text{ foot}; 1 \text{ inch} \quad = \tfrac{1}{12} \text{ foot}$$
$$5{,}280 \text{ feet} = 1 \text{ mile}; 1 \text{ foot} \quad = \tfrac{1}{5280} \text{ mile}$$
$$3{,}600 \text{ seconds} = 1 \text{ hour}; 1 \text{ second} = \tfrac{1}{3600} \text{ hour}$$

Then
$$947 \frac{\text{in.}}{\text{sec}} = 947 \frac{\tfrac{1}{12} \text{ ft}}{\tfrac{1}{3600} \text{ hr}}$$
$$= 947 \frac{(\tfrac{1}{12})\tfrac{1}{5280} \text{ mile}}{\tfrac{1}{3600} \text{ hr}}$$
$$= \frac{947 \times 3{,}600}{12 \times 5{,}280} \frac{\text{miles}}{\text{hr}}$$
$$= 53.9 \text{ miles/hr.}$$

Example 2.—Change K watt-sec/meter into pounds.   First note that

$$746 \text{ watts} = 1 \text{ horsepower} = 550 \text{ ft-lb/sec,}$$

so
$$1 \text{ watt} = \tfrac{550}{746} \text{ ft-lb/sec.}$$

Then
$$K \frac{\text{watt-sec}}{\text{meter}} = K \frac{\dfrac{550}{746} \dfrac{\text{ft-lb}}{\text{sec}} \times \text{sec}}{\dfrac{39.37}{12} \text{ ft}}$$
$$= 0.225 K \text{ lb.}$$

79. Derivation of Formulas.   The Buckingham π Theorem.—The Buckingham π theorem[1] states that if a problem can be formulated in terms of n quantities (for example mass, viscosity, displacement, etc.) and if these n quantities can be expressed in terms of m dimensions (force, length, and time, for example), then there will be $n - m$ independent dimensionless groups that can be formed by combination of the quantities.   Furthermore, if we call these $n - m$ groups π_1, π_2, etc., the solution must be of the form:

$$F(\pi_1, \pi_2, \cdots) = 0. \tag{430}$$

[1] BUCKINGHAM, E., *Phys. Rev.*, Vol. 4, p. 345 (1914).
BRIDGMAN, P. W., "Dimensional Analysis," Yale University Press, New Haven, 1931.

For example if $n - m$ happens to be equal to 1, there is only one independent dimensionless group (or π) that can be formed from these quantities, and the solution must be of the form $F(\pi) = 0$. Since the function is zero for all values of π, then π itself must be a constant, and the solution in this case can be expressed in another way:

$$\pi = \text{constant.} \tag{431}$$

The original example was of this type, for the three quantities t, v, and d could be expressed in terms of two dimensions, length and time. Therefore $n = 3$ and $m = 2$, so $n - m = 1$ and only one dimensionless group is possible: $\pi = vt/d$. The solution is of the form $vt/d = $ a constant, which in this case is unity. The dimensional analysis obviously cannot tell us the value of the constant, and this usually must be determined by experiment.

Observe in the foregoing example that other dimensionless groups are possible but none of them is independent of the first. For example d/vt and $(vt/d)^2$ are also dimensionless but can be derived from the original vt/d. Any one of these groups could be used in forming the solution, for example $d/vt = \text{constant} = 1$.

If $n - m$ happens to be equal to 2, then by Eq. (430) the solution is of the form $F(\pi_1, \pi_2) = 0$. This can also be written:

$$\pi_1 = f(\pi_2), \tag{432}$$

and the form of the function f must in general be determined by experiment. The result could be expressed graphically by plotting π_1 against π_2.

As an example, refer to the mechanical resonance problem of Sec. 68 (see Fig. 74). If we wished to plot the maximum displacement of the mass vs. frequency for zero damping, the problem could be formulated in terms of the following quantities (hereafter called *secondary quantities*): maximum displacement $x_{max.}$, mass M, spring constant K, maximum value of driving force F, and angular velocity ω. These are expressible in terms of three *primary quantities* or dimensions: force, length, and time. Then $n - m = 2$, and two independent dimensionless groups are possible. These could be $\pi_1 = Kx_{max.}/F$ and $\pi_2 = \omega \sqrt{M/K}$, and the solution would then be expressed as

$$\frac{Kx_{max.}}{F} = f\left(\omega \sqrt{\frac{M}{K}}\right).$$

In this particular problem the form of the function f can be found analytically, although the dimensional analysis holds even when an analytical solution cannot be obtained.   The relation between π_1 and π_2 can then be obtained experimentally and plotted as in Fig. 74b (compare Fig. 71).

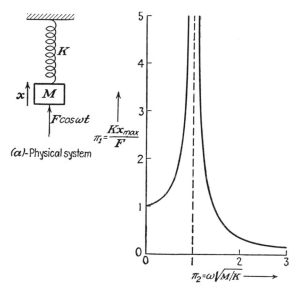

(b)- Graph of $\pi_1 = f(\pi_2)$

Fig. 74.—Problem in mechanical resonance.

If $n - m$ happens to be equal to 3, the solution is of the form $F(\pi_1, \pi_2, \pi_3) = 0$, which can also be expressed as

$$\pi_1 = f(\pi_2, \pi_3). \tag{433}$$

If, for example, in the mechanical resonance problem we wished to plot maximum displacement vs. frequency for various amounts of damping, we would have six secondary quantities: $x_{max.}$, M, K, F, ω, and D.   These could be expressed in terms of three primary quantities: force, length, and time.   Here $n - m = 3$, and three independent dimensionless groups are possible.   These could be $\pi_1 = Kx_{max.}/F$, $\pi_2 = \omega \sqrt{M/K}$, and $\pi_3 = D/(2 \sqrt{MK})$. Figure 75 shows π_1 plotted against π_2 for various values of π_3 (compare Fig. 71).   These curves could be found experimentally from a single physical setup and later used on other mechanical systems of a similar type. However, in this particular case the curves can be found analytically.

In general, for any number of π's, the result can be expressed either as $F(\pi_1, \pi_2, \ldots)$, or as

$$\pi_1 = f(\pi_2, \pi_3, \cdots). \tag{434}$$

Observe that the curves of Fig. 71, Sec. 68, were plotted in terms of dimensionless groups. This is very convenient even

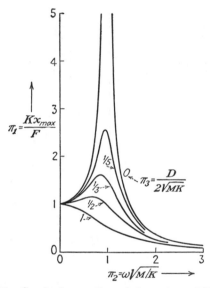

Fig. 75.—Graph of $\pi_1 = f(\pi_2, \pi_3)$ for system of Fig. 74a.

when an analytical solution can be obtained, for it enables one to express or to plot the results with the least number of coordinate axes. Thus, in Fig. 74 we have plotted results involving five quantities as a single curve that will hold regardless of the values of M, K, F, or ω, and in Fig. 75 (or Fig. 71) we have plotted results involving six quantities as a simple family of curves. If we tried to plot this information in the ordinary manner, we would have to choose a wide range of values for each of the parameters and attempt to plot a series of curves for all the possible combinations of these. In comparison with this, the simplicity and compactness of the dimensionless-group method are striking. Furthermore, the use of dimensionless groups reduces the labor of computation or experiment to a minimum.

Analytical results can be put into dimensionless form in a simple manner. For example, consider Eq. (415) in Sec. 68, from which Fig. 71 was plotted:

$$x_{max.} = \frac{F}{\sqrt{(K - \omega^2 M)^2 + (\omega D)^2}}. \tag{415}$$

The quantity F/K has the dimensions of displacement, hence we can make both sides of Eq. (415) dimensionless by multiplying through by K/F:

$$\frac{Kx_{max.}}{F} = \frac{K}{\sqrt{(K - \omega^2 M)^2 + (\omega D)^2}}$$

$$= \frac{1}{\sqrt{\left(1 - \frac{\omega^2 M}{K}\right)^2 + \left(\frac{\omega D}{K}\right)^2}}$$

$$= \frac{1}{\sqrt{\left[1 - \left(\omega\sqrt{\frac{M}{K}}\right)^2\right]^2 + 4\left(\frac{D}{2\sqrt{MK}}\right)^2\left(\omega\sqrt{\frac{M}{K}}\right)^2}}.$$

Thus by manipulation we have reduced the equation to one involving three dimensionless variables, equivalent to

$$\pi_1 = \frac{1}{\sqrt{(1 - \pi_2^2)^2 + 4(\pi_2\pi_3)^2}}.$$

This was the equation from which Fig. 71 was plotted.

The main use, however, of dimensional analysis is in the derivation of relations and the plotting of experimental results when an analytical solution is difficult or impossible to find. The sections that follow will discuss some of the methods by which dimensional analysis can be used for these purposes.

A dimensional analysis will yield results with relatively small labor when other methods become extremely difficult, or virtually impossible. However, it yields less information than a mathematical solution of the original equations, since it does not give the values of constants or the form of the function f. It provides an excellent means of organizing and interpreting experimental data and provides the basis for the use of models in predetermining the performance of full-sized equipment.

Although the use of dimensional analysis requires a comparatively small amount of mathematical knowledge, it is evident that one must choose the proper quantities to enter the analysis. This presupposes a rather intimate knowledge of the physical phenomena involved.

80. Example: Velocity of Sound in a Gas.—Let us suppose that the velocity of sound in a gas is dependent on the following secondary quantities: viscosity, density, and pressure of the gas. The quantity that we are trying to find, velocity, must also be considered a secondary quantity. All of these can be expressed in terms of three primary quantities: force, length, and time.

Velocity of sound, $[v] = LT^{-1}$.

Mass density of gas, $[\rho] = FT^2L^{-4}$.

Pressure of gas, $[p] = FL^{-2}$.

Viscosity of gas, $[\mu] = FTL^{-2}$.

Here there are four secondary quantities $(n = 4)$ and three primary quantities $(m = 3)$, so $n - m = 1$ and we expect that one independent dimensionless group can be formed. The solution must then be $F(\pi) = 0$ or $\pi = $ constant.

A method of finding a dimensionless grouping of v, ρ, p, and μ is to write π as a product of these quantities with unknown exponents:

$$\pi = v^a\rho^b p^c\mu^d,$$

and then write the dimensions of each quantity in place of its symbol:

$$\pi = (LT^{-1})^a(FT^2L^{-4})^b(FL^{-2})^c(FTL^{-2})^d.$$

In order for this to be a dimensionless group, the exponents of the L's, T's, and F's must be separately equal to zero, *i.e.*,

For L: $\qquad\qquad a - 4b - 2c - 2d = 0$.

For T: $\qquad\qquad -a + 2b + d = 0$.

For F: $\qquad\qquad\quad b + c + d = 0$.

Evidently any set of values of a, b, c, and d that simultaneously satisfy these three equations will yield a dimensionless π group. There are four unknowns (since $n = 4$) and only three equations (since $m = 3$); hence a value can be arbitrarily selected for one of the unknowns. We wish eventually to solve for velocity v, and so for convenience select its exponent a equal to 1. Solving the foregoing equations simultaneously, we then obtain

$$b = \tfrac{1}{2}, \qquad c = -\tfrac{1}{2}, \qquad d = 0.$$

Therefore, $\qquad\qquad \pi = v\rho^{\frac{1}{2}}p^{-\frac{1}{2}} = $ constant,

or $\qquad\qquad\qquad v = $ constant $\sqrt{\dfrac{p}{\rho}}.$ $\qquad\qquad$ (435)

It is not necessary to choose the exponent a equal to 1. If we chose it equal to 2, we would obtain

$$\pi = v^2\rho p^{-1} = C,$$

or $\qquad\qquad\qquad v = \sqrt{C}\,\sqrt{\dfrac{p}{\rho}} = C_2\sqrt{\dfrac{p}{\rho}},$

which is the solution obtained previously. The new π is not identical with the old one but can be derived from it and is not independent. Either one will produce the correct result, as shown above.

The constant can be evaluated by experiment, after which the equation can be used for other gases, or for the same gas under different pressure and density conditions. For example, the velocity of sound in air at 20°C and 14.7 lb/in.² is about 1,130 ft/sec. The density of air under these conditions is 2.34×10^{-3} lb-sec²/ft⁴ (slugs/ft³). The constant in Eq. (435) is found from these data to be

$$\text{Constant} = v\sqrt{\dfrac{\rho}{p}}$$

$$= 1,130\sqrt{\dfrac{2.34 \times 10^{-3}}{14.7 \times 144}}$$

$$= 1.187.$$

Now apply the formula to find the velocity of sound in hydrogen at 0°C and 14.7 lb/in.², for which the density is 1.74×10^{-4} lb-sec²/ft⁴:

$$v = 1.187\sqrt{\dfrac{p}{\rho}}$$

$$= 1.187\sqrt{\dfrac{14.7 \times 144}{1.74 \times 10^{-4}}}$$

$$= 4,140 \text{ ft/sec.}$$

This value checks quite well with the results of experiment.

It will be observed that in deriving Eq. (435) the exponent d vanished and the viscosity did not enter the result. This might have been expected, since the propagation of sound involves compression waves and depends upon the mass and elastic properties of the gas, while viscosity would enter as a factor only if there were shear. If viscosity is omitted in the original formulation of the problem, there will be only three secondary quantities, hence to form one π the number of primary quantities must be reducible to two. This is correct, for the dimensional formulas of v, ρ, and p show that wherever F appears, it enters as FL^{-2}, and furthermore T always appears as TL^{-1}. Thus, density could be expressed dimensionally as $(FL^{-2})(TL^{-1})^2$. Considering the two groups FL^{-2} and TL^{-1} as the primary quantities, we would correctly expect one independent dimensionless π. This is again seen in the simultaneous equations involving the exponents, for if d is dropped, the three equations are not independent and the third can be obtained by addition of the first and second.

In the foregoing example the extraneous quantity that we introduced went out automatically. However, this cannot always be depended upon, for if we should introduce a factor which could affect the result under some conditions but which has negligible effect in our problem, the quantity could produce an extra dimensionless group and unnecessarily complicate the solution. Considerable care and sound physical reasoning are necessary in selecting pertinent secondary quantities.

81. Example: Heat Transfer. Correlation of Data.—It is desired to determine an expression for the coefficient of heat transfer for fluids flowing across wires and cylinders. From physical reasoning, pertinent secondary quantities are

1. Coefficient of heat transfer, defined as the quantity of heat transferred in unit time, per unit area, per unit temperature difference between cylinder and fluid, $[h] = FT^{-1}L^{-1}\theta^{-1}$.

2. Diameter of wire or cylinder, $[d] = L$.

3. Conductivity of fluid, $[k] = FT^{-1}\theta^{-1}$.

4. Mass density of fluid, $[\rho] = FT^2L^{-4}$.

5. Velocity of the fluid, $[u] = LT^{-1}$.

6. Viscosity of the fluid, $[\mu] = FTL^{-2}$.

There are six secondary quantities and four primary quantities (F, L, T, and θ). Therefore, $n - m = 2$, and there will be two independent dimensionless groupings of secondary quantities: π_1 and π_2. The solution will be of the form $F(\pi_1, \pi_2) = 0$, or $\pi_1 = f(\pi_2)$.

To find the dimensionless groups, write π as the product of all secondary quantities to unknown powers:

$$\pi = h^a d^b k^c \rho^e u^f \mu^g.$$

Substitute the dimensional formulas for the symbols:

$$\pi = (FT^{-1}L^{-1}\theta)^a (L)^b (FT^{-1}\theta^{-1})^c (FT^2L^{-4})^e (LT^{-1})^f (FTL^{-2})^g.$$

Since π is dimensionless by definition, the exponents of each of the primary quantities must separately add to zero:

For F: $a + c + e + g = 0.$
For T: $-a - c + 2e - f + g = 0.$
For L: $-a + b - 4e + f - 2y - 0.$
For θ: $-a - c = 0.$

Here are four equations with six unknowns. We can therefore choose two of the exponents in a convenient manner and solve for the other four. Since we expect two π's, we can do this twice, making a different original choice for each.

For π_1, choose $a = 1$ since we wish to solve for h eventually, and let $g = 0$ to simplify the equations. Simultaneous solution of the equations then yields $c = -1$, $b = 1$, $e = 0$, and $f = 0$. Therefore,

$$\pi_1 = \frac{hd}{k}.$$

For π_2, choose $a = 0$ so that the quantity h for which we wish to solve does not appear in both π's (otherwise we could not solve for it directly).

Viscosity was dropped in forming π_1, so bring it into π_2 by letting $g = 1$. Solving the simultaneous equations with these choices, we find $b = -1$, $c = 0$, $e = -1$, and $f = -1$. Therefore,

$$\pi_2 = \frac{\mu}{\rho u d}.$$

This is the reciprocal of the Reynolds number; hence invert it (this can be done because the reciprocal is evidently dimensionless also) and use

$$\pi_2' = \frac{\rho u d}{\mu}.$$

The solution is then of the form $\pi_1 = f(\pi_2')$, or,

$$\frac{hd}{k} = f\left(\frac{\rho u d}{\mu}\right). \tag{436}$$

If desired, this can be solved for the heat-transfer coefficient:

$$h = \frac{k}{d} f\left(\frac{\rho u d}{\mu}\right),\qquad(437)$$

in which the function f must be determined from experiment.

We are not limited to the use of the previous two dimensionless groups. For example, if we chose $a = 1$ and $b = 0$ in forming a group, we would obtain $\pi = h\mu/k\rho u$. Observe that this also could be obtained by the multiplication $\pi_1\pi_2$. Other dimensionless groups would include π_1/π_2, $\pi_1{}^2\pi_2$, $\pi_1 + \pi_2$, etc. However, of all the possible dimensionless groups only two can be independent, and we can use any two we please provided that none of the original secondary quantities h, d, k, u, μ, or ρ is left out entirely. The choice of the two groups to be used can be made from the standpoint of convenience.

Equation (436) can be used very effectively to correlate data taken under a wide variety of conditions and, in fact, forms a basis from which one can experiment most effectively. For example, in collecting data on the heat-transfer coefficient for air flowing across pipes and wires, one would not need to take data for every density he could get, then for every velocity he could conveniently obtain, and then for many different sizes of pipes, and so on, which evidently would lead to an enormous mass of data. Instead, the dimensional analysis shows that the required information can be obtained merely by varying the quantity $\rho u d/\mu$ and observing the effect on the quantity hd/k. The quantity $\rho u d/\mu$ can be varied in any convenient manner, perhaps by changing the velocity u or the diameter d, since for any given numerical value of $\rho u d/k$ there should exist only one corresponding numerical value of the group hd/k. Thus, we have reduced a problem involving six variables to one involving effectively only two, *i.e.*, the two π's. Figure 76 shows a correlation of data on this basis.[1] These data were taken by a number of independent investigators, with a range in wire size of over 3,000:1. It will be seen that all the data fall reasonably well along a single smooth curve, which therefore defines the function f.

[1] From KING, W. J., The Basic Laws and Data of Heat Transmission, IV, *Mech. Eng.*, June, 1932, p. 413. The plot of Fig. 76 is reproduced from Fig. 3 of that paper by courtesy of the author and publisher.

The lower part of the curve is almost straight, and in this region the function f can be expressed quite simply by the empirical formula:

$$\frac{hd}{k} = 0.764 \left(\frac{\rho u d}{\mu}\right)^{0.41}.$$

Observe carefully the importance of using consistent units in calculating the numerical value of a dimensionless group. For a given set of physical conditions, any true dimensionless group will have the same numerical value regardless of the set of

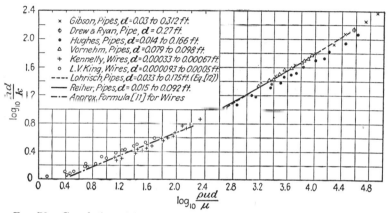

Fig. 76.—Correlation of heat transfer data; air flowing across a wire or pipe [*Reproduced with permission from W. J. King, The Basic Laws and Data of Heat Transmission, Mech. Eng., p. 413 (June, 1932).*]

units used for its factors, provided only that these units are consistent within themselves. This can be assured by a simple dimensional check in which the names, not the symbols, of the units are used.

82. Example : A Nonlinear Electrical Transient.—Suppose that a nonlinear inductance has an iron core for which the saturation curve can be expressed approximately by a ninth-power equation, i.e., $i = K\psi^9$ where K depends upon the number of turns and the size of the core. It is desired to plot in most convenient form the transient current resulting when a resistance R is connected in series and a d-c voltage E is impressed at time $t = 0$. The secondary quantities are i, t, K, R, and E. These are expressible in terms of three primary quantities: E, I, and T.

From the equation $e = \dfrac{d\psi}{dt}$, $[K] = I(ET)^{-9}$.

Also,
$$[i] = I.$$
$$[t] = T.$$
$$[R] = EI^{-1}.$$
$$[E] = E.$$

Since $n = 5$ and $m = 3$, two independent dimensionless groups are expected.   Write π as

$$\pi = K^a i^b t^c R^d E^f,$$

and replace each symbol by its dimensional formula:

$$\pi = (IE^{-9}T^{-9})^a (I)^b (T)^c (EI^{-1})^d (E)^f.$$

For this to be dimensionless we must have

For E: $-9a + d + f = 0.$
For I: $a + b - d = 0.$
For T: $-9a + c = 0.$

We wish to plot i vs. t; hence for the first π let $b = 1$ and $c = 0$. This yields $a = 0$, $d = 1$, and $f = -1$.   Then

$$\pi_1 = i\,\frac{R}{E}.$$

For the second group set $b = 0$ so that i will not enter both groups, and let $c = 1$ so that time enters in a convenient manner. This yields $a = \frac{1}{9}$, $d = \frac{1}{9}$, and $f = \frac{8}{9}$, so that

$$\pi_2 = (KRE^8)^{\frac{1}{9}} t.$$

We can now write the solution in the form of Eq. (432):

$$i\,\frac{R}{E} = f[(KRE^8)^{\frac{1}{9}} t]. \tag{438}$$

The function f could be found by taking an oscillogram for one such physical system, or it could be determined by a graphical or numerical integration of the nonlinear differential equation. The results, when plotted as in Fig. 77, can be used to find the current as a function of time for any values of K, R, or E, limited of course by our assumption of a ninth-power saturation curve.

83. Example: Force on Wing of Airplane.   Use of Models.— The lift and drag on the wing of an airplane depend mainly on the following factors: the shape of the wing, the size of the wing, its relative velocity with respect to the air, the angle with which the wing is inclined to the relative wind direction (angle of attack),

and the density and viscosity of the air. One could investigate
a particular shape of wing by making a *geometrically similar*
model. The shape of the wing would then have no bearing in an
investigation of the relation between forces observed on the
model and those which would exist with the full-sized wing

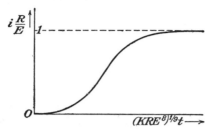

FIG. 77.—Transient current in nonlinear circuit.

(sometimes called the *prototype*). Thus for a given shape of
wing and angle of attack the secondary quantities will be:

1. The force on the wing (either lift or drag), $[F] = F$.

2. A "characteristic dimension" to indicate relative size, say
the chord of the wing, $[l] = L$.

3. The relative velocity, $[v] = LT^{-1}$.

4. The mass density of the air, $[\rho] = FT^2L^{-4}$.

5. The viscosity of the air, $[\mu] = FTL^{-2}$.

There are five secondary quantities and three primary quantities,
so $n - m = 2$ and we expect two independent dimensionless
groups. Write

$$\pi = F^a l^b v^c \rho^d \mu^e,$$

or $$\pi = (F)^a (L)^b (LT^{-1})^c (FT^2L^{-4})^d (FTL^{-2})^e,$$

from which,

For F: $a + d + e = 0.$

For L: $b + c - 4d - 2e = 0.$

For T: $-c + 2d + e = 0.$

We wish to solve for the force, so for the first π let $a = 1$,
and to simplify the equation let $e = 0$. Solving the simultaneous equations with this choice we obtain $b = -2$, $c = -2$,
and $d = -1$, so

$$\pi_1 = \frac{F}{l^2 v^2 \rho}. \tag{439}$$

For the second π let $a = 0$ so as not to bring the force in
more than once, and make $e = 1$ to bring the previously ignored

viscosity into this group. With these selections the simultaneous equations yield $b = -1$, $c = -1$, and $d = -1$. This will produce the reciprocal of the Reynolds number, so invert it and use

$$\pi_2 = \frac{lv\rho}{\mu} = \text{Reynolds number, } R_e. \tag{440}$$

Therefore the solution is of the form

$$\frac{F}{(lv)^2\rho} = f\left(\frac{lv\rho}{\mu}\right). \tag{441}$$

The function f is still unknown, and dimensional analysis can tell us nothing about it. However, the form of this function should depend only on the shape of the wing and its angle of attack, and thus it could be determined by model experiments and finally used on the full-sized wing. One could make a convenient sized model and test it in a wind tunnel, varying

$$\pi_2 = \frac{lv\rho}{\mu},$$

and measuring the resulting force, from which π_1 could be plotted against π_2 after the fashion of Fig. 74. This curve would then define the function f. To apply this curve to the full-sized wing, one would first calculate its π_2 [Eq. (440)] for the operating conditions, then refer to the curve and read the corresponding value of π_1. The force could then be computed numerically using Eq. (439). If the angle of attack is changed, the function f and its curve will be changed also. This effect could be plotted as a family of curves (see Fig. 75), each curve of which would define the function f for a particular angle of attack.

In many problems it is desired to find only one or two conditions of operation, and it is unnecessary to find the form of the whole function f. Since the same curve applies to both model and prototype, it is evident that if the value of π_2 is made the same for both, the curve will yield a particular value of π_1 which will apply to both also. Thus we can say that if the solution is of the form $\pi_1 = f(\pi_2)$, and if we can arrange the testing so that $\pi_{2m} = \pi_{2p}$ where the subscripts m and p refer to the model and prototype, respectively, then it must be true that $\pi_{1m} = \pi_{1p}$ also.

Thus, if we make $$\frac{l_m v_m \rho_m}{\mu_m} = \frac{l_p v_p \rho_p}{\mu_p}, \tag{442}$$

we shall have $\dfrac{F_m}{(l_m v_m)^2 \rho_m} = \dfrac{F_p}{(l_p v_p)^2 \rho_p},$

and the force on the full-sized wing will be

$$F_p = F_m \frac{\rho_p (l_p v_p)^2}{\rho_m (l_m v_m)^2}. \tag{443}$$

By arranging the density, viscosity, and velocity of the air in the test so that Eq. (442) is satisfied, Eq. (443) can be used to calculate the desired force from the measured force on the model.

Equations (442) and (443) bring out some interesting considerations in model testing. If one used atmospheric pressure in the wind tunnel and if the model were scaled down considerably from the full-sized wing (*i.e.*, $l_m \ll l_p$), it is clear from a consideration of Eq. (442) that to make the Reynolds numbers the same, the velocity of air in the tunnel v_m would have to be very much greater than the expected velocity of air past the full-sized wing:

$$v_m = \frac{l_p}{l_m} v_p \qquad \text{for} \qquad \rho_p = \rho_m \qquad \text{and} \qquad \mu_p = \mu_m.$$

This, of course, is quite impracticable. Furthermore, with these relations Eq. (443) shows that $F_m = F_p$, or the force on the model will be as great as that on the actual wing!

There are several ways of at least partly getting around these difficulties. The model could be made to a relatively large scale, thus permitting one to obtain reasonable Reynolds numbers at practical velocities but requiring quite a large wind tunnel. Another method is to use a tunnel built to operate at high pressures so that $\rho_m \gg \rho_p$ (the so-called "variable density" tunnel). Equation (442) shows that this permits reasonably large Reynolds numbers without excessive velocity or size. Furthermore Eq. (443) shows that a high air density in testing will reduce the force on the model, which certainly is desirable. Finally, useful results fortunately can be obtained with Reynolds numbers lower than those encountered with the full-sized wing. Experiment shows that as the Reynolds number is increased the function f in Eq. (441) tends asymptotically toward a constant value, which means physically that turbulence in the air stream is causing viscosity to play a smaller and smaller part in the results. If this asymptotic value can be determined from the model test, we can write Eq. (441) approximately for this region as $F = \text{constant} \times \rho l^2 v^2$.

When the relative velocity approaches or exceeds the velocity of sound, compressibility effects become important. This factor can be introduced by considering the velocity of sound to be a secondary quantity, thus giving rise to a dimensionless group called *Mach's number:* v/v_c, where v_c is the velocity of sound in the fluid. This number is especially important in the investigation of the flight of projectiles.

Although in the foregoing discussion we have been particularly interested in air as the resisting medium, similar considerations and identical dimensionless groups apply to other fluids as well, for example water. The importance of various secondary factors depends entirely on the conditions of the problem, for example the wave resistance offered to a surface ship depends on gravity forces and requires that the acceleration of gravity g be brought into the dimensional analysis as a secondary quantity. Surface tension must also be considered on very small models. These factors give rise to other dimensionless groups, concerning which the reader is referred to standard texts on fluid mechanics. The necessity for selecting the important factors from all the possible ones again emphasizes the importance of a sound physical grasp of the problem.

84. Dimensional Constants.—Consider the expression in the universal law of gravitation for the force of attraction between two bodies of masses M_1 and M_2 which are a distance d apart:

$$F = G \frac{M_1 M_2}{d^2},$$

where G is a constant, the value of which will depend on the system of units used. It is apparent that to make the equation dimensionally homogeneous, the constant G must have dimensions, in particular the dimensions of force times distance squared divided by mass squared. Furthermore, it is possible to choose the units so that the constant G is unity, in which case the equation would normally be written as $F = M_1 M_2/d^2$. Although for this particular system of units the equation is a true one, it is not *complete* but is said to be *adequate*. A dimensional check or dimensional analysis cannot be used on any but complete equations.

A constant (such as G above) which has dimensions and whose value depends on the system of units is called a *dimensional constant*. When making a dimensional analysis of a system for which the underlying relations involve a dimensional constant, it is necessary to include this dimensional constant as a secondary factor. In problems involving electromagnetic fields the velocity of light enters as a dimensional constant.

Problems

CONVERSION TABLE

1 kilogram = 2.205 pounds

980.7 dynes = 1 gram

2.54 centimeters = 1 inch

1 horsepower = 550 foot-pounds per second

745.7 watts = 1 horsepower

778.3 foot-pounds = 1 Btu

1. Change 7.75 grams/cm^3 to pounds per cubic inch.

2. Change W watts into Btu per hour.

3. Find the factor by which a given torque in dyne-centimeters should be multiplied to obtain the torque in pound-inches.

4. A cylindrical buoy is oscillating vertically. Find by a dimensional analysis the frequency of oscillation, using the following as secondary factors: cross-sectional area of the buoy A, mass of the buoy M, density of the water in weight per unit volume ρ, frequency of oscillation f.

5. Find an expression for the velocity of a wave advancing in deep water. Secondary quantities are velocity of the wave v, density of the water ρ expressed in terms of mass per unit volume, acceleration of gravity g, and the wave length (distance between crests) λ.

6. *a.* By means of a dimensional analysis find the equation for the period of a pendulum when oscillating through a small angle, assuming that the period T depends upon the moment of inertia about the axis of suspension, I; the weight W; and the distance between the center of gravity and the point of suspension, L.

b. A pendulum weighing 2 lb has a WR^2 of 800 lb-in.^{2} about the axis of suspension, a distance $L = 20$ in., and a period of 1.425 sec. Calculate the period of a pendulum for which $W = 5$ lb, $L = 1$ ft, and $WR^2 = 2.5$ lb-ft.^{2}

7. If heat is generated uniformly within a homogeneous cylinder, the steady-state temperature rise of the center over the outer surface, $\Delta\theta$, depends upon the following quantities:

K = conductivity, $\dfrac{\text{Btu/hr}}{\text{ft-}^\circ\text{F}}$.

R = radius, ft.

Q = rate of heat generation per unit volume, $\dfrac{\text{Btu/hr}}{\text{ft}^3}$.

By means of a dimensional analysis and the data below, find a complete equation for the temperature rise of the center, $\Delta\theta$. It is suggested that the quantity Btu/hr be used as one of the primary quantities.

Data: For $R = 0.20$ ft, $K = 0.12$ Btu/hr-ft-°F, and $Q = 960$ Btu/hr-ft³, $\Delta\theta = 80$°F.

8. Using a dimensional analysis and the data below, find a complete equation for the velocity of sound along a solid rod. The velocity v will depend on the weight per unit volume w, the acceleration of gravity g, and the modulus of elasticity E.

Data: For steel, $v = 1.98 \times 10^5$ in./sec, $w = 0.284$ lb/in.³, and $E = 28.9 \times 10^6$ lb/in.²

9. Show that if a cylindrical shaft is twisted within the elastic limit, the maximum shearing stress is proportional to the applied torque and inversely proportional to the cube of the diameter.

10. Find an expression for the fundamental frequency f of free vibration of a stretched string, if the frequency depends on the length L, the tension T, and the mass per unit length ρ.

Data: A string 0.031 in. in diameter, 1 ft long, made of steel weighing 0.283 lb/in.³, and stretched with a tension of 20 lb, is found to have a fundamental natural frequency of 250 cycles per second.

11. It is desired to calculate the windage loss of a thin disk 18 in. in diameter, rotating at 1,200 rpm in air at 20°C. Use dimensional analysis and the available test data below.

Windage loss of thin disks rotating at 3,600 rpm in air (20°C):

Diameter of disk, in.	Windage loss, watts	Diameter of disk, in.	Windage loss, watts
6	1.11	14	57.
8	4.20	16	107.
10	12.2	20	294.
12	29.5		

12. In experiments on heat leakage through the walls of refrigerator boxes, a test was made on a cork-insulated box about 3 by 3 by 4 ft in size. With the box initially at 70°F, an incandescent lamp was used to maintain a constant flow of radiant heat to the interior of the box. The outside surface was maintained at 70°F. Data on the temperature rise of inside surface over outside surface are given below.

a. Plot the data on temperature rise vs. time in terms of dimensionless groups so that it can be applied to other problems of a similar nature. One group should contain temperature but not time, and the other should contain time but not temperature. Use consistent units.

b. Determine the temperature difference that should be expected at the end of 15 min under conditions exactly the same as those of the test except with a wall thickness only one-half as great.

Data: Rate of heat flow per unit area, $Q = 6.09$ Btu/hr-ft².
Thickness of insulation, $L = 2$ in.
Conductivity of insulation, $k = 0.0209$ Btu-ft/ft²-hr-°F.
Thermal capacity of insulation (specific heat times density),
$$c\rho = 4.85 \text{ Btu/ft}^3\text{-°F.}$$

Time, hr.	0	0.5	1.0	2.0	3.0	5.0	10
Temperature difference, °F	0	15.9	22.5	30.0	35.5	42.0	48.3

13. When a condenser is charging through a resistance from a full-wave rectifier, charging current flows only on that part of the half cycle when the line voltage exceeds the condenser voltage. As the condenser voltage increases toward the peak a-c voltage, charging current is drawn over a smaller period and is smaller in magnitude.

If the time constant RC of the circuit is much greater than the period of the applied voltage, it will take a large number of cycles to charge the condenser, and a plot of condenser voltage vs. time will rise over a relatively smooth curve. For $C = 186$ μf, $R = 1,000$ ohms, and with an a-c voltage of 440 volts rms, an oscillogram shows the following relation between condenser voltage and time:

Time, sec.	0	0.105	0.187	0.303	0.499	0.917	Steady state
Condenser voltage..	0	176	264	352	440	529	621

a. Using a dimensional analysis, plot these data in terms of dimensionless groups so that they will apply to similar systems satisfying the assumptions. Pertinent secondary quantities will be the applied rms voltage E, the condenser voltage e_c, time t, resistance R, and capacitance C. One dimensionless group should contain condenser voltage but not time, and the other should contain time but not condenser voltage.

b. Find the time required for the condenser voltage to build up to 80 per cent of final value if $E = 220$ volts rms, $C = 150$ μf, and $R = 2,900$ ohms.

14. An eddy-current brake has been built to test fractional horsepower induction motors, and it is desired to determine the necessary size of a geometrically similar brake for loading a larger motor. The brake consists of a disk of conducting material which is fastened to the shaft of the motor and is rotated between the poles of an electromagnet. The eddy currents induced in the disk dissipate energy and cause a resisting torque.

a. Make a dimensional analysis of the eddy-current brake, assuming that the flux density is not greatly decreased by the blocking effect of the eddy currents. The following secondary quantities should be included:

Power absorbed by the brake, P.
Flux density under the pole tip, B.
Speed, s.
A characteristic dimension: the diameter of the disk, D.
The resistivity of the disk material, ρ.

b. The brake now in use has two poles, the disk is made of aluminum and is 9 in. in diameter, and it operates with a flux density of 6,000 lines per square inch under the pole tips. The brake dissipates $\frac{1}{4}$ hp at 1,170 rpm.

For a geometrically similar brake, what flux density would be necessary to load a 1-hp motor at 860 rpm, using a copper disk 14 in. in diameter? At the estimated operating temperature, the resistivity of the copper disk will be approximately 2.15×10^{-6} ohm-cm and that of the aluminum disk will be approximately 3.55×10^{-6} ohm-cm.

15. When a voltage is suddenly impressed on the sending end of a long electrical transmission line, the resulting input current is independent of the load at the far end up to the time of arrival of the first reflection from that end. The data below give the input current that results from the application of 112 volts direct current to a line about 200 miles long, before the arrival of the first reflection. Analyze the problem by dimensional analysis and plot the data below in terms of dimensionless groups, one of which should contain current but not time, and the other of which should contain time but not current. The input current will depend mainly upon

The applied d-c voltage, E.

The resistance per unit length of line, R.

The inductance per unit length of line, L.

The capacitance per unit length of line, C.

The time, t.

Data: For the line on which the test was made, $E = 112$ volts, $L = 3.39 \times 10^{-3}$ henry per mile, $C = 8.47 \times 10^{-9}$ farad per mile, and $R = 10.8$ ohms per mile.

Time, sec	Entering current, amp	Time, sec	Entering current, amp
0	0.177	1.0×10^{-3}	0.062
0.25×10^{-3}	0.123	1.5×10^{-3}	0.049
0.50×10^{-3}	0.093	2.0×10^{-3}	0.042
0.75×10^{-3}	0.074		

CHAPTER X

FOURIER SERIES

85. Introduction.—Many engineering problems are concerned with functions which repeat in form at regular intervals and which

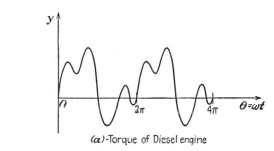

(a)-Torque of Diesel engine

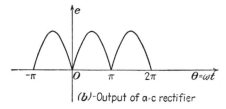

(b)-Output of a-c rectifier

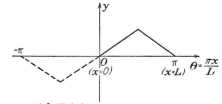

(c)-Initial shape of elastic string

FIG. 78.—Examples of nonsinusoidal periodic functions.

are therefore called *periodic functions.*[1] Alternating currents, mechanical oscillations, the torque of an engine, and the transverse vibration of an elastic string are examples of periodic

[1] More precisely, a periodic function is one in which $f(x) = f(x + C)$, where C is the period.

239

phenomena. The simplest type of periodic function is the sinusoid of the form $y = Y_m \sin \theta$, and this form of driving force and steady-state solution is used whenever it is possible to do so without serious error. However, many periodic phenomena arising in practice cannot be assumed to be of this simple form, as for example those shown in Fig. 78. Functions such as these are conveniently handled by means of the Fourier series.

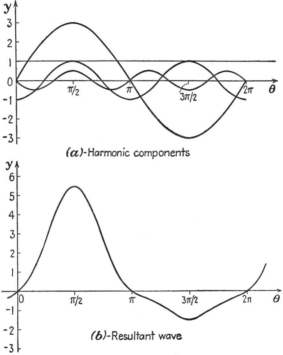

Fig. 79.—Synthesized wave.

As an introduction to the concept, consider the curves of Fig. 79*a*, which consist of a constant and several sinusoidal waves whose frequencies are integral multiples of the lowest frequency present. The algebraic sum of these waves is shown in Fig. 79*b* and is seen to be a periodic nonsinusoidal wave with a period equal to that of the lowest frequency component. This wave can be expressed in terms of its components by the trigonometric polynomial:

$$f(\theta) = 1.0 + 3.0 \sin \theta - 1.0 \cos 2\theta - 0.5 \sin 3\theta.$$

We shall next consider a general trigonometric series by which practical periodic waves can be expressed in terms of their harmonic components and shall derive methods for determining the amplitude and phase position of these components.

86. The Fourier Series.—It can be shown that periodic functions can, with certain restrictions, be expressed by an infinite trigonometric series of the form:

$$f(\theta) = \frac{A_0}{2} + (A_1 \cos \theta + B_1 \sin \theta) + (A_2 \cos 2\theta + B_2 \sin 2\theta)$$
$$+ \cdots . \quad (444)$$

This is the *Fourier series*, and the coefficients A and B are called the *Fourier coefficients*. The series can be written more compactly as

$$f(\theta) = \frac{A_0}{2} + \sum_{n=1}^{\infty} (A_n \cos n\theta + B_n \sin n\theta), \quad (445)$$

or, in the equivalent form,

$$f(\theta) = \frac{A_0}{2} + \sum_{n=1}^{\infty} C_n \cos (n\theta - \phi_n), \quad (446)$$

where $$C_n = \sqrt{A_n^2 + B_n^2},$$

and $$\tan \phi_n = \frac{B_n}{A_n}.$$

The term $A_0/2$ represents the average value of the function over one period, and the factor of $\frac{1}{2}$ is used so that the general formula for determining A_n will apply to this term also. The term $C_1 \cos (\theta - \phi_1)$ is called the *fundamental wave* or *first harmonic* and has a period equal to that of the original function. The nth term, $C_n \cos (n\theta - \phi_n)$, is called the nth harmonic or the harmonic of order n and has a frequency n times as great as the fundamental wave. Although θ is fundamentally an angle, a periodic function of time can be represented by using $\theta = \omega t$ where ω is 2π times the fundamental frequency, and a periodic function of length can be expanded using $\theta = \pi x/L$ where $2L$ is the length in which the function repeats.

The Fourier expansion is an infinite series, but in practice the higher harmonics are ordinarily of such small magnitude that they can be neglected without serious error. The expansion then reduces to a trigonometric polynomial with comparatively few terms.

87. Restrictions.—Almost all periodic functions that arise in engineering work can be expressed in terms of the Fourier series. Any single-valued periodic function can be represented by such a series if it satisfies the following sufficient, but not always necessary, conditions:

1. The function is finite everywhere.

2. The function has at most a finite number of finite discontinuities in one period.

3. The function has at most a finite number of maxima and minima in one period.

88. The Fourier Coefficients.—The magnitudes of the various components in the Fourier expansion of a function depend upon the form and magnitude of the wave. Any periodic wave which satisfies the restrictions of Sec. 87 and which is completely defined over one period can be represented by one and only one Fourier expansion. Observe, however, that if the wave is shifted along the θ-axis, the phase angles ϕ_n in Eq. (446) will be changed, although the magnitudes C_n will remain the same.

We shall now proceed to derive formulas for the Fourier coefficients A_n and B_n. To obtain an expression for the A's, multiply both sides of Eq. (445) by $\cos m\theta \, d\theta$ and integrate from $-\pi$ to π. Now, since

$$\int_{-\pi}^{\pi} \cos m\theta \cos n\theta \, d\theta = 0 \qquad \text{if } n \neq m,$$
$$= \pi \qquad \text{if } n = m,$$

and
$$\int_{-\pi}^{\pi} \cos m\theta \sin n\theta \, d\theta = 0,$$

we find that all terms vanish in the integration except the one containing A_n, leaving the expression

$$A_n = \frac{1}{\pi} \int_{-\pi}^{\pi} f(\theta) \cos n\theta \, d\theta. \tag{447}$$

To find the B's, multiply Eq. (445) by $\sin m\theta \, d\theta$ and integrate from $-\pi$ to π. Here all the terms vanish except the one containing B_n, leaving

$$B_n = \frac{1}{\pi} \int_{-\pi}^{\pi} f(\theta) \sin n\theta \, d\theta. \tag{448}$$

These are the expressions for the Fourier coefficients. When $f(\theta)$ is defined over one period, these integrals can be evaluated to find the magnitude of the harmonic components of the periodic wave.

As already observed, the term $A_0/2$ in Eq. (445) represents the average value of the function over one period and is equal to the area under the graph of the function over one period divided by the base of 2π radians:

$$\frac{A_0}{2} = \frac{1}{2\pi} \int_{-\pi}^{\pi} f(\theta)\, d\theta.$$

From this it is seen that A_0 itself can be obtained from Eq. (447) by letting $n = 0$ and can be regarded as a special case of A_n for the harmonic of zero order.

It can be shown in a similar manner that, if the function is defined in the interval 0 to 2π rather than in the interval $-\pi$ to π, the Fourier coefficients are given by the formulas:

$$\left.\begin{aligned}
A_n &= \frac{1}{\pi} \int_0^{2\pi} f(\theta)\, \cos n\theta\, d\theta \\
B_n &= \frac{1}{\pi} \int_0^{2\pi} f(\theta)\, \sin n\theta\, d\theta.
\end{aligned}\right\} \tag{449}$$

Example.—As an example, we shall derive the Fourier series expansion for the square wave of Fig. 80, which is defined in the interval $-\pi < \theta < \pi$ by

$$\begin{aligned}
f(\theta) &= -Y & &\text{for } -\pi < \theta < 0, \\
&= Y & &\text{for } 0 < \theta < \pi.
\end{aligned}$$

To evaluate the A's, use Eq. (447) and break the integral into two parts as follows:

$$\begin{aligned}
A_n &= \frac{1}{\pi} \int_{-\pi}^{0} (-Y) \cos n\theta\, d\theta + \frac{1}{\pi} \int_0^{\pi} Y \cos n\theta\, d\theta \\
&= -\left[\frac{Y \sin n\theta}{\pi n}\right]_{-\pi}^{0} + \left[\frac{Y \sin n\theta}{\pi n}\right]_0^{\pi} = 0.
\end{aligned}$$

Using Eq. (448) for the B's, we obtain

$$\begin{aligned}
B_n &= \frac{1}{\pi} \int_{-\pi}^{0} (-Y) \sin n\theta\, d\theta + \frac{1}{\pi} \int_0^{\pi} Y \sin n\theta\, d\theta \\
&= \left[\frac{Y \cos n\theta}{\pi n}\right]_{-\pi}^{0} - \left[\frac{Y \cos n\theta}{\pi n}\right]_0^{\pi} \\
&= \frac{2Y}{\pi n} (1 - \cos n\pi).
\end{aligned}$$

The Fourier expansion for the square wave can then be written from Eq. (445) as

$$f(\theta) = \frac{2Y}{\pi} \sum_{n=1}^{\infty} \frac{(1 - \cos n\pi)}{n} \sin n\theta. \qquad (450)$$

This equation can be expressed more simply by observing that the quantity $(1 - \cos n\pi)$ is equal to 2 for n odd and 0 for n even, so the even harmonics

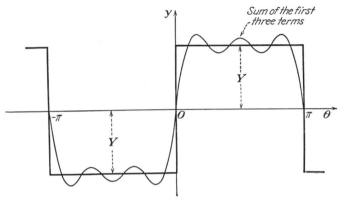

FIG. 80.—Square wave.

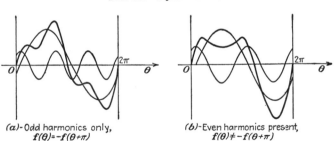

(a)-Odd harmonics only,
$f(\theta)=-f(\theta+\pi)$

(b)-Even harmonics present,
$f(\theta)\neq-f(\theta+\pi)$

FIG. 81.—Effect of even and odd harmonics.

vanish and we can write the series in terms of odd harmonics only:

$$f(\theta) = \frac{4Y}{\pi} \sum_{n=1,3,5\cdots}^{\infty} \frac{\sin n\theta}{n} \qquad (n \text{ odd only}). \quad (451)$$

It is a general rule that even harmonics are absent in waves that have identical positive and negative loops, *i.e.*, when $f(\theta) = -f(\theta + \pi)$. This effect is illustrated in Fig. 81.

Equation (451) can be written in expanded form as

$$f(\theta) = \frac{4Y}{\pi} \left(\sin\theta + \frac{1}{3}\sin 3\theta + \frac{1}{5}\sin 5\theta + \cdots \right).$$

As is true in general with discontinuous functions, this series converges rather slowly, *i.e.*, as $1/n$. The sum of the first three terms is shown superimposed on the original wave in Fig. 80. The addition of more components would produce a better approximation.

89. Expansion of Even and Odd Functions.—It frequently happens that the wave to be analyzed is symmetrical about $\theta = 0$, whereupon the Fourier expansion is simplified to the extent that it contains either sines or cosines only, depending on the type of symmetry. The foregoing example was of this type and could have been analyzed more readily by taking its symmetry into account.

Figure 82 shows a wave that is symmetrical about the y-axis, so that $f(\theta) = f(-\theta)$. Such a function is said to be an "even function," since an expansion of $y = f(\theta)$ in a power series in θ

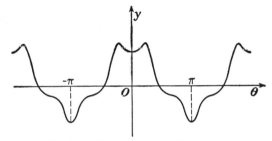

Fig. 82.—Even function, $f(\theta) = f(-\theta)$.

$(y = M_0 + M_1\theta + M_2\theta^2 + \cdots)$ can have this type of symmetry only when the odd powers of θ are absent and only the even powers remain. Using Eq. (447) for A_n and breaking up the integral so that the limits become $-\pi$ to 0 and 0 to π, we see that

$$A_n = \frac{1}{\pi} \int_{-\pi}^{0} f(\theta) \cos n\theta \, d\theta + \frac{1}{\pi} \int_{0}^{\pi} f(\theta) \cos n\theta \, d\theta. \quad (452)$$

These two integrals are equal in value, as can be shown by a change of variable: in the first integral let $\phi = -\theta$. This integral then becomes

$$\int_{\pi}^{0} f(-\phi) \cos (-n\phi)(-d\phi) = \int_{0}^{\pi} f(-\phi) \cos n\phi \, d\phi.$$

However ϕ is merely the variable of integration and disappears after the integration has been performed and the limits substituted. Hence, we may use the symbol θ instead without changing the value of the integral, and write it as

$$\int_0^\pi f(-\theta) \cos n\theta \, d\theta.$$

Moreover for an even function $f(-\theta) = f(\theta)$. So the first integral is equal to the second and we can write for an even function

$$A_n = \frac{2}{\pi} \int_0^\pi f(\theta) \cos n\theta \, d\theta. \tag{453}$$

It can be shown in a similar manner that the B_n's are zero, so that the Fourier series for the even function becomes simply

$$f(\theta) = \frac{A_0}{2} + \sum_{n=1}^{\infty} A_n \cos n\theta. \tag{454}$$

The wave shown in Fig. 83 is symmetrical about the origin, so that $f(\theta) = -f(-\theta)$. This is an odd function and has the

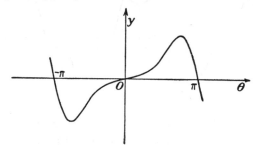

FIG. 83.—Odd function, $f(\theta) = -f(-\theta)$.

type of symmetry possessed by the sine function but not by the cosine function. For this type of wave it can be shown that the A_n's are zero and that

$$B_n = \frac{2}{\pi} \int_0^\pi f(\theta) \sin n\theta \, d\theta. \tag{455}$$

The Fourier series for odd functions then becomes

$$f(\theta) = \sum_{n=1}^{\infty} B_n \sin n\theta. \tag{456}$$

Example.—To illustrate the expansion of an even function, consider the triangular wave of Fig. 84, which is so placed on the θ-axis that $f(\theta) = f(-\theta)$.

The wave is defined in the interval $0 < \theta < \pi$ by the straight-line equation $f(\theta) = -\dfrac{S\pi}{2} + S\theta$, where S is the slope of the line. Using Eq. (453),

$$A_n = \frac{2}{\pi} \int_0^{\pi} S\left(\theta - \frac{\pi}{2}\right) \cos n\theta \; d\theta$$

$$= -\frac{2S(1 - \cos n\pi)}{\pi n^2}$$

$$= -\frac{4S}{\pi n^2} \quad \text{for } n \text{ odd, } 0 \text{ for } n \text{ even.}$$

Using Eq. (454), the Fourier series for the triangular wave becomes

$$f(\theta) = -\frac{2S}{\pi} \sum_{n=1}^{\infty} \frac{(1 - \cos n\pi)}{n^2} \cos n\theta, \qquad (457)$$

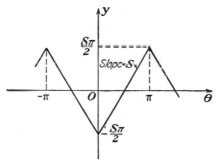

FIG. 84.—Triangular wave.

or, more compactly,

$$f(\theta) = -\frac{4S}{\pi} \sum_{n=1,3,5,\cdots}^{\infty} \frac{\cos n\theta}{n^2} \quad (n \text{ odd only}) \quad (458)$$

In expanded form this series is

$$f(\theta) = -\frac{4S}{\pi}\left(\cos \theta + \frac{1}{9} \cos 3\theta + \frac{1}{25} \cos 5\theta + \cdots\right).$$

Observe that this wave is continuous, that its first derivative is discontinuous, and that its series converges as $1/n^2$. This is true in general with waves that have discontinuous first derivatives.

90. Expansion in Terms of Time or Distance.—In engineering work it is common to have functions of time (such as the force applied to a mechanical system or the current flowing in an electrical circuit) or functions of distance (such as the distribution of static load along a beam). In addition, the solutions of dynamic distributed systems turn out to be functions of both time and distance.

If we wish to expand a periodic function of time $f(t)$ which has a fundamental frequency f, we can express the angle θ in radians as $\theta = \omega t = 2\pi f t$ where t is the instantaneous time. With this change of variable the Fourier series of Eq. (445) can be rewritten as

$$f(t) = \frac{A_0}{2} + \sum_{n=1}^{\infty} (A_n \cos n\omega t + B_n \sin n\omega t), \qquad (459)$$

and the expressions for the Fourier coefficients corresponding to Eqs. (447) and (448) become

$$\left.\begin{aligned} A_n &= \frac{\omega}{\pi} \int_{-\pi/\omega}^{\pi/\omega} f(t) \cos n\omega t \, dt \\ B_n &= \frac{\omega}{\pi} \int_{-\pi/\omega}^{\pi/\omega} f(t) \sin n\omega t \, dt. \end{aligned}\right\} \qquad (460)$$

Equations (449) for a function that is defined in the interval $0 < \theta < 2\pi$ can similarly be expressed in terms of $0 < t < 2\pi/\omega$, and Eqs. (453) and (455) for even and odd functions can be written in terms of $0 < t < \pi/\omega$.

To expand a periodic function of distance $y = f(x)$ which has a fundamental period (length) $2L$, the argument θ can be expressed in radians as $\theta = \pi x/L$ where x is the distance from the origin. The Fourier series of Eq. (445) can then be expressed as

$$f(x) = \frac{A_0}{2} + \sum_{n=1}^{\infty} \left(A_n \cos \frac{\pi n x}{L} + B_n \sin \frac{\pi n x}{L} \right), \qquad (461)$$

and Eqs. (447) and (448) for the Fourier coefficients become

$$\left.\begin{aligned} A_n &= \frac{1}{L} \int_{-L}^{L} f(x) \cos \frac{\pi n x}{L} \, dx \\ B_n &= \frac{1}{L} \int_{-L}^{L} f(x) \sin \frac{\pi n x}{L} \, dx. \end{aligned}\right\} \qquad (462)$$

Equations (449), (453), and (455) can be expressed in terms of length in a similar manner.

In some problems it is more convenient first to expand in terms of angle θ and later change variable ($\theta = \omega t$ or $\theta = \pi x/L$) rather than to use Eq. (460) or (462) directly.

91. Expansion of Nonperiodic Function in an Interval.—The Fourier series is periodic by nature and, for this reason, can be used to represent nonperiodic functions only within an interval, outside of which the series gives an incorrect periodic result. Consider, for example, the initial shape of an elastic string as shown in Fig. 78c. This is not a true periodic function, since the string exists only between $x = 0$ and $x = L$. However, the shape of the string can be expressed correctly in this interval by a Fourier series, while outside the interval in which we are interested the series gives a fictitious result. The dotted lines of Fig. 78c show the shape of the curve which we could assume outside the interval $0 < x < L$ if we wished to expand it as an odd function. On the other hand, we could draw the dotted lines so as to obtain an even function. Since the choice of the function outside the interval of interest is arbitrary and is dictated mainly by convenience, the resulting Fourier series is not unique.

92. Convergence, Derivatives, and Integrals.—The rate of convergence of the Fourier series was mentioned in the examples of Secs. 88 and 89, in which it was seen that the expansion of the discontinuous square wave converged rather slowly, while the series for the continuous triangular wave converged more rapidly. In general, the smoother the wave, the faster its Fourier series will converge, and the fewer the terms necessary to produce a good degree of approximation. It is reasonably evident that waves with square edges or sharp points will require harmonics of high order to fill these spaces in, and hence the corresponding series will converge slowly.

If the Fourier series is to represent a discontinuous function such as the square wave of Fig. 80, an interesting question arises as to the value of the function that the series will give us at the point of discontinuity. It can be shown that if a function $f(\theta)$ satisfies the restrictions of Sec. 87, its Fourier series will converge at $\theta = \theta_0$ to the value:

$$\lim_{\epsilon \to 0} \frac{f(\theta_0 + \epsilon) + f(\theta_0 - \epsilon)}{2} = \frac{f(\theta_0 +) + f(\theta_0 -)}{2}.$$

This is shown graphically in Fig. 85, from which it is seen that if the function is discontinuous at θ_0, the series will converge to the average of the values on opposite sides of the discontinuity. Where the function is continuous, we have

$$f(\theta_0\,+) = f(\theta_0\,-) = f(\theta_0),$$

and the series converges to the correct value $f(\theta_0)$.

If a Fourier series represents a discontinuous function, a plot of the first few terms as in Fig. 80 will show a tendency to overshoot near the discontinuity. This tendency will persist

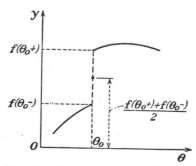

regardless of the number of harmonics taken into consideration. It is known as the *Gibbs phenomenon*. This effect causes unsatisfactory convergence near points of discontinuity.

Many important applications of the Fourier series involve the use of derivatives or integrals. This raises an important question as to the validity of differentiating or integrating the series term by term. It can be shown

Fig. 85.—Value to which a Fourier series converges at a discontinuity.

that if a function is continuous, the derivative of its series will truly represent the derivative of the function wherever that derivative is continuous. Where the derivative is discontinuous, its series will converge to the average of the values on opposite sides of the discontinuity, as noted previously.

It can also be shown that if a function satisfies the restrictions of Sec. 87, the integral of its series will truly represent the integral of the function. Observe that if the function has a constant term its integral will contain a linear term, and the series representing this integral will not be a true Fourier series.

Example.—Consider Eq. (458) for the expansion of the triangular wave of Fig. 84:

$$f(\theta) = -\frac{4S}{\pi} \sum_{n=1,3,5,\cdots}^{\infty} \frac{\cos n\theta}{n^2},$$

or $\qquad f(\theta) = -\frac{4S}{\pi}\left(\cos\theta + \frac{1}{9}\cos 3\theta + \frac{1}{25}\cos 5\theta + \cdots\right).$

This function is continuous; hence we may try to take its first derivative. If we do so in the usual manner, we obtain

$$f'(\theta) = \frac{4S}{\pi} \sum_{n=1,3,5,\cdots}^{\infty} \frac{\sin n\theta}{n}$$

or
$$f'(\theta) = \frac{4S}{\pi} \left(\sin \theta + \frac{1}{3} \sin 3\theta + \frac{1}{5} \sin 5\theta + \cdots \right).$$

This is precisely the series that we obtained for the square wave of Fig. 80 [see Eq. (451)] and is obviously the correct result for the first derivative of the triangular wave. Conversely, integration of the series for the square wave will result in the expansion for the triangular wave provided the constant of integration is set equal to zero.

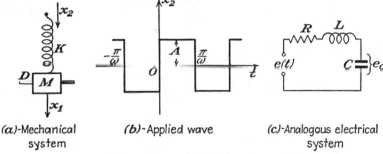

(a)-Mechanical   (b)-Applied wave   (c)-Analogous electrical
system   system

FIG. 86.—Physical systems and applied motion used in example.

The first derivative of the triangular wave is discontinuous and, as we should expect, its second derivative is nonconvergent and meaningless:

$$f''(\theta) = \frac{4S}{\pi} \left(\cos \theta + \cos 3\theta + \cos 5\theta + \cdots \right).$$

Integration of the series for the triangular wave will produce, as we should expect, a continuous succession of parabolas. Observe that integration produces a smoother wave with a more rapidly convergent series and also that the derivative or integral of an odd function produces an even function, and vice versa.

93. Example: Application of Fourier Series.—The Fourier series is useful in so many types of problems that isolated examples can convey only a small part of its usefulness. However, the following example will illustrate some of its power and utility.

Consider the mechanical system of Fig. 86, in which a mass and damper are suspended from a spring. The upper end of the spring is moved with an abrupt periodic motion which approximates the square wave of Fig. 80, and the problem is to find the steady-state motion of the mass. An analogous electrical problem is shown in Fig. 86c, where a square wave of voltage is applied to an RLC series circuit and the resulting voltage across the condenser is required.

The differential equation for the motion of the mass is

$$(Mp^2 + Dp + K)x_1 = Kx_2. \qquad (463)$$

The square-wave motion of the upper end of the spring has been expanded in Eq. (451) and can be expressed as a function of time by the series:

$$x_2 = \frac{4A}{\pi} \sum_{n=1,3,5,\,\cdots}^{\infty} \frac{\sin n\omega t}{n}. \qquad (464)$$

The differential equation (463) can then be written as

$$(Mp^2 + Dp + K)x_1 = \frac{4KA}{\pi} \sum_{n=1,3,5,\cdots}^{\infty} \frac{\sin n\omega t}{n}. \qquad (465)$$

Since this is a linear system, the principle of superposition can be used. Each of the harmonic components on the right will produce a corresponding steady-state harmonic component in the solution x_1. Denoting these components by

$$x_{1n} \qquad (n = 1, 3, 5, \cdots),$$

the solution will be given by addition of the components:

$$x_1 = \sum_{n=1,3,5,\cdots}^{\infty} x_{1n}. \qquad (466)$$

Thus for the nth harmonic component the differential equation is

$$(Mp^2 + Dp + K)x_{1n} = \frac{4KA}{\pi n} \sin n\omega t. \qquad (467)$$

The solution is most easily obtained by the vector methods of Chap. VII. Observe that $\sin n\omega t = \cos (n\omega t - \pi/2)$. To obtain the vector solution, replace the instantaneous x_{1n} by the vector $\bar{X}_{1n}$, the driving force by $(4KA/\pi n)\epsilon^{-j\pi/2}$, and p by $jn\omega$. This yields the solution:

$$\bar{X}_{1n} = \frac{4KA\,\epsilon^{-j\pi/2}}{\pi n[(K - n^2\omega^2 M) + j(n\omega D)]},$$

or
$$\bar{X}_{1n} = \frac{4KA}{\pi n \sqrt{(K - n^2\omega^2 M)^2 + (n\omega D)^2}} \epsilon^{-j[(\pi/2)+\phi_n]}, \quad (468)$$

where
$$\phi_n = \tan^{-1} \frac{n\omega D}{K - n^2\omega^2 M}. \quad (469)$$

The instantaneous value of x_{1n} can be written by the methods of Chap. VII as

$$x_{1n} = C_n \cos\left(n\omega t - \frac{\pi}{2} - \phi_n\right)$$
$$= C_n \sin(n\omega t - \phi_n), \quad (470)$$

where
$$C_n = |\bar{X}_{1n}| = \frac{4KA}{\pi n \sqrt{(K - n^2\omega^2 M)^2 + (n\omega D)^2}} \quad (471)$$

and ϕ_n is given by Eq. (469).

Using Eqs. (466) and (470), the total solution can now be written in Fourier series form as

$$x_1 = \sum_{n=1,3,5,\cdots}^{\infty} C_n \sin(n\omega t - \phi_n), \quad (472)$$

where the values of C_n and ϕ_n are given by the equations above. The analogous electrical problem can be solved by exchanging L for M, R for D, $1/C$ for K, and e_c for x_1.

As a numerical example, consider the following data:

$A = 0.347$ ft.
$\omega = 4$ radians per second.
Fundamental $f = 0.636$ cycles per second.
$M = 0.20$ lb-sec^2/ft (weight $= 6.44$ lb).
$K = 28.8$ lb/ft.
$D = 0.30$ lb-sec/ft.

Using Eqs. (469) and (471), the amplitudes and phase angles of the various harmonics of x_1 are found to be

$C_1 = 0.498$ ft	$\phi_1 = 2.7°$
$C_3 = 1.178$ ft	$\phi_3 = 90°$
$C_5 = 0.0494$ ft	$\phi_5 = 173.3°$
$C_7 = 0.0142$ ft	$\phi_7 = 176.2°$
$\cdots\cdots\cdots\cdots$	$\cdots\cdots\cdots$

Using Eq. (472), the motion of the mass can be expressed as

$x_1 = 0.498 \sin(\omega t - 2.7°) + 1.178 \sin(3\omega t - 90°)$
$\qquad\qquad + 0.049 \sin(5\omega t - 173.3°) + \cdots .$

The sum of the first three terms is plotted in Fig. 87.   The system is resonant to the third harmonic frequency, and this harmonic is predominant in the motion of the mass.   Similar constants in the analogous electrical system will produce a like selective action with regard to the third harmonic.

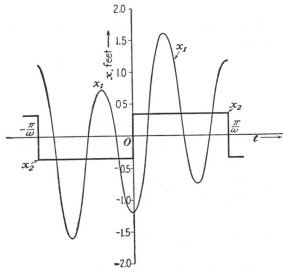

FIG. 87.—Solution for systems of Fig. 86.

94. Complex Form of the Fourier Series.—The trigonometric form of the Fourier series is cumbersome in that it contains either two terms for each harmonic or one term with a phase angle, and requires the use of two different formulas [Eqs. (447) and (448)] for evaluation of the constants.   The complex form of the Fourier series is more compact and requires only one formula for the coefficients.   Its exponential form makes it easy to manipulate, and in many problems it has a distinct advantage over the trigonometric form.

The Fourier series was written in Eq. (459) as

$$f(t) = \frac{A_0}{2} + \sum_{n=1}^{\infty} (A_n \cos n\omega t + B_n \sin n\omega t), \qquad (473)$$

where

$$\left. \begin{array}{l} A_n = \dfrac{\omega}{\pi} \displaystyle\int_{-\pi/\omega}^{\pi/\omega} f(t) \cos n\omega t \, dt \\[2ex] B_n = \dfrac{\omega}{\pi} \displaystyle\int_{-\pi/\omega}^{\pi/\omega} f(t) \sin n\omega t \, dt. \end{array} \right\} \qquad (474)$$

Now express the sine and cosine in terms of exponentials:

$$\left.\begin{aligned} \sin n\omega t &= \frac{\epsilon^{jn\omega t} - \epsilon^{-jn\omega t}}{2j} \\ \cos n\omega t &= \frac{\epsilon^{jn\omega t} + \epsilon^{-jn\omega t}}{2}. \end{aligned}\right\} \quad (475)$$

Substituting these relations into Eq. (473) we obtain

$$f(t) = \frac{A_0}{2} + \sum_{n=1}^{\infty} \left(\frac{A_n - jB_n}{2} \epsilon^{jn\omega t} + \frac{A_n + jB_n}{2} \epsilon^{-jn\omega t} \right). \quad (476)$$

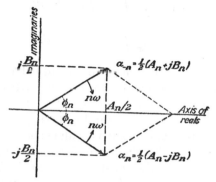

FIG. 88.—Vector representation of harmonic terms.

This can be simplified by defining new coefficients:

$$\left.\begin{aligned} \alpha_n &= \frac{A_n - jB_n}{2} \\ \alpha_{-n} &= \frac{A_n + jB_n}{2}. \end{aligned}\right\} \quad (477)$$

Equation (476) can then be expressed more simply as

$$f(t) = \frac{A_0}{2} + \sum_{n=1}^{\infty} (\alpha_n \epsilon^{jn\omega t} + \alpha_{-n} \epsilon^{-jn\omega t}). \quad (478)$$

This will be further simplified directly. However, consider for a moment the meaning of the coefficients α_n and α_{-n} in terms of the vectors of Fig. 88. The term $\alpha_n \epsilon^{jn\omega t}$ can be represented by a vector rotating counterclockwise at an angular velocity $n\omega$ radians per second. At $t = 0$ its value is the complex number α_n

given by Eq. (477). Furthermore, the term $\alpha_{-n}\epsilon^{-jn\omega t}$ represents the conjugate vector of Eq. (477) rotating oppositely at the same speed. The vector sum of the two is always real and varies sinusoidally, correctly representing the instantaneous value of the nth harmonic. Its amplitude is $|\alpha_n| + |\alpha_{-n}| = 2|\alpha_n|$, and its phase angle is given by the initial position of the vectors as denoted by the complex numbers α_n and α_{-n}.

Let us return to the process of simplification. To obtain formulas for the α's, substitute Eqs. (474) into (477) and reduce to exponentials by use of Eqs. (475). This results in

$$\alpha_n = \frac{\omega}{2\pi} \int_{-\pi/\omega}^{\pi/\omega} f(t)\epsilon^{-jn\omega t}\, dt, \qquad (479a)$$

$$\alpha_{-n} = \frac{\omega}{2\pi} \int_{-\pi/\omega}^{\pi/\omega} f(t)\epsilon^{jn\omega t}\, dt. \qquad (479b)$$

However, these two expressions are identical except that one contains n where the other contains $-n$. Although we have previously considered only positive integral values of n, we could let Eq. (479a) also serve for Eq. (479b) merely by letting n have both positive and negative values: $n = \cdots -3, -2, -1, 1, 2, 3, \cdots$. Furthermore for the harmonic of zero order, Eq. (479a) yields the constant term in the Fourier expansion without the factor of $\frac{1}{2}$ which was necessary before:

$$\alpha_0 = \frac{\omega}{2\pi} \int_{-\pi/\omega}^{\pi/\omega} f(t)\, dt = \frac{A_0}{2}.$$

Now return to the exponential series of Eq. (478). Note that by substituting n for $-n$ and properly changing the limits of summation, we can write

$$\sum_{n=1}^{\infty} \alpha_{-n}\epsilon^{-jn\omega t} = \sum_{n=-\infty}^{-1} \alpha_n\epsilon^{jn\omega t}.$$

In addition $A_0/2 = \alpha_0$, so the whole series can be telescoped into the simple expression:

$$f(t) = \sum_{n=-\infty}^{\infty} \alpha_n\epsilon^{jn\omega t}, \qquad (480)$$

where $$\alpha_n = \frac{\omega}{2\pi} \int_{-\pi/\omega}^{\pi/\omega} f(t)\epsilon^{-jn\omega t}\, dt. \qquad (481)$$

This is the complex form of the Fourier series. Its simplicity and ease of manipulation are evident. The terms arising from equal positive and negative values of n can be visualized as conjugate vectors rotating oppositely at harmonic speed, with their vector sum representing the real instantaneous value of the harmonic component.

It will be interesting to compare the trigonometric and complex Fourier expansions for the square and triangular waves. Using Eqs. (480) and (481) it can be shown that

For the square wave:

$$f(t) = \frac{Y}{\pi} \sum_{n=-\infty}^{\infty} \frac{(1 - \cos n\pi)}{jn} \epsilon^{jn\omega t} = \frac{2Y}{\pi} \sum_{n=-\infty}^{\infty} \frac{\epsilon^{jn\omega t}}{jn} \quad (n \text{ odd only}).$$

This should be compared with Eq. (451), setting $\theta = \omega t$.
For the triangular wave:

$$f(t) = -\frac{S}{\pi} \sum_{n=-\infty}^{\infty} \frac{(1 - \cos n\pi)}{n^2} \epsilon^{jn\omega t} = -\frac{2S}{\pi} \sum_{n=-\infty}^{\infty} \frac{\epsilon^{jn\omega t}}{n^2} \quad (n \text{ odd only}),$$

provided that the slope of the line is taken to be $S\omega$ along the time axis. This should be compared with Eq. (458).

Example.—Consider the rectified voltage wave of Fig. 78b applied to a load of resistance R through a smoothing inductance L. Using Eq. (480) to express the voltage, the differential equation for load current can be written as

$$(R + pL)i = \sum_{n=-\infty}^{\infty} E_n \epsilon^{jn\omega t}, \tag{482}$$

where E_n is obtained by Eq. (481), using $e = -E \sin \omega t$ for $-(\pi/\omega) < t < 0$, and $e = E \sin \omega t$ for $0 < t < (\pi/\omega)$. Then

$$E_n = \frac{\omega}{2\pi} \left[\int_{-\pi/\omega}^{0} (-E \sin \omega t)\epsilon^{-jn\omega t} \, dt + \int_{0}^{\pi/\omega} (E \sin \omega t)\epsilon^{-jn\omega t} \, dt \right]$$

$$= -\frac{E(1 + \cos n\pi)}{\pi(n^2 - 1)}$$

$$= -\frac{2E}{\pi(n^2 - 1)} \quad \text{for } n \text{ even, 0 for } n \text{ odd.} \tag{483}$$

Using superposition as before, the differential equation for the nth harmonic component of current is

$$(R + pL)i_n = E_n \epsilon^{jn\omega t}. \tag{484}$$

Following the methods of Chap. VII, we shall assume a steady-state solution $i_n = \bar{I}_n \epsilon^{jn\omega t}$, substitute into Eq. (484), perform the indicated differentiation, and obtain the relation:

$$\bar{I}_n = \frac{E_n}{R + jn\omega L} = \frac{E_n}{\bar{Z}_n}. \tag{485}$$

We could now substitute from Eq. (483) for E_n and sum the harmonic components to obtain the Fourier series for i. However, we are interested mainly in the magnitude of the components and shall compute these only.

Take $E = 1,000$ volts peak, $\omega = 377$ radians per second corresponding to 60 cycles, $R = 500$ ohms, and $L = 10$ henrys. The following table of magnitudes can then be computed, using Eq. (483) for E_n and Eq. (485) for $\bar{I}_n$.

n	$|E_n|$	$|\bar{Z}_n|$	$|\bar{I}_n|$	Actual magnitude of current
0	637	500	1.247	1.247
±1	0			
±2	212	7,560	0.028	0.056
±3	0			
±4	42.5	15,080	0.003	0.006
..	.....	......	.....	.....

Except for the d-c component the actual magnitudes of the harmonics of voltage and current are double the values of $|E_n|$ and $|\bar{I}_n|$. It will be seen that the smoothing choke substantially reduces the a-c components of load current.

95. Numerical Methods of Harmonic Analysis.—In many cases the wave to be analyzed is given in graphical or numerical form and cannot conveniently be broken into analytically expressed segments. One method of determining the Fourier coefficients is by numerical integration of Eqs. (447) and (448) for each important harmonic. The Runge schedule of harmonic analysis simplifies this procedure by making use of certain symmetries in the computation.

Another method, devised by Fischer-Hinnen and sometimes called the *method of selected ordinates*, is particularly convenient when the number of harmonics to be found is not great. It is based on the fact that if one period of the wave is divided into k equal parts and the corresponding ordinates added algebraically, the sum is affected only by the harmonics of order k and multiples thereof. To illustrate this effect, consider the wave of Fig. 89, which has been synthesized from a fundamental plus third and fifth harmonics. For $k = 1$ the line of division has been placed at a, and the corresponding ordinate y_a is seen to be affected not only by the fundamental but also by the multiple frequencies. For $k = 3$ the lines of division have been placed at b, c, and d.

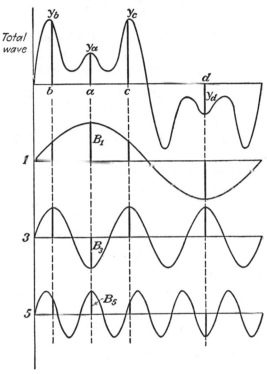

FIG. 89.—Illustration of principle used in Fischer-Hinnen harmonic analysis.

The algebraic sum of the ordinates $y_b + y_c + y_d$ is seen to contain the components

$$(0.5B_1 + 0.5B_1 - B_1) + (B_3 + B_3 + B_3)$$
$$+ (0.5B_5 + 0.5B_5 - B_5) = 3B_3$$

and is not affected by the nonmultiple frequencies. Since harmonics of high order are usually negligible, it is possible to evaluate the highest appreciable harmonic first and then proceed to the lower harmonics, correcting them for the presence of their multiples. Furthermore, by proper placement of the divisions, sine and cosine components of the harmonics can be separated.

To determine the relations involved, the wave will be expressed as a complex Fourier series:

$$y = \sum_{n=-\infty}^{\infty} \alpha_n \epsilon^{jn\theta}. \tag{486}$$

Divide one period into k equal parts, starting at a general point $\theta = \beta$. The angle between increments is $\Delta\theta = 2\pi/k$, so the sum of the k ordinates can be written from Eq. (486) as

$$\sum y_k = \sum_{n=-\infty}^{\infty} \alpha_n \left[\epsilon^{jn\beta} + \epsilon^{jn\left(\beta + \frac{2\pi}{k}\right)} + \cdots + \epsilon^{jn\left(\beta + \frac{k-1}{k}2\pi\right)} \right].$$

$$= \sum_{n=-\infty}^{\infty} \alpha_n \epsilon^{jn\beta} (1 + \epsilon^{j\frac{n}{k}2\pi} + \cdots + \epsilon^{j\frac{n}{k}(k-1)2\pi}).$$

Two cases must now be considered. When the ratio n/k is an integer, the arguments of the exponentials become multiples of 2π, and the sum of the terms in parentheses becomes equal to k. When n/k is not an integer, the terms in parentheses can be considered as a geometrical progression of the form

$$1 + x + x^2 + \cdots + x^{r-1},$$

the sum of which is shown in algebra to be $(1 - x^r)/(1 - x)$. Thus for n/k not an integer the sum of the terms in parentheses is

$$\frac{1 - \epsilon^{j2\pi n}}{1 - \epsilon^{j(n/k)2\pi}} = 0.$$

Then the algebraic sum of the k ordinates can be written more simply as

$$\sum y_k = k \sum_{n=-\infty}^{\infty} \alpha_n \epsilon^{jn\beta} \quad \left(\frac{n}{k} \text{ integers only}\right). \tag{487}$$

If the constant component of the wave is removed, Eq. (487) can be written as

$$\sum y_k = k \sum_{n=k,2k,\cdots}^{\infty} \alpha_n \epsilon^{jn\beta} + k \sum_{n=k,2k,\cdots}^{\infty} \alpha_{-n} \epsilon^{-jn\beta}. \tag{488}$$

But by Eqs. (477),

$$\alpha_n = \frac{A_n - jB_n}{2}, \qquad \alpha_{-n} = \frac{A_n + jB_n}{2}.$$

Also by Euler's formula, $\epsilon^{\pm jn\beta} = \cos n\beta \pm j \sin n\beta$, so Eq. (488) for the sum of the k ordinates becomes

$$\sum y_k = k \sum_{n=k,2k,\cdots}^{\infty} (A_n \cos n\beta + B_n \sin n\beta). \qquad (489)$$

To separate the cosine components, let the k divisions be made starting at $\beta = 0$. Equation (489) then yields

$$\frac{\sum y_k}{k} = A_k + A_{2k} + A_{3k} + \cdots = A_k'. \qquad (490)$$

To find the sine components, let the divisions start at $\beta = \pi/2k$. Then

$$\frac{\sum y_k}{l_0} = B_k - A_{2k} - B_{3k} + A_{4k} + B_{5k} - \cdots = B_k'. \qquad (491)$$

Thus the coefficients of the kth harmonic can be expressed in terms of the algebraic sum of the k ordinates and the coefficients of the harmonics of multiple frequency. The procedure will now be summarized in a more convenient manner.

Procedure.—If the wave has a constant component, compute its magnitude Y_0 by graphical or numerical integration (area over one period divided by the base) and remove this component by subtracting it algebraically from each ordinate.

First compute the coefficients of the highest desired harmonic and work down. For the kth harmonic, divide the period into $4k$ equal parts starting at $\theta = 0$, and let the ordinates be denoted by $y_0, y_1, y_2, \ldots$. Define

$$\left.\begin{array}{l} A_k' = \dfrac{1}{k}(y_0 + y_4 + y_8 + \cdots + y_{4k-4}) \\[2mm] B_k' = \dfrac{1}{k}(y_1 + y_5 + y_9 + \cdots + y_{4k-3}). \end{array}\right\} \qquad (492)$$

If there are no higher harmonics whose order is an integral multiple of k, then the coefficients of the kth harmonic are given directly by

$$\left.\begin{array}{l} A_k = A_k' \\ B_k = B_k'. \end{array}\right\} \qquad (493)$$

If there are harmonics whose order is an integral multiple of k, the coefficients of the kth harmonic must be corrected:

$$\left.\begin{array}{l} A_k = A_k' - (A_{2k} + A_{3k} + \cdots) \\ B_k = B_k' + (A_{2k} + B_{3k} - A_{4k} - B_{5k} + \cdots). \end{array}\right\} \quad (494)$$

If the positive and negative halves of the wave are alike, there are no even harmonics present. Then $f(\theta) = -f(\theta + \pi)$, and in general $y_m = -y_{m+2k}$. It is then only necessary to divide the first half period **into** $2k$ equal parts, and Eqs. (492) can be expressed as

$$\left.\begin{array}{l} A_k' = \dfrac{1}{k}(y_0 - y_2 + y_4 - \cdots + y_{2k-2}) \\[2mm] B_k' = \dfrac{1}{k}(y_1 - y_3 + y_5 - \cdots + y_{2k-1}). \end{array}\right\} \quad (495)$$

The even multiples now can be eliminated from Eqs. (494), leaving

$$\left.\begin{array}{l} A_k = A_k' - (A_{3k} + A_{5k} + A_{7k} + \cdots) \\ B_k = B_k' + (B_{3k} - B_{5k} + B_{7k} - \cdots). \end{array}\right\} \quad (496)$$

In any case the Fourier polynomial approximately representing the wave is given by

$$y = Y_0 + \sum_n (A_n \cos n\theta + B_n \sin n\theta),$$

or

$$y = Y_0 + \sum_n C_n \cos(n\theta - \phi_n),$$

where

$$C_n = \sqrt{A_n^2 + B_n^2}, \qquad \tan \phi_n = \frac{B_n}{A_n}.$$

Example.—Consider the wave of Fig. 90. There are no even harmonics and, since the wave is comparatively smooth, all harmonics above the fifth will be ignored. The wave has zero average value, *i.e.*, $Y_0 = 0$. For the fifth harmonic, $k = 5$; so divide the first half period into 10 equal parts as shown by the letters a. Taking the ordinates at these divisions, we obtain from Eq. (495):

$$A_5' = \tfrac{1}{5}(0.163 - 0.244 + 0.460 - 0.457 + 0) = -0.016,$$
$$B_5' = \tfrac{1}{5}[0.200 - 0.332 + 0.542 - 0.250 + (-0.122)] = 0.007.$$

Since higher harmonics are neglected,

$$A_5 = A_5' = -0.016, \quad \text{and} \quad B_5 = B_5' = 0.007,$$
$$C_5 = \sqrt{(-0.016)^2 + (0.007)^2} = 0.017,$$
$$\phi_5 = \tan^{-1}\frac{0.007}{-0.016} = 156°.$$

For the third harmonic, $k = 3$; so divide the half period into six equal parts as shown by the letters b.   From Eqs. (495)

$$A_3' = \tfrac{1}{3}(0.163 - 0.370 + 0.305) = 0.033,$$
$$B_3' = \tfrac{1}{3}[0.232 - 0.542 + (-0.059)] = -0.123.$$

Harmonics whose orders are multiples of three have been ignored; hence $A_3 = A_3'$ and $B_3 = B_3'$, from which

$$C_3 = 0.127 \qquad \text{and} \qquad \phi_3 = -75°$$

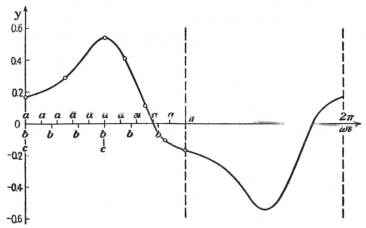

FIG. 90.—Wave used in example of harmonic analysis. The circled points are calculated from the equation

$$y = 0.437 \cos(\omega t - 70.5°) + 0.127 \cos(3\omega t + 75°) + 0.017 \cos(5\omega t - 156°).$$

For the fundamental, $k = 1$; so divide the half period into two equal parts as indicated by the letters c.   Then

$$A_1' = 0.163 \qquad \text{and} \qquad B_1' = 0.542.$$

Multiple frequencies are present; so use Eqs. (496) to correct the coefficients:

$$A_1 = 0.163 - [0.033 + (-0.016)] = 0.146,$$
$$B_1 = 0.542 + (-0.123 - 0.007) = 0.412,$$

from which $C_1 = 0.437$ and $\phi_1 = 70.5°$.

Thus the wave can be expressed approximately as

$$y = 0.437 \cos(\omega t - 70.5°) + 0.127 \cos(3\omega t + 75°)$$
$$+ 0.017 \cos(5\omega t - 156°).$$

Several points obtained from this equation are shown in Fig. 90 and are seen to agree quite well with the original wave.

96. Estimation of Harmonic Content.—When a wave contains one harmonic that is especially predominant, as is often the case, it is possible to determine by inspection the order of this harmonic and to obtain some idea of the relative magnitudes of the main components and their approximate phase positions. This can be done by visualizing or sketching by eye a sine curve of fundamental frequency over the wave to be analyzed, so that the wave alternately crosses the sine curve in a regular manner. This is illustrated by the dotted curve of Fig. 91a. When this is properly done, the algebraic difference between the two waves will look somewhat as in Fig. 91b and will be a residual wave

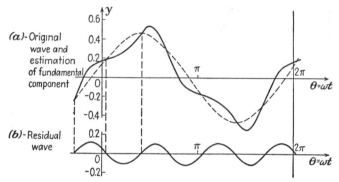

(a)-Original wave and estimation of fundamental component

(b)-Residual wave

Fig. 91.—Estimation of harmonic content.

with perhaps a more or less constant period and amplitude. This residual wave will indicate the approximate magnitude and phase position of the main harmonic, while the original sine wave will show the approximate magnitude and phase position of the fundamental. If desirable, the residual wave can be broken down into components as was the original wave, although in doing this by eye all semblance of accuracy is quickly lost. Obviously, the method works best on waves that are made up mainly of a few simple components.

This type of visual estimation for the curve of Fig. 91a indicates that the fundamental component has a magnitude of about 0.45 unit and is a cosine curve shifted to the right about two-tenths of a period, or roughly 70°. The main harmonic is seen to be the third, since the residual wave has three loops to every one of the fundamental. The magnitude is estimated to be something over 0.1 unit and is a cosine wave shifted to the left about two-tenths of its period, or again roughly 70°. Thus our rough estimate of the main components of the wave would be

$$y \approx 0.45 \cos (\omega t - 70°) + 0.1 \cos (3\omega t + 70°).$$

The curve of Fig. 91a is identical with that of Fig. 90, and our result should be compared with the harmonic analysis of that wave.

When the wave has a constant component, as that of Fig. 92a, the positive and negative loops will have unequal areas. The

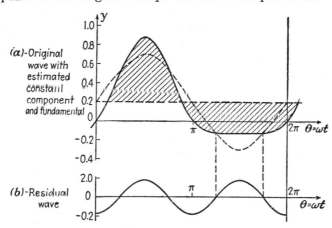

FIG. 92.—Estimation with constant component present.

constant component can be estimated by placing a horizontal line through the wave so that approximately equal areas appear to fall above and below, as shown by the shaded areas of Fig. 92a. Then, visualizing or sketching a fundamental curve on top of the original wave, the residual wave indicates the principal harmonic. In this case the main harmonic is the second, as the residual wave of Fig. 92b has two loops for every loop of the fundamental. Again observe the dissymmetry that an even harmonic produces in the positive and negative loops of the original wave. A rough estimate of the principal components of the original wave will be

$$y \approx 0.2 + 0.5 \sin \omega t - 0.2 \cos 2\omega t.$$

Although the method given above for estimating harmonic content is of quite limited accuracy and indeed is only semiquantitative, it is often quite useful and permits a ready visualization of the components of reasonably simple waves.

97. The Fourier Integral.—The concept of resolving a nonsinusoidal periodic wave into fundamental and harmonic components is a particularly convenient one, not only because it provides a powerful method for calculating the performance of systems involving such functions, but also because it can be used in a semiquantitative way to explain many interesting and physically important phenomena. For example, it was found in Sec. 88 that a square wave contains odd harmonics of considerable magnitude. From this we should expect that if the wave were applied to a system that was resonant at one of the harmonic frequencies, this harmonic might predominate in the response. This was illustrated in Sec. 93 and Figs. 86 and 87.

The Fourier integral bears much the same relation to nonperiodic functions that the Fourier series does to periodic waves and is used in the analysis of such problems as the response of systems to sudden shocks, the transient analysis of electrical networks including transmission lines and filters, structural problems involving nonperiodic loading, and the transient conduction of heat. Like the Fourier series, it is of aid both in calculation and in semiquantitative reasoning. We can give here only a brief introduction to the subject and trust that it will encourage the reader to pursue the matter further.

We shall here regard the Fourier integral as a development of the Fourier series concept and, as an introduction to the subject, shall consider the problem of Sec. 93 and Fig. 86 in more detail. A square wave of motion was applied at the upper end of the spring, and the motion of the mass was calculated in terms of a Fourier series. Since the harmonic frequencies are multiples of the fundamental frequency, the difference in frequency between adjacent harmonics is in general equal to the fundamental frequency. To keep this in mind, let us denote the fundamental angular velocity by $\Delta\omega$, and reserve the symbol ω to represent angular velocity in general. Thus, we can write the frequencies present in a periodic wave as $\omega = 0$, $\Delta\omega$, $2\Delta\omega$, etc. With this change in nomenclature, the complex expression given in Sec. 94 for the square wave can be expressed as the following Fourier series:

$$f(t) = \frac{Y \, \Delta\omega}{\pi} \sum_{\omega = -\infty}^{\infty} \frac{\left(1 - \cos \dfrac{\omega}{\Delta\omega} \pi\right)}{j\omega} \epsilon^{j\omega t}$$

$$(\omega = \cdot \cdot \cdot -\Delta\omega, \, 0, \, \Delta\omega, \, 2\Delta\omega, \, \cdot \cdot \cdot \,). \quad (497)$$

The magnitudes of the various harmonic components of this wave are plotted against frequency in Fig. 93a. They appear as a

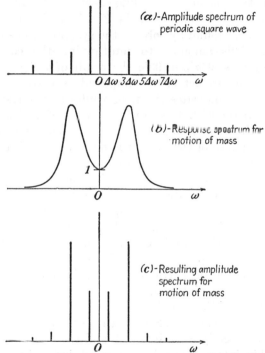

(a)-Amplitude spectrum of periodic square wave

(b)-Response spectrum for motion of mass

(c)-Resulting amplitude spectrum for motion of mass

FIG. 93.—Amplitude spectra obtained by Fourier series analysis, system of Fig. 86.

series of isolated points separated by increments of $2 \, \Delta\omega$ since even harmonics are absent, and diminish in magnitude as $1/\omega$. This can be regarded as the amplitude spectrum of the square wave.

Plotted in Fig. 93b is the amplitude ratio of displacement of the mass to displacement of the upper end of the spring as found in the example of Sec. 93 for steady-state sinusoidal conditions.

This can be obtained from the differential equation (463) by replacing the operator p by $j\omega$ and taking the absolute value of the ratio:

$$\frac{|\bar{X}_1|}{|\bar{X}_2|} = \frac{K}{\sqrt{(K - \omega^2 M)^2 + (\omega D)^2}} \tag{498}$$

For the data given in that problem this ratio is a maximum at the third harmonic frequency. The plot of Fig. 93b can be regarded as the response amplitude spectrum for the system.

The harmonic components in the Fourier series for the motion of the mass were found by solving the system for each harmonic separately. This amounts to multiplying the corresponding ordinates of Figs. 93a and 93b, the result of which is shown in Fig. 93c. The product is the amplitude spectrum for motion of the mass and indicates the magnitudes of the resulting harmonics (compare with the results of Sec. 93). The effect of changing either the frequency of the applied motion or the frequency response of the system is now easy to visualize. For example, if the resonant frequency of the system were changed to coincide with the seventh harmonic, this frequency would be brought into prominence but its response would be comparatively weak. Similar considerations will, of course, apply to the corresponding electrical system. Although we have concentrated our attention on the amplitudes, the phase angles can similarly be treated in a simple manner. We shall find the concept of frequency spectra of particular value in understanding and applying the Fourier integral.

Consider next the problem of representing a nonperiodic function. It was stated in Sec. 91 that such a function could be represented correctly in an interval, and the question now arises whether this interval can be extended indefinitely in length so as correctly to express a nonperiodic $f(t)$ for $-\infty < t < \infty$, and also whether the results so obtained can be interpreted in a useful manner. For this purpose refer to the Fourier series of Eqs. (480) and (481) and rewrite them in terms of our new nomenclature:

$$f(t) = \sum_{\omega = -\infty}^{\infty} \alpha_\omega \epsilon^{j\omega t} \quad (\omega = \cdots, -\Delta\omega, 0, \Delta\omega, 2\Delta\omega, \cdots), \tag{499}$$

where
$$\alpha_\omega = \frac{\Delta\omega}{2\pi} \int_{-\pi/\Delta\omega}^{\pi/\Delta\omega} f(t)\epsilon^{-j\omega t}\, dt. \tag{500}$$

Substitute Eq. (500) into Eq. (499) and obtain

$$f(t) = \frac{1}{2\pi} \sum_{\omega = -\infty}^{\infty} \left[\int_{-\pi/\Delta\omega}^{\pi/\Delta\omega} f(t)\epsilon^{-j\omega t}\, dt \right] \epsilon^{j\omega t}\, \Delta\omega. \qquad (501)$$

This form of the Fourier series emphasizes the fact that if we put $f(t)$ into the interior of the equation as a set of analytically expressed segments, we get $f(t)$ out in more usable form as a series of harmonic components. The period of this wave is $2\pi/\Delta\omega$. To make the period indefinitely large we shall let the fundamental frequency $\Delta\omega$ approach zero as a limit. The form of Eq. (501) then suggests that $\Delta\omega$ should be replaced by the infinitesimal $d\omega$, the summation by an integral, and the limits on the internal integral by $-\infty$ and ∞. We then obtain the following expression:

$$f(t) = \frac{1}{2\pi} \int_{-\infty}^{\infty} \left[\int_{-\infty}^{\infty} f(t)\epsilon^{-j\omega t}\, dt \right] \epsilon^{j\omega t}\, d\omega. \qquad (502)$$

This is the *Fourier integral.* In general $f(t)$ must be continuous over finite intervals, and the integral $\int_{-\infty}^{\infty} |f(t)|\, dt$ must exist for the internal integral of Eq. (502) to converge.

The Fourier integral of Eq. (502) can be broken into two parts:

$$f(t) = \frac{1}{2\pi} \int_{-\infty}^{\infty} g(\omega)\epsilon^{j\omega t}\, d\omega, \qquad (503)$$

where
$$g(\omega) = \int_{-\infty}^{\infty} f(t)\epsilon^{-j\omega t}\, dt. \qquad (504)$$

The functions $g(\omega)$ and $f(t)$ are said to be the *Fourier transforms* of each other. Observe that the symmetry of the equations is such that the Fourier integral can be turned inside out.

Next examine the significance of these expressions. Reasoning from the Fourier series of Eq. (499), we can regard $f(t)$ in Eq. (503) to be made up of harmonic components of infinitesimal magnitude $g(\omega) \cdot d\omega$ and, since the fundamental frequency approaches zero in magnitude, all possible frequencies are present in the function. Since $g(\omega) \cdot d\omega$ is infinitesimal, we shall regard $g(\omega)$ itself as given in Eq. (504) to be the frequency spectrum of $f(t)$.

As an example, consider the pulse function shown in Fig. 94a. This might be regarded as a shock impressed on a mechanical system, a telegraphic dot, or a television pulse.   It is defined by $f(t) = 0$ for $-\infty < t < -T$, E for $-T < t < T$, and zero for $T < t < \infty$.   Break the integral (504) into three corresponding parts.   The first and last of these are zero, leaving

$$g(\omega) = \int_{-T}^{T} E\epsilon^{-j\omega t}\, dt = \frac{2E}{\omega} \sin \omega T. \tag{505}$$

This amplitude spectrum is plotted in Fig. 94b and shows the relative amplitudes of the various harmonic components of the

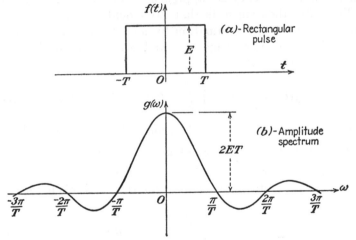

FIG. 94.—Rectangular pulse and its spectrum.

rectangular pulse.   The pulse is expressed as a function of time by summing (integrating) these components as in Eq. (503).

Since a shock contains all possible frequency components, it is not hard to see how it could rouse transient oscillations corresponding to the natural frequencies of the system.   Considering the pulse as an electrical voltage, it is evident that an amplifier or transmission system that refuses to pass frequencies as high as $1/2T$ cycles per second ($\omega = \pi/T$) will considerably distort the signal by rounding off the corners.   Similarly, a system that will not pass reasonably low frequencies may respond unduly to the steep sides but not reproduce the flat top, while one having a pronounced resonant frequency may show, a transient oscillation.

As a simple example, consider a voltage pulse applied to the
RL series circuit of Fig. 95. Using vector notation, the ratio
of current to voltage as a function of frequency is easily shown
to be

$$h(\omega) = \frac{I}{E} = \frac{1}{R + j\omega L} \qquad (506)$$

This is, of course, the a-c admittance of the circuit. Reasoning

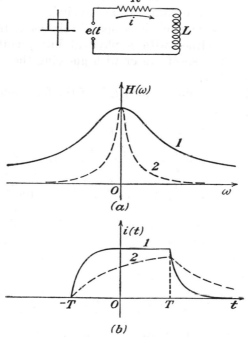

FIG. 95.—Response amplitude spectra for two different RL series circuits, and
solutions for rectangular pulse applied.

again from our Fourier series procedure, we can regard this as
giving the response spectrum for the system, and its magnitude
$H(\omega)$ is plotted in Fig. 95a. The harmonic components of the
current can be obtained by multiplying the response spectrum
by the impressed spectrum (505):

$$\frac{2E}{\omega(R + j\omega L)} \sin \omega T \qquad (507)$$

The resulting current as a function of time is obtained by integrating these components as in Eq. (503):

$$i(t) = \frac{1}{2\pi} \int_{-\infty}^{\infty} \frac{2E \sin \omega T}{\omega(R + j\omega L)} \epsilon^{j\omega t} \, d\omega. \tag{508}$$

Such integrals are difficult to evaluate by ordinary means, but fortunately the methods of contour integration supplied by the theory of functions of a complex variable can be used to integrate many of these functions in a simple manner.[1] Furthermore, extensive tables of such integrals are available.[2]   The theory of such integration is beyond the scope of this book, and we must be content here either with a physical interpretation of the resulting frequency spectrum or with guessing the solution and proving its validity.

Assume that the solution for $i(t)$ is of the form plotted in Fig. 95b and is given by

$$i = 0 \qquad \text{for } -\infty < t < -T,$$

$$i = \frac{E}{R} (1 - \epsilon^{-\frac{R}{L}(t+T)}) \qquad \text{for } -T < t < T,$$

$$i = \frac{E}{R} (1 - \epsilon^{-\frac{2RT}{L}})\epsilon^{-\frac{R}{L}(t-T)} \text{ for } T < t < \infty.$$

If the frequency spectrum for the solution as defined above checks with its spectrum as indicated in Eq. (507) or (508), the assumed solution is correct. To check this, substitute the assumed solution into Eq. (504):

$$\int_{-T}^{T} \frac{E}{R} (1 - \epsilon^{-\frac{R}{L}(t+T)})\epsilon^{-j\omega t} \, dt + \int_{T}^{\infty} \frac{E}{R} (1 - \epsilon^{-\frac{2RT}{L}})\epsilon^{-\frac{R}{L}(t-T)}\epsilon^{-j\omega t} \, dt.$$

Upon integration and substitution of limits this becomes

$$\frac{2E \sin \omega T}{\omega(R + j\omega L)},$$

which checks with Eq. (507), and our assumed solution is correct.   The solution is plotted in Fig. 95b for two different sets of parameters.   As one would expect by reasoning from the

[1] See, for example, McLachlan, N. W., "Complex Variable and the Operational Calculus," Cambridge University Press, London, 1939.

[2] Campbell, G. A., and R. M. Foster, Fourier Integrals for Practical Applications, *Bell Telephone System Tech. Pub., Monograph* B-584, 1942.

frequency spectra, the circuit that severely suppresses the higher frequencies produces a greatly rounded response. Figure 96 shows the corresponding current in an RC series circuit for two sets of parameters. Here the low frequencies are suppressed, and the response tends to be peaked. Observe the important point that the transient behavior of a system is completely

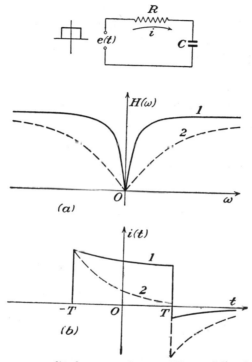

FIG. 96.—Response amplitude spectra for two different RC series circuits, and solutions for rectangular pulse applied.

determined by its steady-state sinusoidal response expressed as a function of ω. This principle forms a rigorous basis for proving the validity of various operational processes involving the differential operator p.

A particularly important nonperiodic function is the unit step function, which is defined as zero for $-\infty < t < 0$ and unity for $0 < t < \infty$. This can be regarded as a force or displacement suddenly applied to a mechanical system or as a battery voltage applied at $t = 0$ to an electrical circuit and can be used in combination with other functions to indicate discontinuity. Its spectrum can be obtained by using $f(t) = \epsilon^{-\alpha t}$ for $t > 0$ to make the integral (504) converge, and then let α approach zero as a limit. This yields the spectrum for the unit step function:

$$g(\omega) = \frac{1}{j\omega}.$$

The general procedure in analyzing a system is first to find the frequency spectrum for the driving force $f(t)$ using Eq. (504). In general, this is complex in form and can be expressed as

$$g(\omega) = G(\omega) \cdot \epsilon^{j\phi(\omega)}, \tag{509}$$

where $G(\omega)$ represents the relative magnitudes of the harmonics and is the amplitude spectrum, and $\phi(\omega)$ represents the phase angles and is the phase spectrum.

Next the steady-state vector ratio between response and sinusoidal driving force is found. When the differential equation for the system can be written in the form

$$D(p)y = M(p)f(t),$$

this ratio is given by

$$\frac{M(j\omega)}{D(j\omega)} = h(\omega) = H(\omega) \cdot \epsilon^{-j\theta(\omega)}, \tag{510}$$

where $H(\omega)$ and $\theta(\omega)$ are, respectively, the response amplitude and phase spectra for the system. The negative sign is placed before θ in Eq. (510) merely to make lag angles positive.

The product of driving force and system spectra is the spectrum of the response $y(t)$, and is given by

$$G(\omega) \cdot H(\omega) \cdot \epsilon^{j(\phi-\theta)}. \tag{511}$$

Thus the response can be written as a Fourier integral of the form of Eq. (503):

$$y(t) = \frac{1}{2\pi} \int_{-\infty}^{\infty} H(\omega) \cdot G(\omega)\epsilon^{j(\phi-\theta)}\epsilon^{j\omega t} \, dt. \tag{512}$$

Evaluation of this integral will yield the solution as a function of time. Moreover, in many problems the desired information can be obtained merely by reasoning from the spectrum of the solution, Eq. (511). Observe that the amplitude spectrum of the solution, $G(\omega) \cdot H(\omega)$, is the *product* of the amplitude spectra for the driving force and the system, and that the resulting phase spectrum, $\phi - \theta$, is given by the *difference* between the driving force and system phase spectra.

The foregoing treatment has given only a brief glimpse into the power and utility of the Fourier integral concept. When the integral (512) is evaluated, the resulting function of time will, of course, be the same as would be obtained by the classical methods of differential equations. However, the present methods cover a wider range of problems, in many practical cases are more simple and direct, and yield useful information in addition to giving the formal solution. The Fourier integral is closely allied to the operational calculus and has been made the basis for entire treatments of this subject. In combination with the theory of functions of a complex variable it is a powerful and convenient tool in transient analysis; on the other hand, it can be used in an intuitive manner in many direct practical applications such as the square-wave testing of circuits. Furthermore, the concept of the harmonic components of a non-periodic wave is important for its own sake, for it serves to explain many interesting and important physical phenomena.

Problems

1. Find the Fourier series expansion for the periodic triangular wave defined by $f(\theta) = \theta$ for $-\pi < \theta < \pi$.

2. *a.* Obtain the Fourier series for the wave defined by

$$f(\theta) = -Y \qquad \text{for } -\pi < \theta < -\frac{\pi}{2}.$$

$$f(\theta) = Y \qquad \text{for } -\frac{\pi}{2} < \theta < \frac{\pi}{2}.$$

$$f(\theta) = -Y \qquad \text{for } \frac{\pi}{2} < \theta < \pi.$$

b. Express the wave as a function of time if the fundamental angular velocity is ω radians per second.

c. Express the wave as a function of distance if L is the length of one half period.

3. Find the Fourier series expansion for the wave given by

$$f(\theta) = 0 \qquad \text{for } -\pi < \theta < 0.$$

$$f(\theta) = 2Y \qquad \text{for } 0 < \theta < \frac{\pi}{2}.$$

$$f(\theta) = Y \qquad \text{for } \frac{\pi}{2} < \theta < \pi.$$

4. The following periodic wave represents a function of time which has a fundamental frequency of 1,000 cycles per second. Expand in a Fourier series as a function of time. The function is defined in terms of angle by

$$f(\theta) = 0 \qquad \text{for } -180° < \theta < -120°,$$
$$f(\theta) = -E \qquad \text{for } -120° < \theta < -60°,$$
$$f(\theta) = 0 \qquad \text{for } -60° < \theta < 60°,$$
$$f(\theta) = E \qquad \text{for } 60° < \theta < 120°,$$
$$f(\theta) = 0 \qquad \text{for } 120° < \theta < 180°.$$

5. *a.* Expand the odd function defined over one half period by

$$f(\theta) = S\theta \qquad \text{for } 0 < \theta < \frac{\pi}{3},$$
$$f(\theta) = \frac{S}{2}(\pi - \theta) \qquad \text{for } \frac{\pi}{3} < \theta < \pi,$$

and examine the expansion for the absence of certain harmonics.

b. Express the wave as a function of distance if L is the length of one half period.

c. Differentiate the expression obtained in (*a*) with respect to θ. What wave is represented?

6. A function is defined by $f(\theta) = e^{\theta}$ over the interval $0 < \theta < \pi$. Expand this in a Fourier series (*a*) as an even function, (*b*) as an odd function. Sketch the waves and discuss the difference in the rates of convergence.

7. Expand the even function defined in the interval $0 < \theta < \pi$ by $f(\theta) = \theta$. Place $\theta = 0$ in the series and from the resulting expression deduce the relation:

$$\pi = \sqrt{8\left(1 + \frac{1}{3^2} + \frac{1}{5^2} + \frac{1}{7^2} + \cdots\right)}.$$

8. Use the complex form of the Fourier series to expand the periodic square wave defined by

$$f(t) = -Y \qquad \text{for } -\frac{\pi}{\omega} < t < 0,$$
$$f(t) = Y \qquad \text{for } 0 < t < \frac{\pi}{\omega}.$$

9. Using the complex form of the Fourier series, expand the half-wave rectifier voltage defined by

$$f(t) = 0 \qquad \text{for } -\frac{\pi}{\omega} < t < -\frac{\pi}{2\omega},$$
$$f(t) = E\cos\omega t \qquad \text{for } -\frac{\pi}{2\omega} < t < \frac{\pi}{2\omega},$$
$$f(t) = 0 \qquad \text{for } \frac{\pi}{2\omega} < t < \frac{\pi}{\omega}.$$

Tabulate the values of α_n for n from -4 to $+4$ inclusive, and also tabulate the amplitudes of the harmonic components up to and including the fourth harmonic.

10. *a.* Accurately plot the wave indicated by the following table of values and make a harmonic analysis starting with the fifth harmonic.

θ	y	θ	y
0°	0	105°	9.80
15°	4.42	120°	10.00
30°	6.02	135°	8.38
45°	5.60	150°	6.08
60°	4.08	165°	3.10
75°	4.40	180°	0
90°	7.70		

The negative loop is identical in shape with the positive loop, *i.e.*, at $\theta = 240°$, $y = -4.08$; at $\theta = 270°$, $y = -7.70$; etc.

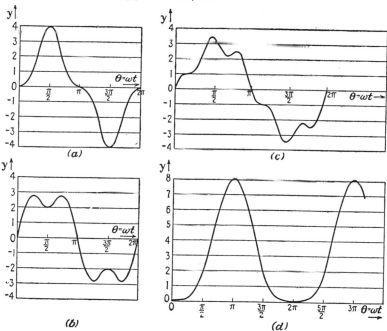

FIG. P11.—Exercises in estimation of harmonic content.

b. If the foregoing wave represents a voltage with a fundamental frequency of 60 cycles per second, find an expression for the current that would be drawn by a pure inductance of 0.0352 henry; by a pure capacitance of 200μf. Compare the harmonic components of the two currents.

11. Apply the method of estimation given in Sec. 96 to the waves of Fig. P11. Determine the order of the principal harmonic and the approximate magnitude and phase angle of each of the main components of the wave.

12. The frequency-selective properties of a tuned circuit are employed in the vacuum tube frequency doubler, which is a Class C amplifier with

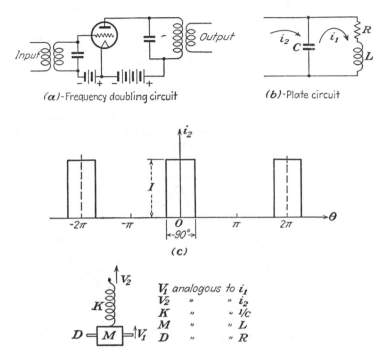

(a)-Frequency doubling circuit   *(b)*-Plate circuit

(c)

(d)-Analogous mechanical system

Fig. P12.—Vacuum-tube frequency doubler and analogous mechanical system.

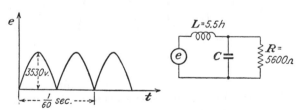

Fig. P13.—Filter circuit.

the plate circuit tuned to the second harmonic. Figure P12a shows the circuit diagram. Figure P12b shows the plate circuit, in which the plate current will be assumed to have the idealized form of Fig. P12c. Figure P12d shows an analogous mechanical system.

a. For the data below, find the amplitudes of the following components of the plate current i_2: constant (d-c) component, fundamental, second harmonic, and third harmonic.

b. Using vector methods, find the amplitudes of the corresponding components of i_1. Tabulate the two sets of values side by side and compare.

Data: The angle of conduction is $-45° < \theta < 45°$. The fundamental frequency is 10^6 cycles per second. $I = 0.400$ amp, $L = 37.5 \times 10^{-6}$ henry, $C = 169 \times 10^{-12}$ farad, $R = 39.2$ ohms.

13. A full-wave rectifier is supplied from a 60-cycle line. The output wave has the form shown in Fig. P13 and has a peak value of 3,530 volts.

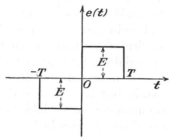

FIG. P15.—Nonperiodic wave.

The load is a 5,600-ohm resistance which is supplied through a filter consisting of a 5.5-henry series inductance and a shunt capacitor. Find the capacitance necessary to reduce the second harmonic voltage at the load to 2 per cent of the d-c voltage. Find the fourth harmonic voltage as a percentage of the d-c voltage.

14. Show that the frequency spectrum for the unit step function is $g(\omega) = 1/j\omega$. The unit function is defined by $f(t) = 0$ for $-\infty < t < 0$, $f(t) = 1$ for $0 < t < \infty$.

15. *a.* Find the frequency spectrum for the wave shown in Fig. P15 and sketch the spectrum roughly to scale.

b. If $T = 10^{-4}$ sec, approximately what frequency range should an amplifier have in order to pass all components that have an amplitude greater than about 10 per cent of the maximum component?

CHAPTER XI

SYSTEMS WITH DISTRIBUTED CONSTANTS

98. Introduction.—Our attention so far has been directed mainly to systems with lumped parameters. For example, we have assumed ideally rigid masses, springs with inappreciable distributed mass, and inductances with negligible distributed capacity. In a complicated system we have had to define a number of dependent variables, for example, the displacement of different parts of a system or currents in the various meshes of an electrical network, but in all cases these variables have been functions of one independent variable, usually time. This led to a description of these systems in terms of ordinary differential equations.

It is important to recognize, however, that the parameters of these systems are lumped by assumption only. Each element inherently has distributed-parameter characteristics: the masses are somewhat elastic, the springs have some distributed mass, inductances have distributed capacity, and even two adjacent short wires have inductance and capacity effects that are important at high frequencies. Fortunately, the distributed effects are often negligible and the ordinary differential equations then give accurate results, but it is essential to recognize the assumptions behind these equations and to realize that for some important phenomena it is necessary to take the distribution of parameters into account for an understanding of the effects.

To gain some idea of how a distribution of parameters will affect the results, let us examine more carefully our assumptions concerning the properties of a simple spring. The assumption of zero mass implies that for each small element of the spring there is no inertia reaction force, and hence any force applied to one end of the element will be passed on undiminished to the other end. Therefore, at any instant the force will be uniform throughout the spring, each element will be deflected a proportional amount, and the net force will be related to the net deflection by a constant factor called the spring constant. Now, however, assume that each element of the spring has appreciable mass. When the element is accelerating, the forces on its two ends will be different by the inertia reaction, hence the force will not be uniform throughout the spring, and our previous simple relationship breaks down. This will happen whenever the elements are caused to accelerate at a relatively high rate; for example, by a comparatively high-frequency oscillation or by shock excitation. The waves that are set up in a spring by such excitation are a matter of common experience, and the spring then loses its simple properties. Under these conditions the force on an element and its deflection not only are functions of time but also depend on the position of the element along the spring, *i.e.*, they are functions of two independent variables: distance and time. It is clear that the phenomena depend upon rates of change and hence involve derivatives. Since more than one independent variable is present, these will have to be partial derivatives, and the resulting equations will therefore be partial differential equations.

An even more obvious function of two independent variables would be the distribution of temperature on, say, the floor of a room at some particular time. We would presumably set up x- and y-coordinates on the floor and measure temperature as a function of the two variables x and y. If we wished to express this temperature as a function of time, we would have to add time as a third independent variable, and to express the temperature in the whole room we would need four independent variables: three space coordinates and time. In the simple case of two independent variables we could plot temperature vs. x and y along three mutually perpendicular axes as shown in Fig. 97 (or use a family of plane curves as in an isothermal chart), but as more independent variables are added, more coordinate axes are needed and graphical representation breaks down. In this type of problem we might have to consider the conduction of heat caused by temperature gradients and also the storage of heat caused by the time rate of change of temperature, thus again giving rise to partial differential equations.

The field of partial differential equations is large and has extensive physical applications. As a matter of fact, the applications of even a single set of partial differential equations may deserve an entire volume to discuss their important aspects, for example, the transmission line equations or Maxwell's field equations. Furthermore, the field of partial differential equations is inherently more difficult than that of ordinary differential equations. Hence we shall confine our attention here to some of the important physical ideas involved and to a solution of some of the simpler linear equations of considerable physical interest.

99. Partial Derivatives.—This section assumes that the reader is somewhat familiar with partial differentiation, and is given mainly as a brief review and an aid in visualizing the significance of partial derivatives.

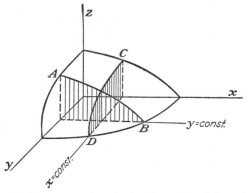

FIG. 97.—Graphical representation of a function of two independent variables, $z = f(x, y)$.

Consider a dependent variable z which is a function of two independent variables x and y. This might be visualized as the temperature distribution at any instant along the floor of a room, for example, and could be represented graphically as a surface (see Fig. 97). The derivative of z with respect to x as y remains constant is called the partial derivative of z with respect to x and is denoted by $\partial z/\partial x$. It can be visualized geometrically by imagining the surface to be cut by a plane $y = $ constant parallel to the xz plane as in Fig. 97, thus forming the curve of intersection AB. The partial derivative $\partial z/\partial x$ then represents the slope of this curve at any point. In general, the slope will depend upon both the value of y chosen for the intersecting plane and the position on the curve as denoted by x; *i.e.*, the partial derivative will in general be a function of both x and y.

In a similar way, the derivative of z with respect to y as x remains constant is called the partial derivative of z with respect to y and is denoted by $\partial z/\partial y$.   It can be visualized as the slope at any point of the curve CD formed by the intersection of some plane $x =$ constant with the surface.

Since in general both of the foregoing partial derivatives will be functions of both x and y, it is possible to take their derivatives

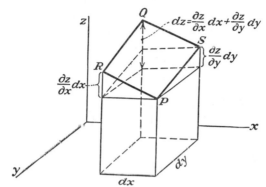

Fig. 98.—Infinitesimal portion of surface.

partially, thus leading to partial derivatives of higher order.   For example,

$$\frac{\partial}{\partial x}\left(\frac{\partial z}{\partial x}\right) = \frac{\partial^2 z}{\partial x^2}, \qquad \frac{\partial}{\partial y}\left(\frac{\partial z}{\partial x}\right) = \frac{\partial^2 z}{\partial y\,\partial x},$$

$$\frac{\partial}{\partial y}\left(\frac{\partial z}{\partial y}\right) = \frac{\partial^2 z}{\partial y^2}, \qquad \frac{\partial}{\partial x}\left(\frac{\partial z}{\partial y}\right) = \frac{\partial^2 z}{\partial x\,\partial y},$$

and similarly for higher derivatives.   It can be shown that when mixed derivatives are continuous functions of x and y, the order of differentiation is immaterial.   Thus, for example,

$$\frac{\partial^2 z}{\partial y\,\partial x} = \frac{\partial^2 z}{\partial x\,\partial y}.$$

We shall next interpret geometrically the total differential of a function of two independent variables.   Assume that the slope of the surface shown in Fig. 97 is continuous, and imagine that Fig. 98 shows a portion of this surface so small in size that, for the purpose of taking first derivatives, we can regard it as being flat.[1] We wish to find an expression for the total differential change in z, dz, between points P and Q, as x and y change by the infinitesimal amounts dx and dy, respectively. The slope of the line joining P and R is $\partial z/\partial x$ by the definitions above and the horizontal distance is dx, so the change in z between these two points is given by $(\partial z/\partial x)\, dx$. The line RQ has the same slope as the line PS, namely $\partial z/\partial y$, and the horizontal distance is dy, so between points R and Q the variable z changes an additional amount $(\partial z/\partial y)\, dy$. Therefore, between points P and Q the total differential change in z is

$$dz = \frac{\partial z}{\partial x}\, dx + \frac{\partial z}{\partial y}\, dy. \qquad (513)$$

In general, if z is a function of n independent variables x_1, x_2, . . . , x_n, the total differential is given by

$$dz = \frac{\partial z}{\partial x_1}\, dx_1 + \frac{\partial z}{\partial x_2}\, dx_2 + \cdots + \frac{\partial z}{\partial x_n}\, dx_n. \qquad (514)$$

We have so far assumed that the variables x and y are independent. However, x and y may both be functions of some independent variable t, which may be visualized in Fig. 97 as a point moving along some path on the surface as a function of t. In this case z may have a derivative with respect to t:

$$\frac{dz}{dt} = \frac{\partial z}{\partial x}\frac{dx}{dt} + \frac{\partial z}{\partial y}\frac{dy}{dt}. \qquad (515)$$

More generally, if z is a function of the n variables x_1, x_2, . . . , x_n and if each x is a function of a single variable t, then

$$\frac{dz}{dt} = \frac{\partial z}{\partial x_1}\frac{dx_1}{dt} + \frac{\partial z}{\partial x_2}\frac{dx_2}{dt} + \cdots + \frac{\partial z}{\partial x_n}\frac{dx_n}{dt}. \qquad (516)$$

Furthermore, if z is a function of the n variables x_1, x_2, . . . , x_n, $z = f(x_1, x_2, \cdots, x_n)$, and if each x is a function of m independent variables t_1, t_2, . . . , t_m, then the partial derivative of z

----

[1] The reader should recognize that the argument given here does not constitute a proof. Proofs of these relations will be found in textbooks on advanced calculus.

with respect to each of the latter will be

$$\left.\begin{aligned}
\frac{\partial z}{\partial t_1} &= \frac{\partial f}{\partial x_1}\frac{\partial x_1}{\partial t_1} + \frac{\partial f}{\partial x_2}\frac{\partial x_2}{\partial t_1} + \cdots + \frac{\partial f}{\partial x_n}\frac{\partial x_n}{\partial t_1} \\
\frac{\partial z}{\partial t_2} &= \frac{\partial f}{\partial x_1}\frac{\partial x_1}{\partial t_2} + \frac{\partial f}{\partial x_2}\frac{\partial x_2}{\partial t_2} + \cdots + \frac{\partial f}{\partial x_n}\frac{\partial x_n}{\partial t_2} \\
&\cdots\cdots\cdots\cdots\cdots\cdots\cdots\cdots\cdots\cdots\cdots\cdots\cdots \\
\frac{\partial z}{\partial t_m} &= \frac{\partial f}{\partial x_1}\frac{\partial x_1}{\partial t_m} + \frac{\partial f}{\partial x_2}\frac{\partial x_2}{\partial t_m} + \cdots + \frac{\partial f}{\partial x_n}\frac{\partial x_n}{\partial t_m}.
\end{aligned}\right\} \qquad (517)$$

100. The Nature of a Partial Differential Equation. The Vibrating String.—In order to illustrate something of the nature of a partial differential equation, we shall first develop the equation for the transverse vibration of a stretched elastic string. A string with a weight w per unit length is placed under a tension

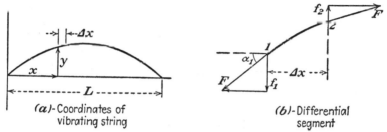

(a)-Coordinates of
vibrating string

(b)-Differential
segment

Fig. 99.—Vibrating string.

F and is then caused to vibrate, perhaps by applying a sinusoidally varying deflection to one end, or merely by displacing the string and then suddenly releasing it. The deflections are assumed to be small enough so that the tension in the string is not appreciably altered during vibration. We shall neglect damping and assume that the string offers no resistance to bending. The coordinate system is shown in Fig. 99a, and Fig. 99b shows a differential segment of the string in a general deflected position. Two types of force must be considered: the net vertical component of tension that acts as an elastic restoring force, and the inertia force caused by acceleration of the segment. The vertical component of tension will be proportional to the sine of the angle that the segment makes with the x-axis, but for small deflections $\sin \alpha \approx \tan \alpha$. So for the left side of the differential segment we can write this component for any given instant of time as

$$f_1 = F \sin \alpha_1 \approx F \tan \alpha_1 = F \left(\frac{\partial y}{\partial x}\right)_1, \qquad (518)$$

and similarly for the right side,

$$f_2 = F \left(\frac{\partial y}{\partial x}\right)_2. \qquad (519)$$

The net vertical component of tension on the segment is, therefore,

$$f_2 - f_1 = F \left(\frac{\partial y}{\partial x}\right)_2 - F \left(\frac{\partial y}{\partial x}\right)_1, \qquad (520)$$

where positive force is taken to be upward.

Still considering time to be "frozen," however, we can relate the slopes at the two points by the mean value theorem of calculus.[1] This theorem states that if a function $f(x)$ has a finite derivative everywhere between two points $x = a$ and $x = b$, there is some point M lying on the arc between a and b at which the slope of the curve is parallel to the chord joining the points $f(a)$ and $f(b)$. In equation form this can be expressed as $f(b) = f(a) + (b - a)(df/dx)_M$. Thus we can write from Eq. (520)

$$f_2 - f_1 = F \left[\left(\frac{\partial y}{\partial x}\right)_1 + \Delta x \left(\frac{\partial^2 y}{\partial x^2}\right)_M \right] - F \left(\frac{\partial y}{\partial x}\right)_1$$

$$= F \left(\frac{\partial^2 y}{\partial x^2}\right)_M \Delta x, \qquad (521)$$

where M is some point in the interval Δx.

The mass of the segment is $(w/g) \Delta x$, and if the segment accelerates in the positive direction (upward), its inertia reaction will be downward:

$$- \frac{w}{g} \Delta x \left(\frac{\partial^2 y}{\partial t^2}\right)_{M'}, \qquad (522)$$

in which the last factor is the upward acceleration of the center of mass of the segment, M'. Observe that, in general, M and M' are different points. Neglecting damping, the algebraic sum of the net restoring force (521) and the inertia force (522) must be equal to zero:

$$F \left(\frac{\partial^2 y}{\partial x^2}\right)_M \Delta x - \frac{w}{g} \Delta x \left(\frac{\partial^2 y}{\partial t^2}\right)_{M'} = 0. \qquad (523)$$

[1] See, for example, FINE, H. B., "Calculus," Chap. XII, The Macmillan Company, New York, 1938.

Divide through by Δx and then imagine the length of the segment to approach zero as a limit. Since the points M and M' are within the interval Δx, in the limit they both approach the same point of abscissa x, and we can write

$$\frac{\partial^2 y}{\partial t^2} = a^2 \frac{\partial^2 y}{\partial x^2}, \qquad (524)$$

where $a = \sqrt{Fg/w}$ and has the dimensions of a velocity. Equation (524) expresses the relations that must hold at a point and, since the point that we were considering was a perfectly general one, the equation must hold at all points. This, therefore, is the partial differential equation for the motion of the stretched elastic string.

Now observe that in setting up the equation we paid attention to only a segment of the string and took no regard of its length, its initial shape, the conditions at the ends, or any driving forces that might conceivably be present. Thus Eq. (524) contains considerably less information than we have found in ordinary differential equations, and we might expect that it would be correspondingly more difficult to find a solution that would both satisfy the differential equation and fit the boundary conditions. As a matter of fact, it would be possible to consider each element of the string as having one degree of freedom and, therefore, from the point of view of ordinary differential equations, the string as a whole would have an infinite number of degrees of freedom. This would lead to an infinite number of simultaneous ordinary differential equations. To get around this difficulty we introduce another independent variable and write a differential equation for only a general element of the string, at the expense of including less information in the equation itself.

The solution of partial differential equations often involves arbitrary functions in much the same manner that the solutions of ordinary differential equations involve arbitrary constants. Out of the infinitude of possible solutions we must then choose and combine those which will enable us to satisfy the physical conditions that were not contained in the original differential equation. We shall refer to these additional conditions as *boundary conditions*, and for the vibrating string these would relate to the conditions at the ends (whether fixed or moving in a prescribed manner) and to the initial shape of the string just before its release.

To illustrate how the solution of a partial differential equation can involve arbitrary functions, consider the following possible solution of Eq. (524):

$$y = f(x - at),$$ (525)

where f can be any function. For example, the function might be $C \sin (x - at)$, $C \sin k(x - at)$, or $C(x - at)^2$, to name but three possibilities. For convenience define the argument of the function as s: $s = x - at$, so that $y = f(s)$. Take the first partial derivative of Eq. (525) with respect to t:

$$\frac{\partial y}{\partial t} = \frac{\partial f}{\partial s} \frac{\partial s}{\partial t} = -af'(x - at),$$

where the prime denotes the first derivative of the function with respect to its argument. Taking the second derivative, we obtain

$$\frac{\partial^2 y}{\partial t^2} = a^2 f''(x - at).$$ (526)

Similarly $$\frac{\partial^2 y}{\partial x^2} = f''(x - at).$$ (527)

Eliminating $f''(x - at)$ between these two equations we obtain

$$\frac{\partial^2 y}{\partial t^2} = a^2 \frac{\partial^2 y}{\partial x^2},$$

which is identical with the differential equation (524). Thus we have shown that Eq. (525) is a solution of the differential equation (524), and furthermore we have succeeded in eliminating the function f without specifying its form; so the function is arbitrary. It can be shown in a similar manner that a second possible solution is $f_2(x + at)$ where f_2 is a second arbitrary function. In addition, it is easy to show that, because the differential equation is linear and homogeneous in y, the sum $f_1(x - at) + f_2(x + at)$ is also a solution. The functions f_1 and f_2 must be chosen so as to satisfy the particular boundary conditions of the problem.

We shall next consider some relatively simple methods of solving certain important, although special, linear partial differential equations.

101. The Product Solution. Continuation of the Vibrating String Problem.—There is a comparatively simple method of attack which works surprisingly often in solving partial differential equations that arise in physical problems. In this method, particular solutions of the equation are found by a process described below, and these solutions are then combined so as to satisfy the boundary conditions.

The method is probably best shown by an example. Consider again the differential equation (524) for the vibrating string, and try to find a solution which will fit the boundary conditions that the ends are fixed on the y-axis and that the string is initially displaced into a sinusoidal shape and released with zero velocity. The differential equation is

$$\frac{\partial^2 y}{\partial t^2} = a^2 \frac{\partial^2 y}{\partial x^2}, \tag{524}$$

where $a^2 = Fg/w$. To find some particular solutions of this equation, assume that a solution exists as a product of two functions: one a function of x alone which we shall call $X(x)$, and the other a function of t alone which we shall call $T(t)$. That is, assume

$$y = X(x) \cdot T(t). \tag{528}$$

To check the validity of our assumption, take the partial derivatives of Eq. (528) for substitution into Eq. (524):

$$\left.\begin{aligned}
\frac{\partial^2 y}{\partial t^2} &= X \frac{d^2 T}{dt^2} \\
\frac{\partial^2 y}{\partial x^2} &= \frac{d^2 X}{dx^2} T,
\end{aligned}\right\} \tag{529}$$

and

where we now use total derivatives because X and T are functions of single variables only. Substitution into the differential equation (524) then yields

$$X \frac{d^2 T}{dt^2} = a^2 T \frac{d^2 X}{dx^2}. \tag{530}$$

Dividing through by TX now separates the variables, and we shall also divide through by a^2 for future convenience, obtaining

$$\frac{1}{a^2 T} \frac{d^2 T}{dt^2} = \frac{1}{X} \frac{d^2 X}{dx^2}. \tag{531}$$

Now observe that the left side is a function of t alone and will not change when x varies. Similarly, the right side is a function of x alone and will not change when t varies. Therefore, neither member can change when both t and x vary. So they must be equal to an undetermined constant which we shall denote for convenience by $-k^2$:

$$\frac{1}{a^2 T}\frac{d^2 T}{dt^2} = \frac{1}{X}\frac{d^2 X}{dx^2} = -k^2. \tag{532}$$

From the first and last members we can write an ordinary differential equation involving only one independent variable, t:

$$\frac{d^2 T}{dt^2} + a^2 k^2 T = 0. \tag{533}$$

Similarly, from the middle and last members of Eq. (532) we can write

$$\frac{d^2 X}{dx^2} + k^2 X = 0. \tag{534}$$

These are linear equations with constant coefficients and can be solved by the methods of Chap. VI. The characteristic equation for Eq. (533) is $m^2 + a^2 k^2 = 0$. The constant k^2 is as yet undetermined, and the best form of the solution will depend on whether it is positive, negative, or zero. The choice must be made on the basis of which type of solution can best be fitted to the boundary conditions. We have the following possibilities for the form of the solution of Eq. (533):

If k^2 is a positive number, the characteristic equation yields $m = \pm jak$, and we write the solution in trigonometric form:

$$T = A \sin akt + B \cos akt, \tag{535a}$$

where A and B are constants of integration.

If k^2 is zero, the characteristic equation yields $m = 0$ twice, and the solution will be

$$T = (C_1 + C_2 t)\epsilon^0 = C_1 + C_2 t. \tag{535b}$$

If we regard k^2 as a negative number, we can write $k^2 = -k_2^2$ where k_2^2 is positive. This amounts to writing $+k_2^2$ on the right side of Eq. (532) in the first place. From the characteristic equation we have $m = \pm k_2$; so we can write the solution in either exponential or the equivalent hyperbolic form (see Sec. 53, Chap. VI):

$$T = C_1 \epsilon^{k_2 t} + C_2 \epsilon^{-k_2 t}, \tag{535c}$$

or

$$T = A \sinh k_2 t + B \cosh k_2 t. \tag{535d}$$

Since we expect periodic motion of the string, we shall tentatively choose the trigonometric solution (535a) as the one most likely to fit our boundary conditions.

Proceeding next to a solution of Eq. (534), we can write the characteristic equation as $m^2 + k^2 = 0$ where k is precisely the same constant as was used in the solution of Eq. (533). Thus we obtain $m = \pm jk$, and the solution is

$$X = C \sin kx + D \cos kx. \tag{536}$$

From our assumption of a product solution (528) we can then write a particular solution for the deflection:

$$y = (A \sin akt + B \cos akt)(C \sin kx + D \cos kx). \tag{537}$$

We shall now try to find values of the constants k, A, B, C, and D, that will satisfy the boundary conditions of fixed ends, initial sinusoidal shape, and zero initial velocity. Expressed more precisely, these conditions are

$$y = 0 \text{ for } x = 0 \text{ and all values of } t,$$
$$y = 0 \text{ for } x = L \text{ and all values of } t,$$
$$\frac{\partial y}{\partial t} = 0 \text{ for } t = 0 \text{ and all values of } x,$$

and

$$y = Y \sin \frac{\pi x}{L} \qquad \text{for } t = 0.$$

Substituting these conditions successively into Eq. (537), we obtain

$$0 = (A \sin akt + B \cos akt)(0 + D), \quad \text{from which } D = 0.$$
$$0 = (A \sin akt + B \cos akt)(C \sin kL),$$

which can be satisfied by choosing $k = n\pi/L$ where n is any integer, so that $\sin kL$ will be zero. Observe that we cannot choose $C = 0$ or our solution will be the trivial one $y \equiv 0$. Substituting this value of k into Eq. (537) and applying the third and fourth conditions, we find

$$0 = \left(\frac{an\pi}{L} A - 0\right)\left(C \sin \frac{n\pi x}{L}\right), \text{from which } A = 0.$$

$$Y \sin \frac{\pi x}{L} = (0 + B)\left(C \sin \frac{n\pi x}{L}\right), \text{from which } n = 1, BC = Y.$$

Therefore the solution (537) becomes

$$y = Y \sin \frac{\pi x}{L} \cos \frac{a\pi t}{L}. \tag{538}$$

Observe that the success of the method depended upon our being able to separate the variables after the fashion of Eq. (531) and that we had no assurance in the beginning that this would be possible. Furthermore, the product solution (537) is only one of many possible solutions. For example, $C(x - at)^2$ will satisfy differential equation (524), and we could not be sure in advance that the product solution could be fitted in with our boundary conditions. However, we have seen that the method works quite well for this particular problem, as indeed it does for a great many problems of a practical nature.

Discussion of the Vibrating-string Solution.—Aside from affording a practical example of the use of a product solution, several features of the foregoing problem are particularly interesting from a physical standpoint and deserve discussion. Many of the considerations that we shall develop are not restricted to vibrating strings but find important application in such problems as the characteristics of springs and structural elements, the phenomenon of water hammer, the propagation of sound, and the characteristics of electrical transmission lines.

First observe that, because of our neglect of damping, the solution (538) will indicate a vibration continuing indefinitely with undiminished amplitude. However, this solution will hold approximately over short periods of time, and the presence of a moderate amount of damping will not greatly affect the properties that we shall discuss. We can recognize physically that damping will result in a continual decrease in the amplitude of free vibration. With this in mind we can proceed to a discussion of the useful and comparatively simple undamped solution.

Examination of the solution (538) will show that at any given instant the shape of the string is sinusoidal and that this space sinusoid moves transversely in a harmonic manner with time.

This type of motion is called a *standing wave*. The stationary points (at the ends in this case) are called *nodes*, and a point of maximum amplitude (in the middle for this vibration) is called a *loop* or *antinode*. Now, from trigonometry, it is possible to write Eq. (538) as

$$y = \frac{Y}{2} \sin \frac{\pi}{L} (x - at) + \frac{Y}{2} \sin \frac{\pi}{L} (x + at). \qquad (539)$$

The first term of this can be thought of as representing a wave of amplitude $Y/2$ traveling in the positive x-direction at a velocity a. This can be seen by imagining that we are moving with the wave so that we remain opposite a point of constant value. For this speed of motion the argument $(x - at)$ must remain constant, since the sine function is not changing in value. Therefore, setting $x - at =$ constant and taking the derivative of this with respect to time, we obtain the velocity $dx/dt = a$. This represents the velocity of a point of constant phase on the traveling wave and is therefore called the *phase velocity*.

In a similar fashion the second term of Eq. (539) can be thought of as a wave traveling in the negative x-direction with a phase velocity a. The sum of the two waves traveling in opposite directions at the same speed gives rise to a standing wave. This concept is shown graphically in Fig. 100. The traveling wave coming away from either end can be regarded as the reflection of the incident wave at that end. From this point of view the undamped vibration consists of an unbroken succession of reflected waves.

Now recall that, in applying the boundary conditions to the solution (537), the value of k was found to be $n\pi/L$ and that the value of unity for n was not fixed until we applied the last condition relating to the initial shape of the string. It would be quite possible for the initial shape to be different from that assumed above and, while we shall postpone the investigation of complicated shapes until the next section, there are some simple shapes of considerable interest. Returning to the point where we introduced the last boundary condition, assume the initial displacement shown in Fig. 101*b*: $Y \sin 2\pi x/L$. This will force us to choose $n = 2$ and will give rise to a standing wave with a node in the middle. In general n can be any integer, thus leading to the solution

$$y = Y \sin \frac{n\pi x}{L} \cos \frac{n a \pi t}{L} \tag{540}$$

$$= \frac{Y}{2} \sin \frac{n\pi}{L} (x - at) + \frac{Y}{2} \sin \frac{n\pi}{L} (x + at), \tag{541}$$

where $n = 1, 2, 3, \cdots$. The solutions obtained for the various integral values of n correspond to what are called the *character-*

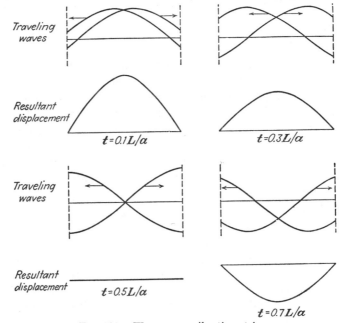

Fig. 100.—Waves on a vibrating string.

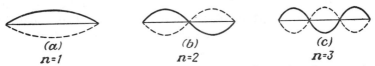

Fig. 101.—Vibrating string; first three modes of vibration.

istic modes of oscillation, the first three of which are shown in Fig. 101. In general, shock excitation will cause all the various modes to be present simultaneously in varying degrees.

If we investigate the phase velocity of the traveling waves indicated by Eq. (541), we find that it is numerically equal to a for all modes, and hence is a function only of the mass per unit length and the tension in the string:

$$\text{Phase velocity} = a = \sqrt{\frac{Fg}{w}}. \qquad (542)$$

The frequency of vibration can be obtained from the time factor in Eq. (540), for $(na\pi/L)t = \omega t = 2\pi ft$. So

$$f = \frac{na}{2L} = \frac{n}{2L}\sqrt{\frac{Fg}{w}}. \qquad (543)$$

The values obtained from Eq. (543) by successively placing $n = 1, 2, 3, \cdot\cdot\cdot$ are the natural frequencies of the stretched string and are seen to be theoretically infinite in number. The frequency corresponding to the first mode ($n = 1$) is the fundamental, and the harmonics corresponding to the other modes are called *overtones* in acoustics. The fundamental frequency evidently depends upon the length of the string, its mass, and the tension. Excitation by striking or plucking the string will in general arouse all natural frequencies except those which would have a node at the point of excitation, but the higher harmonics are relatively weak. In a musical instrument the quality of tone depends upon the relative magnitudes of the harmonics and is influenced greatly by the presence of resonant cavities and surfaces.

If a sinusoidal driving force is applied to the string, the steady-state frequency of vibration will be that of the applied force. Maximum amplitude, or *resonance*, will be obtained when the applied frequency coincides with one of the natural frequencies given by Eq. (543). Thus, a stretched string has a great number of possible resonant frequencies, starting with the fundamental ($n = 1$) and including all multiples of that frequency.

The wave length of a traveling wave is frequently of interest. This is the distance between successive maxima, and in Fig. 101 is evidently twice the distance between successive nodes. The reciprocal of frequency is the time required for one time cycle, during which the wave has progressed one wave length at a velocity a. Therefore the wave length λ, in space units, must be

$$\lambda = \frac{\text{velocity}}{\text{frequency}} = \frac{a}{f}. \qquad (544)$$

The wave length is therefore inversely proportional to frequency when the phase velocity is constant (see Fig. 101).

It should again be mentioned that many of the above-developed concepts such as those of traveling waves, modes of oscillation, phase velocity, and wave length are not restricted to vibrating strings but find similar application in many problems involving distributed mass and elasticity, or distributed inductance and capacity.

102. Extension to Other Boundary Conditions by Fourier Series.—The success of the product solution depends partly on whether or not the particular solutions we obtain can be fitted in with the known physical boundary conditions. In the previous problem this was particularly simple, for we had assumed an initial sinusoidal displacement, and the product solution came out in this same form. Now, however, suppose that the vibrations are excited by stretching the string transversely from the middle as in Fig. 102 and releasing it from rest at $t = 0$. In this case it will be impossible to fit any one solution of the form (537) into the boundary condition of initial shape. Next observe that

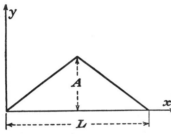

Fig. 102.—Initial shape of string.

the original differential equation (524) is linear, since it involves the dependent variable and its partial derivatives in the first degree only, and that it is homogeneous in the sense that every term involves y. Solutions of this type of equation enjoy a property that we found in ordinary linear homogeneous equations:

If for a linear homogeneous partial differential equation any finite number of solutions are multiplied by constants and added together, the sum will also be a solution of the equation. The solution can take the form of an infinite series if this series is uniformly convergent.

For our particular problem of the vibrating string we have the solution (540) or (541) which satisfies the first three boundary conditions relating to fixed ends and zero initial velocity, and in which n can be given any integral value. Therefore, we can obtain any number of solutions by successively giving n the values 1, 2, 3, . . . , next we can give the coefficients of these solutions appropriate values, and finally we can add the solutions together to form a new solution which may fit the boundary conditions.

We shall denote the coefficients of the solutions by B_n and write the sum as

$$y = \sum_{n=1}^{\infty} B_n \sin \frac{n\pi x}{L} \cos \frac{n a \pi t}{L}, \tag{545}$$

which will be recognized as a Fourier series. Moreover, we can show by the methods of Chap. X that the triangular initial shape of the string (Fig. 102) can be represented by the Fourier series:

$$(y)_{t=0} = \frac{8A}{\pi^2} \sum_{n=1,3,5,\cdots}^{\infty} \frac{(-1)^{(n-1)/2}}{n^2} \sin \frac{n\pi x}{L} \quad (n \text{ odd only}). \tag{546}$$

It now appears that the solution (545) will fit the desired initial shape, for by setting $t = 0$ in Eq. (545) and equating to (546), we obtain

$$B_n = 0 \qquad \text{for } n \text{ even.}$$

$$B_n = \frac{8A(-1)^{(n-1)/2}}{\pi^2 n^2} \qquad \text{for } n \text{ odd.}$$

The solution for an initial triangular shape then becomes

$$y = \frac{8A}{\pi^2} \sum_{n=1,3,5,\cdots}^{\infty} \frac{(-1)^{(n-1)/2}}{n^2} \sin \frac{n\pi x}{L} \cos \frac{n a \pi t}{L}, \tag{547}$$

or, alternatively in a form that emphasizes the traveling wave concept,

$$y = \frac{4A}{\pi^2} \sum_{n=1,3,5,\cdots}^{\infty} \frac{(-1)^{(n-1)/2}}{n^2} \left[\sin \frac{n\pi}{L}(x - at) + \sin \frac{n\pi}{L}(x + at) \right].$$

$$\tag{548}$$

The amplitudes of the various components vary inversely as the square of their order. Each harmonic component can be thought of as being made up of two waves of half amplitude moving oppositely at a speed a and with a wave length inversely proportional to frequency. Observe that all even harmonics, which would have a node in the middle, are absent.

103. Equations Homogeneous with Respect to Derivatives.— Some of the linear partial differential equations with constant coefficients that arise in practical work involve partial derivatives of the same order in each term. Such an equation is of the general form

$$a_0 \frac{\partial^n y}{\partial t^n} + a_1 \frac{\partial^n y}{\partial t^{n-1} \partial x} + \cdots + a_{n-1} \frac{\partial^n y}{\partial t\, \partial x^{n-1}} + a_n \frac{\partial^n y}{\partial x^n} = 0. \quad (549)$$

For example, it happens that Eq. (524) is of this type, although if we had included viscous damping of the string, one term would have contained a first derivative and the equation could not have been put into the form (549). Because all the derivatives above are of the same order, such equations are sometimes said to be homogeneous, but it should be observed that this definition of homogeneity is different from that of the preceding section where equations homogeneous in y were considered.

Equations of the type (549) can be solved by a method analogous to that used in Chap. VI for ordinary linear homogeneous equations with constant coefficients. First define the operators

$$p_t \equiv \frac{\partial}{\partial t} \quad \text{and} \quad p_x \equiv \frac{\partial}{\partial x}. \quad (550)$$

Equation (549) can then be written as

$$(a_0 p_t^n + a_1 p_t^{n-1} p_x + \cdots + a_n p_x^n) y = 0. \quad (551)$$

Just as we were led in the ordinary differential equation to try an exponential solution because its derivatives retained the exponential form, the appearance of Eq. (549) suggests that we find a solution for which all the nth partial derivatives have the same form. Such a solution is

$$y = f(x + mt), \quad (552)$$

where m is an undetermined constant and f is an arbitrary function. To show this, we take the nth partial derivative of this solution, k times with respect to t and $n - k$ times with respect to x, and obtain

$$\frac{\partial^n y}{\partial t^k \partial x^{n-k}} = p_t^k p_x^{n-k} y = m^k f^{(n)}(x + mt), \quad (553)$$

where the superscript in parentheses (n) indicates the nth derivative of the function with respect to its argument. Substituting the solution (552) into Eq. (551) we find

$$(a_0 m^n + a_1 m^{n-1} + \cdots + a_n) f^{(n)}(x + mt) = 0. \quad (554)$$

Therefore, Eq. (552) will be a solution provided that m is a root of the auxiliary equation

$$a_0 m^n + a_1 m^{n-1} + \cdots + a_n = 0. \tag{555}$$

Furthermore, we see that we can write the auxiliary equation by inspection of the partial differential equation (551). There will be n roots of Eq. (555), each corresponding to a separate solution of the form (552) and, since the differential equation is linear and homogeneous in y, the sum of these solutions will also be a solution. Therefore the general solution of Eq. (551) will be

$$y = f_1(x + m_1 t) + f_2(x + m_2 t) + \cdots + f_n(x + m_n t), \tag{556}$$

where $m_1, m_2, \ldots, m_n$ are the roots of the auxiliary equation (555) and the f's are arbitrary functions.

If some of the roots are repeated, we shall proceed as we did with repeated roots in ordinary differential equations. For example, if we encounter $m = m_1$ twice, the corresponding terms in the solution can be written

$$f_1(x + m_1 t) + t \cdot f_2(x + m_1 t).$$

It is interesting to observe that the operators p_t and p_x, as used in equations of the type (549), formally obey the laws of algebra in a manner similar to the operator $p \equiv d/dt$ which we used in ordinary differential equations. Thus, for example, we can factor Eq. (551) into the form

$$a_0(p_t - m_1 p_x)(p_t - m_2 p_x) \cdots (p_t - m_n p_x)y = 0, \tag{557}$$

and show that the commutative law holds for the factors.

As an example, consider the equation for the vibrating string without damping:

$$\frac{\partial^2 y}{\partial t^2} - a^2 \frac{\partial^2 y}{\partial x^2} = 0, \tag{558}$$

which is of the type (549). We can write this in operator form:

$$(p_t^2 - a^2 p_x^2)y = 0, \tag{559}$$

from which we can write the auxiliary equation by inspection:

$$m^2 - a^2 = 0. \tag{560}$$

The two roots are $m = \pm a$. The general solution is then

$$y = f_1(x + at) + f_2(x - at). \tag{561}$$

Comparison of this with the solutions (539), (541), and (548) obtained by the product method show that they were special forms of the general solution (561). This does not mean, however, that the product solution is of less value, for, aside from the fact that the product method applies to equations that cannot be put into the form (549), it is helpful in many practical problems where it is difficult to particularize the general solution.

We shall next derive a few of the partial differential equations that are of considerable physical interest.

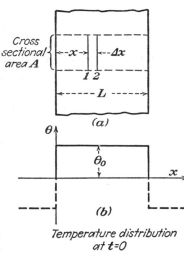

Temperature distribution at $t=0$

FIG. 103 —Variable one-dimensional heat flow.

104. Variable One-dimensional Heat Flow.[1]—Consider a homogeneous conducting body in which heat is flowing in one direction. This might be a rod whose sides are well insulated so that all the heat must flow longitudinally, or a large slab such as a furnace wall or a flat plate with all the heat flowing in a direction normal to the surface. The x-axis will be chosen parallel to the direction of heat flow as shown in Fig. 103. Although it makes no difference in setting up the differential equation, we shall visualize the problem more specifically as follows: A slab of thickness L is raised to a uniform temperature θ_0 and at $t = 0$ is quenched by reducing the surface temperature to zero. The problem is to find the internal temperature at any point as a function of time, assuming the conductivity and specific heat to be independent of temperature. It should be observed here that any temperature can be used as the reference zero, so that θ can be taken as the number of degrees above the final quenching temperature as a reference.

Consider a differential length Δx with a cross-sectional area A as shown in Fig. 103. It is known experimentally that heat

[1] For a more extensive treatment of heat flow problems, see for example Carslaw, "Mathematical Theory of the Conduction of Heat in Solids," The Macmillan Company, New York, 1921.

flows from a higher to a lower temperature and that the rate of conduction at any point is proportional to the temperature gradient at that point, *i.e.*,

$$\text{Conducted } Q = -kA\,\frac{\partial\theta}{\partial x} \qquad \text{heat units per unit time,} \quad (562)$$

where k is the conductivity of the material, A is the cross-sectional area, and θ is temperature. The negative sign indicates that heat is conducted in the positive x-direction if the temperature is *decreasing* in this direction. Thus, we can write the rate of heat conduction through plane 1 in Fig. 103 as

$$Q_1 = -kA\left(\frac{\partial\theta}{\partial x}\right)_1, \qquad (563)$$

and through plane 2 we have similarly

$$Q_2 = -kA\left(\frac{\partial\theta}{\partial x}\right)_2. \qquad (564)$$

However, we can relate these two gradients by the mean value theorem:

$$\left(\frac{\partial\theta}{\partial x}\right)_2 = \left(\frac{\partial\theta}{\partial x}\right)_1 + \left(\frac{\partial^2\theta}{\partial x^2}\right)_M \Delta x, \qquad (565)$$

where M is located in the interval Δx. We then get for the difference between the heat passing in through plane 1 and that passing out through plane 2:

$$\Delta Q = Q_1 - Q_2 = kA\,\Delta x\left(\frac{\partial^2\theta}{\partial x^2}\right)_M. \qquad (566)$$

This difference is being stored in the volume $A\,\Delta x$, and will cause an increase in temperature with time according to the experimental law

$$\Delta Q = c(\rho A\,\Delta x)\left(\frac{\partial\theta}{\partial t}\right)_{M'} \qquad \text{heat units per unit time,} \quad (567)$$

where c is the specific heat of the material, ρ is the density, $\rho A\,\Delta x$ represents the mass of the elementary volume, and M' is located within the interval Δx. Equating the two expressions for ΔQ, (566) and (567), we obtain

$$c\rho A\,\Delta x\left(\frac{\partial\theta}{\partial t}\right)_{M'} = kA\,\Delta x\left(\frac{\partial^2\theta}{\partial x^2}\right)_M.$$

Divide this equation through by $A \Delta x$ and let the size of the element approach zero as a limit so that the values at M and M' become values at the point of abscissa x. This point is a perfectly general one; hence the resulting equation must hold at every point in the body:

$$\frac{\partial \theta}{\partial t} = \alpha \frac{\partial^2 \theta}{\partial x^2}, \tag{568}$$

where $\alpha = k/c\rho$. This is the desired partial differential equation for one-dimensional heat flow. Observe that it assumes no generation of heat within the body.

Let us try a product solution of this equation and attempt to fit it to the particular conditions stated at the beginning. Assume

$$\theta = X \cdot T, \tag{569}$$

where X is a function of x alone and T is a function of t alone. Taking partial derivatives and substituting into Eq. (568), we obtain

$$X \frac{dT}{dt} = \alpha T \frac{d^2 X}{dx^2}.$$

We can separate the variables by dividing through by XT, and we shall also divide by α for convenience. This yields

$$\frac{1}{\alpha T} \frac{dT}{dt} = \frac{1}{X} \frac{d^2 X}{dx^2}. \tag{570}$$

Following the reasoning of Sec. 101 we see that the two sides are entirely independent but equal, hence they must both be equal to an undetermined constant which we shall call $-b^2$. From this we can write the two equations

$$\frac{dT}{dt} + b^2 \alpha T = 0 \tag{571}$$

and $$\frac{d^2 X}{dx^2} + b^2 X = 0, \tag{572}$$

which are ordinary differential equations since each contains but one independent variable. The general solution of Eq. (571) is, by the methods of Chap. VI,

$$T = C\epsilon^{-b^2 \alpha t}, \tag{573}$$

where C is a constant of integration.

The most convenient form for the solution of Eq. (572) will depend upon the boundary conditions. Thus, we can regard b^2 as positive, zero, or negative, and write the corresponding solutions as

$$X = A \cos bx + B \sin bx \qquad \text{for } b^2 > 0, \qquad (574a)$$

or

$$X = C_1 + C_2 x \qquad \text{for } b^2 = 0, \qquad (574b)$$

or

$$X = C_1 \epsilon^{b_2 x} + C_2 \epsilon^{-b_2 x} \qquad \left.\begin{array}{l} \text{for } b^2 < 0, \qquad (574c) \\ = A \cosh b_2 x + B \sinh b_2 x \end{array}\right\} \; b^2 = -b_2^2. \qquad (574d)$$

For any particular choice, the value of b^2 in solution (573) would have to be chosen to correspond.

We shall find the trigonometric solution (574a) to be most convenient, whereupon our attempted solution (569) can be written in the form

$$\theta = \epsilon^{-b^2\alpha t}(D \cos bx + F \sin bx), \qquad (575)$$

where for convenience we have defined new constants $D = AC$ and $F = BC$. The boundary conditions for the problem of the quenched slab are that the surfaces are maintained at zero temperature and that the initial internal temperature is uniform at θ_0, *i.e.*,

$$\theta = 0 \text{ at } x = 0 \text{ for all values of } t,$$
$$\theta = 0 \text{ at } x = L \text{ for all values of } t,$$

and $\theta = \theta_0$ for $t = 0$ and $0 < x < L$. The latter condition is shown by the solid graph of Fig. 103b. If we imagine the graph to extend as shown by the dotted lines, we can represent it by the Fourier series for a square wave (see Chap. X, Sec. 88), and at $x = 0$ and $x = L$ the series will converge to the correct value of zero temperature.[1] The Fourier series for the square wave will therefore be used in applying the third condition.

Applying the above conditions successively to the solution (575), we obtain

$$0 = \epsilon^{-b^2\alpha t}(D) \qquad \text{from which } D = 0,$$
$$0 = \epsilon^{-b^2\alpha t}(F \sin bL),$$

from which, since F cannot be zero, we obtain $b = n\pi/L$ where n is any integer. Thus, after application of the first two conditions,

[1] The value to which a Fourier series converges at a point of discontinuity is discussed in Chap. X, Sec. 92.

our product solution takes the form

$$\theta = F\epsilon^{-n^2\beta t} \sin \frac{n\pi x}{L}, \tag{576}$$

where we have defined $\quad \beta = \dfrac{\pi^2 \alpha}{L^2} = \dfrac{\pi^2 k}{L^2 c\rho} \tag{577}$

and n is any integer. Moreover, since the original equation (568) is linear and homogeneous in y, we can give n the successive values 1, 2, 3, . . . , multiply the resulting particular solutions by constants, and add them together to form a new solution. This will be in the form of a Fourier series:

$$\theta = \sum_{n=1}^{\infty} F_n \epsilon^{-n^2\beta t} \sin \frac{n\pi x}{L}. \tag{578}$$

We must now attempt to fit this at $t = 0$ to the Fourier series for a square wave. This results in [compare Eq. (451) Chap. X]

$$\frac{4\theta_0}{\pi} \sum_{n=1,3,5,\cdots}^{\infty} \frac{\sin \dfrac{n\pi x}{L}}{n} = \sum_{n=1}^{\infty} F_n \epsilon^0 \sin \frac{n\pi x}{L},$$

from which F_n can be determined by comparison and the solution (578) written as

$$\theta = \frac{4\theta_0}{\pi} \sum_{n=1,3,5,\cdots}^{\infty} \frac{\epsilon^{-n^2\beta t}}{n} \sin \frac{n\pi x}{L} \quad (n \text{ odd only}), \tag{579}$$

where β is defined in terms of parameters by Eq. (577). The distribution of temperature in the slab is plotted as a function of distance for various values of time in Fig. 104. It will be observed that as time increases the temperature distribution approaches a sine curve. This is because the exponential factor rapidly becomes appreciable as βt increases, and causes the Fourier series to converge quickly. It is also interesting to note that the center remains substantially at its original temperature for some time and then cools at a reasonably rapid rate.

Inspection of the original differential equation (568) shows that it will be satisfied by the solution $\theta = $ constant; so we could add a constant to our previous solution and use θ in, say, degrees Fahrenheit. However it is probably easier to use Eq. (579) as it stands and regard the quenching temperature as an arbitrary

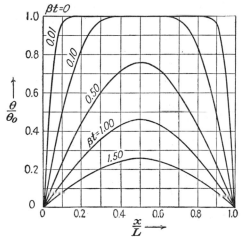

Fig. 104.—Temperature distribution in quenched slab.

zero point, with θ and θ_0 taken as temperature differences above this level.

105. Two- and Three-dimensional Heat Flow. Laplace's Equation.—Next consider a homogeneous and isotropic conducting body in which heat flows in the x- and y-directions but

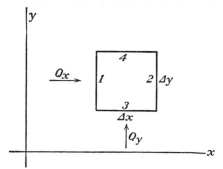

Fig. 105.—Two-dimensional heat flow.

not in the z-direction, and assume no heat generation within the body. This might, for example, represent the flow of heat through the insulation of a refrigerator near the junction between the wall and the top, or the flow of heat along a flat plate of uniform thickness when the surfaces are insulated and the edges are maintained at specified temperatures. We shall assume, as before, that the specific heat and thermal conductivity are independent of temperature. Figure 105 shows an elementary area in the plane of heat flow. Consider a depth d normal to the figure, and designate the x- and y-components of heat flow by Q_x and Q_y. The rate of heat conduction through face 1 is

$$Q_{x1} = -k(d\,\Delta y)\left(\frac{\partial\theta}{\partial x}\right)_1 \qquad \text{heat units per unit time.}$$

The heat conducted out through face 2 is

$$Q_{x2} = -k(d\,\Delta y)\left(\frac{\partial\theta}{\partial x}\right)_2 = -k(d\,\Delta y)\left[\left(\frac{\partial\theta}{\partial x}\right)_1 + \left(\frac{\partial^2\theta}{\partial x^2}\right)_M \Delta x\right],$$

where M is within the interval Δx. The rate of heat storage due to conduction in the x-direction is the difference between these two quantities:

$$\Delta Q_x = Q_{x1} - Q_{x2} = kd\,\Delta x\,\Delta y\left(\frac{\partial^2\theta}{\partial x^2}\right)_M. \tag{580}$$

Similarly, the rate of storage caused by conduction in the y-direction is

$$\Delta Q_y = kd\,\Delta x\,\Delta y\left(\frac{\partial^2\theta}{\partial y^2}\right)_{M'}, \tag{581}$$

where M' is within the interval Δy. The net rate of storage in the elementary volume $d\,\Delta x\,\Delta y$ is $\Delta Q_x + \Delta Q_y$ and will cause a time rate of increase in temperature similar to that expressed by Eq. (567):

$$\Delta Q_x + \Delta Q_y = c(\rho d\,\Delta x\,\Delta y)\left(\frac{\partial\theta}{\partial t}\right)_{M''}, \tag{582}$$

in which M'' is within the area $\Delta x\,\Delta y$. Substituting (580) and (581) into (582), dividing through by the volume $d\,\Delta x\,\Delta y$, and letting the size of the increment approach zero in size, we obtain the equation:

$$\frac{\partial\theta}{\partial t} = \alpha\left(\frac{\partial^2\theta}{\partial x^2} + \frac{\partial^2\theta}{\partial y^2}\right), \tag{583}$$

where $\alpha = k/c\rho$. This is the equation for variable heat flow in two dimensions. When the temperature within the body does not vary in the y-direction, this equation reduces to Eq. (568).

Suppose now that the heat flow is in steady state, so that the temperature at any point does not change with time. Then $\partial\theta/\partial t$ will be zero and Eq. (583) reduces to

$$\frac{\partial^2\theta}{\partial x^2} + \frac{\partial^2\theta}{\partial y^2} = 0, \tag{584}$$

which is called *Laplace's equation*. This equation is of great importance, for it arises not only in the steady-state conduction

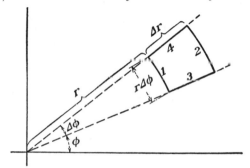

FIG. 106.—Polar coordinates.

of heat but also in many other problems including the conduction of electricity and the calculation of inductance and capacity. A solution of Laplace's equation is called a *harmonic function*.

In problems involving circular boundaries it is convenient to have Eqs. (583) and (584) expressed in polar coordinates. Although the change of variable can be made from Eq. (583) with the aid of Eq. (517), the reason for the form of the equation may be clearer if we derive the equation from the beginning. Consider the elementary area 1-2-3-4 of depth d in Fig. 106. Face 1 has an area $r \, \Delta\phi \, d$, and the heat conducted through this face is

$$Q_{r1} = -kr \, \Delta\phi \, d \left(\frac{\partial\theta}{\partial r}\right)_1 .$$

Face 2 has an area $(r + \Delta r) \, \Delta\phi \, d$; so the heat flowing out is

$$Q_{r2} = -k(r + \Delta r) \, \Delta\phi \, d \left[\left(\frac{\partial\theta}{\partial r}\right)_1 + \left(\frac{\partial^2\theta}{\partial r^2}\right)_M \Delta r\right],$$

where M is within the interval Δr. Expanding the expression for Q_{r2}, subtracting it from Q_{r1}, and neglecting the second-order infinitesimal $(\Delta r)^2$, we obtain for the heat storage due to radial flow:

$$\Delta Q_r = Q_{r1} - Q_{r2} = k \, \Delta r \, \Delta \phi \, d \left[r \left(\frac{\partial^2 \theta}{\partial r^2} \right)_M + \left(\frac{\partial \theta}{\partial r} \right)_1 \right]. \quad (585)$$

Although the corresponding expression in rectangular coordinates had only one term, the foregoing has two terms because of the increase in area of face 2 over face 1.

The temperature gradient in the ϕ-direction is $\partial \theta / \partial (r \phi)$; so the heat flowing in through face 3 is

$$Q_{\phi 3} = -k \, \Delta r \, d \left(\frac{\partial \theta}{\partial (r \phi)} \right)_3 = - \frac{k \, \Delta r \, d}{r_{\text{av.}}} \left(\frac{\partial \theta}{\partial \phi} \right)_3.$$

Similarly, for the heat flowing out through face 4,

$$Q_{\phi 4} = - \frac{k \, \Delta r \, d}{r_{\text{av.}}} \left[\left(\frac{\partial \theta}{\partial \phi} \right)_3 + \left(\frac{\partial^2 \theta}{\partial \phi^2} \right)_{M'} \Delta \phi \right],$$

where M' is within the interval $\Delta \phi$. The heat storage in the element due to flow in the ϕ-direction is then

$$\Delta Q_\phi = \frac{k \, \Delta r \, \Delta \phi \, d}{r_{\text{av.}}} \left(\frac{\partial^2 \theta}{\partial \phi^2} \right)_{M'}. \quad (586)$$

Relating the net rate of storage, $\Delta Q_r + \Delta Q_\phi$, to the rate of temperature increase in the volume $d(r_{\text{av.}} \, \Delta \phi) \, \Delta r$ (after the fashion of Eq. 582), we obtain the equation

$$r \left(\frac{\partial^2 \theta}{\partial r^2} \right)_M + \left(\frac{\partial \theta}{\partial r} \right)_1 + \frac{1}{r_{\text{av.}}} \left(\frac{\partial^2 \theta}{\partial \phi^2} \right)_{M'} = \frac{c\rho}{k} \, r_{\text{av.}} \left(\frac{\partial \theta}{\partial t} \right)_{M''}, \quad (587)$$

where M, M', and M'' are all within the area 1-2-3-4 in Fig. 106. Letting the size of the element approach zero as a limit, the values above approach values at the point (r, ϕ), and the partial differential equation can be written as

$$\frac{\partial \theta}{\partial t} = \alpha \left(\frac{\partial^2 \theta}{\partial r^2} + \frac{1}{r} \frac{\partial \theta}{\partial r} + \frac{1}{r^2} \frac{\partial^2 \theta}{\partial \phi^2} \right), \quad (588)$$

where $\alpha = k/c\rho$. This is the equation for heat flow in polar coordinates. When the flow is in steady state, it reduces to

$$\frac{\partial^2 \theta}{\partial r^2} + \frac{1}{r}\frac{\partial \theta}{\partial r} + \frac{1}{r^2}\frac{\partial^2 \theta}{\partial \phi^2} = 0, \tag{589}$$

which is Laplace's equation in polar coordinates.

When the flow is three-dimensional the steady-state equation corresponding to Eq. (584) is

$$\frac{\partial^2 \theta}{\partial x^2} + \frac{\partial^2 \theta}{\partial y^2} + \frac{\partial^2 \theta}{\partial z^2} = 0, \tag{590}$$

which is Laplace's equation in three dimensions.

Example: Laplace's Equation.—Consider a rectangular plate of conducting material such as that shown in Fig. 107. Since the

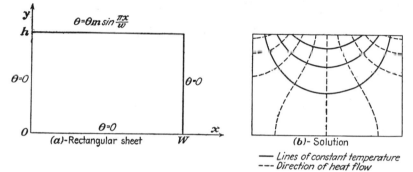

(a)-Rectangular sheet   W   (b)- Solution

— Lines of constant temperature
--- Direction of heat flow

Fig. 107.—Heat flow in rectangular sheet.

two flat surfaces are well insulated, we can assume that there is zero heat flow in the z-direction. Three edges are maintained at zero temperature (or a reference temperature), and the fourth edge has maintained a sinusoidal distribution of temperature as shown in Fig. 107. Find the steady-state distribution of temperature throughout the sheet.

Since the flow is in steady state and there are no sources of heat within the sheet, Laplace's equation (584) will apply:

$$\frac{\partial^2 \theta}{\partial x^2} + \frac{\partial^2 \theta}{\partial y^2} = 0. \tag{591}$$

Try to use a product solution: $\theta = X \cdot Y$. Taking partial derivatives and substituting into Eq. (591), we can separate the variables and obtain

$$-\frac{1}{X}\frac{d^2 X}{dx^2} = \frac{1}{Y}\frac{d^2 Y}{dy^2}. \tag{592}$$

Following our previous reasoning, this must be equal to a constant that may be considered positive, zero, or negative, depending upon which choice can best be fitted to our boundary conditions.   Call this constant b^2, and obtain from Eq. (592) the following two ordinary differential equations:

$$\frac{d^2X}{dx^2} + b^2X = 0, \tag{593}$$

$$\frac{d^2Y}{dy^2} - b^2Y = 0. \tag{594}$$

The first of these leads to a trigonometric solution and the second to either an exponential or a hyperbolic solution.   We shall use a hyperbolic solution for convenience.   Then we have

$$X = A \cos bx + B \sin bx,$$
$$Y = C \cosh by + D \sinh by.$$

The attempted product solution now becomes

$$\theta = (A \cos bx + B \sin bx)(C \cosh by + D \sinh by). \tag{595}$$

The boundary conditions are

$$\theta = 0 \qquad \text{at } y = 0 \text{ for all values of } x,$$
$$\theta = 0 \qquad \text{at } x = 0 \text{ for all values of } y,$$
$$\theta = 0 \qquad \text{at } x = w \text{ for all values of } y,$$
$$\theta = \theta_m \sin \frac{\pi x}{w} \qquad \text{at } y = h \text{ for all values of } x.$$

Applying these conditions successively to solution (595), we find

$$0 = (A \cos bx + B \sin bx)(C), \qquad \text{so } C = 0.$$
$$0 = (A)(0 + D \sinh by), \qquad \text{so } A = 0.$$
$$0 = (0 + B \sin bw)(0 + D \sinh by),$$

which can be satisfied by making $b = n\pi/w$ where n is any integer.   The last condition yields

$$\theta_m \sin \frac{\pi x}{w} = \left(B \sin \frac{n\pi x}{w}\right)\left(D \sinh \frac{n\pi h}{w}\right),$$

which is satisfied if $n = 1$ and $\theta_m = BD \sinh (\pi h/w)$.   Therefore, we can solve for BD and write the product solution (595) as

$$\theta = \theta_m \frac{\sinh \dfrac{\pi y}{w}}{\sinh \dfrac{\pi h}{w}} \sin \frac{\pi x}{w}. \tag{596}$$

This solution is plotted in Fig. 107b after the fashion of an isoclinic chart. The solid lines are curves of constant temperature, with the temperature difference between adjacent lines constant at $\theta_m/4$. The direction of heat flow is, of course, everywhere normal to the lines of constant temperature, as shown by the dotted curves of Fig. 107b.

106. Electrical Transmission Lines.—The study of electrical transmission lines under their various conditions of use forms a sizable subject by itself, and we shall give here only a brief introduction to the topic.[1] Consider a transmission line composed of two parallel conductors as shown in Fig. 108. Denote the resistance per unit length of both conductors in series by R ohms per unit length, and the shunt leakage conductance from one conductor to the other by G mhos per unit length. When a current flows in the conductors, a flux will be set up around the wires, and a change in this flux will induce a voltage. Although inductance is defined on a static basis (flux linkages per ampere) and we are here dealing with decidedly nonstatic conditions, it has been found convenient and sufficiently accurate for most purposes to ascribe the effect of the flux to a distributed inductance L henrys per unit length. Similarly, we shall assume a uniformly distributed capacitance between wires, C farads per unit length. The reader who is interested in the approximations made here will find a discussion of these in the first chapter of Guillemin, *op. cit.* In particular, we shall assume that radiation of energy is negligible.

---

[1] The reader who wishes to pursue the subject further should consult the literature. For example, see E. A. Guillemin, "Communication Networks," Vol. 2, John Wiley & Sons, Inc., New York, 1935; L. F. Woodruff, "Electric Power Transmission and Distribution," 2d ed., John Wiley & Sons, Inc., New York, 1938; A. E. Kennelly, "Electric Lines and Nets," McGraw-Hill Book Company, Inc., New York, 1928; L. A. Ware and H. R. Reed, "Communication Circuits," 2d ed., John Wiley & Sons, Inc., New York, 1944.

A differential segment of the line is shown in Fig. 108b. The distance x is measured from the receiving end for convenience. At any instant the voltages between conductors at planes 1 and 2 are related by

$$e_2 = e_1 + \left(\frac{\partial e}{\partial x}\right)_M \Delta x, \tag{597}$$

where M is some point located within the interval Δx. However, at any instant the drop in voltage from point 2 to 1 is

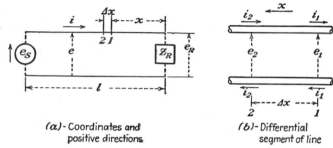

(a)- Coordinates and positive directions

(b)- Differential segment of line

FIG. 108.—Transmission line.

caused by the resistance $R\,\Delta x$ and inductance $L\,\Delta x$ of the segment.

Hence $$e_2 - e_1 = (R\,\Delta x)(i)_{M'} + (L\,\Delta x)\left(\frac{\partial i}{\partial t}\right)_{M''}, \tag{598}$$

where M' and M'' are both in the interval Δx. Eliminate the quantity $e_2 - e_1$ between Eqs. (597) and (598), divide through by Δx, and let the size of the segment approach zero as a limit so that the values at M, M', and M'' become those at a point. This results in

$$\frac{\partial e}{\partial x} = L\frac{\partial i}{\partial t} + Ri. \tag{599}$$

In a similar way, the current i_2 is related to i_1 at any instant by

$$i_2 = i_1 + \left(\frac{\partial i}{\partial x}\right)_P \Delta x, \tag{600}$$

where P is some point within Δx.

However, the difference between i_2 and i_1 at any instant is due to the leakage between conductors and to the displacement current through the capacity between wires. Hence

$$i_2 - i_1 = (G\,\Delta x)(e)_{P'} + (C\,\Delta x)\left(\frac{\partial e}{\partial t}\right)_{P''}. \tag{601}$$

Eliminating the quantity $i_2 - i_1$ between Eqs. (600) and (601), dividing through by Δx, and letting the increment approach zero in size, we obtain

$$\frac{\partial i}{\partial x} = C\frac{\partial e}{\partial t} + Ge. \tag{602}$$

Equations (599) and (602) are simultaneous partial differential equations in two dependent variables, e and i.

To eliminate i between these equations, take the partial derivative of (599) with respect to x, obtaining

$$\frac{\partial^2 e}{\partial x^2} = L\frac{\partial^2 i}{\partial x\,\partial t} + R\frac{\partial i}{\partial x}. \tag{603}$$

Next take the partial derivative of Eq. (602) with respect to t:

$$\frac{\partial^2 i}{\partial t\,\partial x} = C\frac{\partial^2 e}{\partial t^2} + G\frac{\partial e}{\partial t}. \tag{604}$$

Substitute Eqs. (602) and (604) into the right side of Eq. (603) and obtain the differential equation in terms of e:

$$\frac{\partial^2 e}{\partial x^2} = LC\frac{\partial^2 e}{\partial t^2} + (RC + LG)\frac{\partial e}{\partial t} + RGe. \tag{605}$$

In a similar fashion we can show that the current must satisfy an equation identical in form with Eq. (605):

$$\frac{\partial^2 i}{\partial x^2} = LC\frac{\partial^2 i}{\partial t^2} + (RC + LG)\frac{\partial i}{\partial t} + RGi. \tag{606}$$

Although the foregoing equations look formidable, their solutions for a great many conditions of practical interest are not difficult to obtain.

It is interesting to observe that for a cable with small inductance and leakage, Eqs. (605) and (606) reduce to the same form as Eq. (568) for one-dimensional heat flow. If voltage is taken to be analogous to temperature, then the distributed resistance is analogous to the reciprocal of thermal conductance, and the quantity (specific heat times density) can be considered as a thermal capacitance per unit volume.

It is of more practical interest to note that in the idealized case of a line with negligible dissipation ($R = G = 0$), the transmission line equations reduce to

$$\frac{\partial^2 e}{\partial t^2} = \frac{1}{LC} \frac{\partial^2 e}{\partial x^2} \qquad (607)$$

and

$$\frac{\partial^2 i}{\partial t^2} = \frac{1}{LC} \frac{\partial^2 i}{\partial x^2}, \qquad (608)$$

which have precisely the same form as Eq. (524) or (558) for the stretched elastic string. Therefore, the general solution (561) for that problem will apply:

$$e \text{ or } i = f_1 \left(x + \frac{1}{\sqrt{LC}} t \right) + f_2 \left(x - \frac{1}{\sqrt{LC}} t \right), \qquad (609)$$

where the f's are arbitrary functions and the quantity $1/\sqrt{LC}$ has the dimensions of a velocity. For open-wire lines without added inductance this velocity is only slightly less than that of light in free space, 3×10^8 meters per second. This is a most interesting result, for, recalling the traveling wave concept of Sec. 101, it indicates that signals and also disturbances such as those caused by lightning strokes will be propagated along the line at the finite velocity $1/\sqrt{LC}$. Upon reaching one of the ends of the line the wave will in general be reflected in a manner depending on the terminal conditions: whether the line is open, short-circuited, or terminated in an impedance. In time, of course, the dissipation, which we have neglected, will absorb the energy of the wave, but it is possible to have a number of reflections back and forth between the two ends of the line before the wave is greatly attenuated. Furthermore, if we apply sinusoidal driving forces of the proper frequency, we may expect to encounter the phenomenon of resonance.

The simplified equations (607) and (608) are also of particular interest in high-frequency lines carrying more or less sinusoidal voltages and currents. For a nondissipative line the phase velocity, $1/\sqrt{LC}$, is independent of frequency. Hence, the wave length along the line for a sinusoidal wave is inversely proportional to frequency and [compare Eq. (544)] is given by

$$\lambda = \frac{\text{velocity}}{\text{frequency}} = \frac{1}{f \sqrt{LC}} \qquad \text{length units.}$$

For high-frequency waves the wave length may be relatively small. Thus a physically short line may be "electrically long" for high frequencies, *i.e.*, be of a length comparable with a wave length. For these physically short high-frequency lines, dissipation can often be neglected without serious error in steady-state calculations. Note that for a 100-megacycle wave, with a wave length of 3 meters, two parallel wires 1 meter in length would be an electrically long transmission line, not just a pair of simple connecting leads!

Steady-state Solution with Sinusoidal Applied Voltage.—We shall next find a steady-state solution for the dissipative line with sinusoidal applied voltage. The product method can be used to find solutions of Eqs. (605) and (606) and, if applied in the usual manner, will yield both steady state and transients. However, for the steady-state solution we shall find it simpler to recognize that if a sinusoidal voltage is applied to the linear system of Fig. 108, the steady-state current and voltage will everywhere vary sinusoidally with time. Using the vector methods of Chap. VII, we shall assume that the voltage at any point can be expressed by the modified product solution:

$$e = \Re_e[\bar{E}(x) \cdot \epsilon^{j\omega t}], \qquad (610)$$

where $\bar{E}(x)$ is a function of x alone. We can drop the symbol $\Re_e$ after the usual fashion of representing a-c voltages and currents by plane vectors, but we should recognize that the actual instantaneous values will be given by the projection of the rotating vector on the real axis, as indicated by Eq. (610). Substitute the assumed solution into the partial differential equation (605), cancel $\epsilon^{j\omega t}$, and denote $\bar{E}(x)$ simply by $\bar{E}$. This yields an ordinary differential equation:

$$\frac{d^2\bar{E}}{dx^2} - \alpha^2\bar{E} = 0, \qquad (611)$$

where we have defined $\alpha^2 = (R + j\omega L)(G + j\omega C).$ (612)

We could write the solution in either exponential or hyperbolic form, but we shall choose the latter:

$$\bar{E} = A \cosh \alpha x + B \sinh \alpha x. \qquad (613)$$

For the current we can assume a solution $i = \Re_e[\bar{I}(x) \cdot \epsilon^{j\omega t}]$, whereupon Eq. (606) will yield a solution of the same form as

Eq. (613). However, the solutions for current and voltage are related; so we shall use Eq. (599) instead: Substitute Eq. (613) into Eq. (610) and thence into Eq. (599), together with the assumed solution for current, and obtain

$$\bar{I} = \frac{1}{\bar{Z}_0} (A \sinh \alpha x + B \cosh \alpha x), \tag{614}$$

where

$$\bar{Z}_0 = \sqrt{\frac{R + j\omega L}{G + j\omega C}}. \tag{615}$$

There are a great many equivalent forms for these solutions, but we shall assume that the receiving-end impedance and desired voltage are known. Then the end conditions are $(\bar{E})_{x=0} = \bar{E}_R$, and $(\bar{E}/\bar{I})_{x=0} = \bar{Z}_R$. Substituting these into Eqs. (613) and (614) and evaluating A and B, we obtain

$$\bar{E} = \bar{E}_R \left(\cosh \alpha x + \frac{\bar{Z}_0}{\bar{Z}_R} \sinh \alpha x \right) \tag{616}$$

and

$$\bar{I} = \frac{\bar{E}_R}{\bar{Z}_R} \left(\cosh \alpha x + \frac{\bar{Z}_R}{\bar{Z}_0} \sinh \alpha x \right). \tag{617}$$

These equations give the steady-state voltage and current in vector form for any point x on the line. In particular, if $x = l$ (see Fig. 108a), they will yield the sending-end voltage and current.

The quantity $\bar{Z}_0$ defined by Eq. (615) has the dimensions of an impedance and is a characteristic of the line. Thus it is given the name *characteristic impedance*. It is readily shown that the impedance of a line of infinite length is equal to the characteristic impedance, and furthermore a finite line terminated in a load equal to the characteristic impedance will have no reflection from that end. According to the equations the latter statement is mathematically correct, but physically it is an approximation only, for even though the load has an impedance equal to the nonexistent remainder of the infinite line, it cannot supply the necessary continuation of the electric and magnetic fields. This is to say that there may be end effects not taken into account in our replacement of magnetic and electric field effects by distributed inductance and capacity. Reference to Eq. (615) shows that in general $\bar{Z}_0$ is a complex impedance and furthermore is a function of frequency. However for a dissipationless line ($R = G = 0$) and for the so-called "distortionless" line where $RC = GL$, the characteristic impedance is a real number (pure resistance) independent of frequency.

The quantity α defined by Eq. (612) is seen to be a complex number and, because it governs the variation of $\bar{E}$ and $\bar{I}$ with x, it is called the *propagation constant* or *propagation function* of the line. The solutions (616) and (617) can be interpreted by the traveling wave concept, and the real and imaginary parts of α are then found to determine, respectively, the decrease in magnitude (attenuation) of the wave as it travels along the line and its phase velocity. The attenuation and phase velocity will in general depend somewhat upon frequency. Hence, if a periodic nonsinusoidal voltage is applied to the sending end of the line, the various frequency components may be attenuated differently and have different phase velocities, resulting in distortion of the received wave.

The steady-state solutions (616) and (617) will involve hyperbolic functions of a complex argument. Charts and tables of these are available, or they can be expressed in terms of functions of a real argument by use of Eqs. (264) of Chap. VI, Sec. 53.

As indicated previously, the foregoing discussion has given only a brief introduction to the subject. The reader who is interested in the steady-state and transient properties of transmission lines will do well to pursue the matter further in the literature.

107. Graphical Field Plotting.—In Sec. 105 it was shown that the steady-state temperature distribution in a conducting body satisfies Laplace's equation when there is no heat generated within the body itself, and application to the conduction of electricity and to the space distribution of stationary magnetic and electric fields was mentioned. In addition, numerous other problems can be reduced by superposition to a solution of Laplace's equation; for example, the laminar flow of incompressible viscous fluids and the torsion of shafts of odd cross section. When the geometry is not simple, the application of boundary conditions to the mathematical solution becomes quite difficult. For such problems the graphical methods of field plotting are relatively simple and of sufficient accuracy for most practical purposes.[1] Examples of specific problems that can be solved by this means include the calculation of end effects in condensers, the flux distribution around field poles and the inductance of field windings, the resistance of nonuniform electrical conductors, the seepage of water through earth dams, stresses in a shaft with a keyway, and the conduction of heat from pipes embedded in a wall. Ordinary plots made with reasonable care should show an accuracy of 5 per cent or better.

Two-dimensional problems are easiest to plot (*i.e.*, when the field is uniform in the third dimension), but three-dimensional problems with an axis of symmetry can also be plotted.

The method will be derived in terms of the steady-state flow of heat because this type of problem is comparatively easy to visualize. The "small-squares" method of plotting which we shall develop can then be applied to other problems reducible to a solution of Laplace's equation.

The Small-squares Plot.—Refer to Fig. 107b, which shows the two-dimensional temperature distribution in a rectangular conducting sheet of uniform depth. The solid lines are curves of constant temperature, which we might call lines of constant thermal potential. The dotted lines show the direction of heat flow, and we might regard them as forming the boundaries of imaginary "tubes" through which the heat is flowing. If such a plot were graphically obtained and we wished to do quantitative work with it, it would be convenient to place the boundaries of the tubes so that the same amount of heat would be flowing in each tube. Similarly, it would be convenient to place the equipotential (temperature) lines so that adjacent lines would have the same difference in temperature everywhere in the plot.

To attack the first condition, we wish to define a flow or "flux" function u such that u will be constant along any flow line, and, if we denote some particular flow line by $u = 0$, then the value of u for any other flow line will be equal to the total

[1] Some references to the subject of graphical field plotting are: A. R. Stevenson, Jr., and R. H. Park, Graphical Determination of Magnetic Fields, *General Elec. Rev.*, February, 1928, pp. 99–109, and March, 1928, pp. 153–164 (gives a method of plotting into current-carrying conductors). H. Poritsky, Graphical Field Plotting Methods in Engineering, *Trans. A.I.E.E.*, 1938, pp. 727–732 (gives theory and numerous applications). A. D. Moore, "Fundamentals of Electric Design," Chaps. IV to IX, McGraw-Hill Book Company, Inc., New York, 1927.

amount of heat flowing between this line and the original line $u = 0$, considering unit depth.   Figure 109 shows an elementary portion of a field plot.   If we denote the density of heat flow by q (heat units flowing per unit time per unit area) and proceed along an equipotential line for a short distance Δs, the change in u will be

$$\Delta u = (q) \times (\text{area, considering unit depth}) = q \, \Delta s. \quad (618)$$

The change in temperature over a distance Δn normal to the equipotential lines is, from the fundamental conduction equation (562),

$$\Delta\theta = -\frac{q}{k} \Delta n. \quad (619)$$

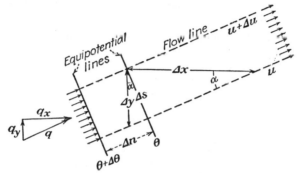

FIG. 109.—Elementary area of field plot.

If we divide Eq. (618) by Eq. (619), we obtain the relation

$$\frac{\Delta u}{-k \, \Delta\theta} = \frac{\Delta s}{\Delta n}. \quad (620)$$

This equation shows us that if we have a constant amount of flow Δu per unit depth between adjacent flow lines and the same difference in temperature $\Delta\theta$ between adjacent equipotential lines, then the ratio $\Delta s/\Delta n$ is a constant.   This indicates that the region will be broken into small rectangles of width Δs and length Δn.   The size of the rectangles will vary inversely with the flow density throughout the plot, as indicated by Eq. (618), but the ratio $\Delta s/\Delta n$ will be the same for all.   In particular, if we let the flow per unit depth in each small tube be

$$\Delta u = -k \, \Delta\theta, \quad (621)$$

then
$$\Delta s = \Delta n, \quad (622)$$

and the region is broken into small squares. This is the most convenient method, for any deviation is easier to see.

It will be seen in Fig. 107 that, except for a perfectly uniform field, the blocks will not be geometrically perfect squares unless they are made infinitesimally small, in which case they become true squares just as an infinitesimal portion of the arc of a circle approaches a straight line. When the blocks are of finite size we shall call them *curvilinear squares*. The sides of a curvilinear square intersect at right angles, and it has approximately the same width as length. If it is properly subdivided an equal number of times in length and width, its subdivisions will approach geometric squares. Furthermore, between opposite edges it has the same physical properties per unit depth (such as resistance to heat flow) as any true geometric square of the same material.

In making a field map the general procedure is to divide the space into curvilinear squares by trial, at the same time satisfying the given boundary conditions. If there is any doubt whether a block is a curvilinear square, it should be divided once lengthwise and once crosswise and, if necessary, these subdivisions further divided in the same manner, to determine whether all the subdivisions can be made to approach geometric squares. Examples of this can be seen in the illustrative plots that follow.

Functional Relations.—Returning to the elementary section of a plot shown in Fig. 109, the perpendicular distance between flow lines can be expressed as $\Delta s = \Delta y \cdot \cos \alpha$. Hence we can write Eq. (618) as $\Delta u = q \cdot \Delta y \cdot \cos \alpha$. However, the quantity $q \cos \alpha$ is the x-component of the flow density q, so we can also write $\Delta u = q_x \Delta y$. As the size of the elementary area approaches zero, this can be written as a partial derivative:

$$\frac{\partial u}{\partial y} = q_x. \tag{623}$$

In a similar way we can demonstrate that

$$\frac{\partial u}{\partial x} = -q_y, \tag{624}$$

where the negative sign arises because u decreases in the positive x-direction when q_y is positive.

Furthermore, from the fundamental equation for heat conduction, we can write

$$q_x = -k \frac{\partial \theta}{\partial x} \quad \text{and} \quad q_y = -k \frac{\partial \theta}{\partial y}. \quad (625)$$

To get rid of the conductivity k, define a potential function v such that $v = k\theta$. From this definition and Eqs. (623) to (625), we see that

$$\frac{\partial u}{\partial x} = \frac{\partial v}{\partial y} \quad \text{and} \quad \frac{\partial u}{\partial y} = -\frac{\partial v}{\partial x}. \quad (626)$$

These are known as the *Cauchy-Riemann differential equations* and imply the existence of a small-squares representation of u and v. Functions u and v satisfying Eqs. (626) are said to be *conjugate functions*.

Taking the partial derivative of the first of Eqs. (626) with respect to x and of the second with respect to y and adding, we obtain

$$\frac{\partial^2 u}{\partial x^2} + \frac{\partial^2 u}{\partial y^2} = 0.$$

Similarly, we can show that

$$\frac{\partial^2 v}{\partial x^2} + \frac{\partial^2 v}{\partial y^2} = 0.$$

Thus both the flow and potential functions satisfy Laplace's equation and are conjugate harmonic functions.

Making a Field Plot.—For any particular problem there is one and only one field plot that will satisfy all the boundary conditions and at the same time divide the area into small squares. Field plotting is a freehand trial-and-error process in which one first draws a trial set of flow or equipotential lines, starting with those lines which can be visualized or estimated most readily, and then checks this trial set by attempting to draw lines of the conjugate function so as to form curvilinear squares. Large curvilinear squares are checked by subdividing them once in each direction, then similarly dividing the subdivisions as necessary, always attempting to approach geometric squares. When the crosslines fail to produce curvilinear squares, the deficiency in width or height of the blocks will indicate the direction in which the original trial set of lines should be moved to correct this deficiency. This procedure is continued until the entire region has been satisfactorily subdivided. Care should be taken in drawing the lines to satisfy the conditions at the boundaries. When the boundary conditions are not violated, there is one necessary and sufficient test of accuracy: the entire region must be broken up into curvilinear squares.

Several rules will aid in making a plot: (1) Always draw intersections at right angles as nearly as can be judged by eye. Skewing angles to avoid rectangular blocks is a waste of time and makes subsequent work useless. Rectangular blocks are useful in that they show the direction in which the trial lines should be moved. (2) Make the plot large enough to be useful but not so large that it cannot be visualized as a unit. (3) Be prepared to erase and correct errors without compunction. (4) Work freehand, without mechanical aids. The eye is surprisingly accurate in judging squares and right angles, so good, in fact, that even a relatively poor looking plot may yield surprising accuracy if the angles are maintained correctly. (5) Work on the plot as a whole. Do not attempt to make the plot section by section, as one portion of the plot will affect all the others.

The evolution of a plot is shown in Fig. 110. This might represent the conduction of heat through some homogeneous medium between a cylinder and rectangular tube, the conduction of electricity, or the electric flux between conductors of this shape. The cylinder and tube are supposed to be of sufficient length (in a direction normal to the plot) that end effects can be neglected and the field assumed to be two-dimensional. In addition it is assumed that the surfaces are highly conductive; so they are equipotentials and the flow lines enter them at right angles. Only one quarter of the plot is shown, as the other three quarters are the same by symmetry. The line a-a' in Fig. 110b was drawn as a first trial line to represent a potential midway between that of the cylinder and that of the tube. The flow line b-b' was next drawn so as to make S_1 a curvilinear square and extended to enter the top wall at right angles. The block S_2 is seen to be too wide for its height, indicating that the line a-a' should be moved in the direction of the arrows.

With a-a' and b-b' changed, the plot proceeds as in Fig. 110c, with further subdivisions made as needed. However, as soon as the line c-c' is drawn, it is apparent that the blocks S_3, S_4, and

S_5 are too flat, indicating that the lower end of a-a' must be moved to the left.   When this is done, most of the plot back to S_1 and S_2 must be erased and the flow lines redrawn to correspond to the new position of a-a'.   This results in the final plot of Fig. 110d.

Observe that in the corner the lines eventually form an "arrowhead" pattern.   Subdivision produces three squares plus a smaller arrowhead and, since this could be continued indefinitely into the corner, the arrowhead itself must be a curvilinear square!

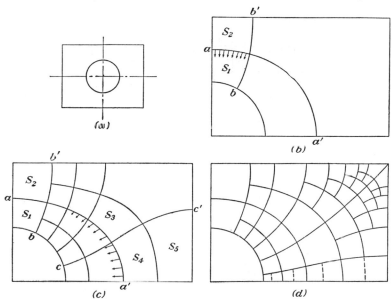

Fig. 110.—Evolution of a plot.

It will be seen that the flow tends to avoid an inside corner, and that the density at the corner is theoretically zero.   Observe that one line bisects the angle at the corner.   Also note that if one chooses an integral number of tubes in one direction, the number of tubes in the other direction will not in general be an integer, and the plot will end with a fractional tube composed of similar curvilinear rectangles.

Figure 111 shows a deep, uniform slot between two magnetic pole pieces.   The two-dimensional field near the edge of the slot has been plotted with the following boundary conditions: (1) The iron surfaces are assumed to have a high permeability ("infinite" compared with the surrounding space), so that they can be considered to be equipotential surfaces, and the flux lines enter them at right angles. (2) The field deep within

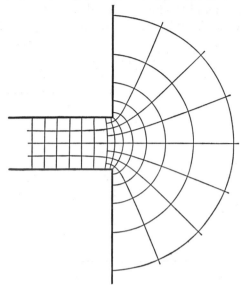

FIG. 111.—Field near the edge of a slot.

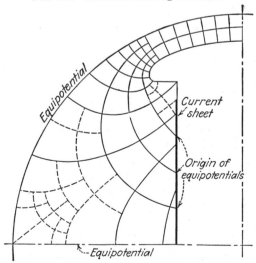

FIG. 112.—Plot of flux for a two-pole machine; current sheet assumed.

the slot is approximately uniform. (3) Outside the slot the flux lines tend to become circular and the equipotentials tend toward radial lines. Observe that the lines tend to hug an outside corner, resulting in a large potential gradient, and that the flux lines concentrate in that region.

Figure 112 shows the magnetic field around the pole of a machine. The current is assumed to flow in a sheet on the surface of the pole, and the boundary condition is that the equipotentials come out of the sheet at equal intervals. The iron surfaces are assumed to be equipotentials. Note the use of one line of symmetry as an equipotential line and of another as a flux line, so that only one quarter of the machine need be plotted. The equipotential and flux lines are refracted at the current sheet and can enter the sheet at any angle.

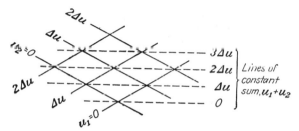

FIG. 113.—Superposition of plots.

Superposition of Plots.—Two plots can be superposed provided that the values of Δu and Δv between adjacent lines are the same for both, assuming, of course, a linear medium. The flow lines of one plot are first properly positioned over the flow lines of the other, as in Fig. 113. If the values of u are added together at the intersections, it will be found that the dotted lines representing constant values of total u are merely the diagonals of the four-sided figures formed by the original u-lines. Subtraction of the two original plots will result in diagonals in the other direction. The superposition can be done conveniently by making the two original plots on separate sheets of tracing paper, placing one sheet in proper position on top of the other, and then drawing in the proper diagonals.

After the flow lines have been superposed, the equipotentials can be superposed also. Sometimes it is more convenient to sketch the equipotentials by making curvilinear squares on the final plot, and in many cases it is not necessary to draw the equipotentials at all.

An example of the use of superposition is shown in Fig. 114. A conductor carrying a steady current runs parallel with an iron surface of high permeability, and it is desired to find the magnetic field in and around the conductor. Laplace's equation does not hold inside the current-carrying region; so superposition will be used as follows: The field due to a cylindrical

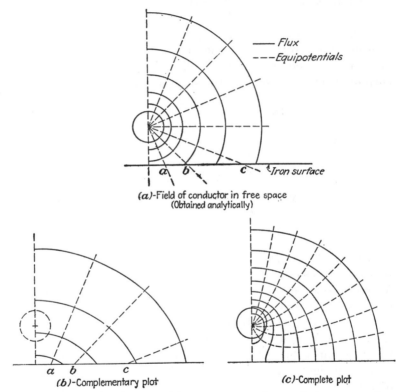

(a)-Field of conductor in free space
(Obtained analytically)

(b)-Complementary plot

(c)-Complete plot

Fig. 114.—Example of superposition: current-carrying conductor near an iron surface.

current-carrying conductor in free space is readily calculated by analytical means because of the symmetry. This is shown in Fig. 114a. However, this field violates the iron boundary, since this must be an equipotential surface and some of the equipotential lines from the conductor pass through it. This condition can be corrected by adding to the field of Fig. 114a a Laplacian (small-squares) field which will have equipotential lines of opposite potential coming out of the iron boundary where those of the conductor go in. This plot is shown in Fig. 114b. The two plots are superposed, resulting in the plot of Fig. 114c which satisfies all boundary conditions.

Calculations. Conduction of Heat.—Imagine that the plot of Fig. 110 represents the conduction of heat between a cylinder and a rectangular tube of depth d normal to the paper. We can choose any curvilinear square or any of its subdivisions to be a unit curvilinear square and count the number of potential and flow tubes on this basis. For example, we can choose the block in the upper left corner to be the unit. On this basis there are two potential tubes (continuing around the whole figure) with $3\frac{1}{4}$ flow tubes in one quarter of the plot, or 13 flow tubes total. On the other hand, if we choose the block in the lower right corner to be the unit, there would be 8 potential tubes and a total of 52 flow tubes.

If the temperature difference between the two bodies is θ degrees and there are N_p potential tubes, then the temperature difference across one potential tube is

$$\Delta\theta = \frac{\theta}{N_p}. \tag{627}$$

This temperature difference, together with the width of the potential tube at the point in question, can be used to calculate the temperature gradient at any point in the plot.

Since each curvilinear square has the physical properties of a geometric square and has, effectively, equal length and width, the rate of heat conduction in each of the unit curvilinear squares is

$$\Delta Q = k(d \cdot \text{average width})\left(\frac{\Delta\theta}{\text{average length}}\right)$$
$$= kd\,\Delta\theta = kd\,\frac{\theta}{N_p},$$

where k is the conductivity of the material between the bodies and d is the depth of the bodies normal to the plot. This expresses the rate of heat conduction in each flow tube. So, if there are N_f flow tubes, the total rate of heat conduction is

$$Q = kd\theta\,\frac{N_f}{N_p} \qquad \text{heat units per unit time.} \tag{628}$$

The conductivity k must be expressed in consistent length units, for example, as $\dfrac{\text{Btu}}{\text{hr-ft-}^\circ\text{F}}$ rather than as $\dfrac{\text{Btu}}{\text{hr-ft}^2\text{-}^\circ\text{F/in.}}$.

Observe that in Eq. (628) the number of flow and potential tubes enters only as a ratio. Hence, the choice of a unit curvilinear square makes no difference in the result.

It will be seen that the calculation of the total rate of heat flow has proceeded as though the curvilinear squares were true geometric squares. Therefore, it is possible to replace a field plot such as the one of Fig. 110 with a rectangular system of squares that will have the same amount of flow per tube, the same temperature drop across potential tubes, and the same total heat flow as the actual configuration. The rectangular

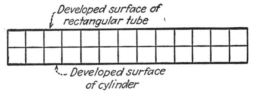

FIG. 115.—Rectangular representation of the plot of Fig. 110.

system in Fig. 115 represents the field plot of Fig. 110 and has 13 flow tubes, 2 potential tubes, and the same thermal conductance. Conversely, Fig. 110 can be regarded as a remapping of Fig. 115. This process is called *conformal mapping* and can be done analytically for certain geometric shapes.[1] Field plotting methods do the equivalent process graphically. Any small angle or small geometric figure is transferred from one plot to the other without change in shape, hence the name *conformal*. It is evident that, although the thermal conductance and total heat flow are the same in both plots, the temperature gradients are in general different at corresponding points.

Conduction of Electricity.—The plot of Fig. 110 could represent the steady flow of electric current through a conducting medium between cylinder and rectangular tube. If the medium has a resistivity ρ, then the electrical resistance of one block per unit depth is numerically equal to ρ, and the total resistance of a conductor with depth d normal to the plot is

[1] See, for example, WALKER, MILES, "Conjugate Functions for Engineers," Oxford University Press, London, 1933.

$$R = \frac{\rho}{d} \frac{N_p}{N_f} \quad \text{ohms.} \tag{629}$$

Electrostatics; Capacitance.—Suppose that the plot of Fig. 110 represents the electric field between oppositely charged conducting bodies. If the bodies have a potential difference of V volts, the potential difference across one potential tube is V/N_p volts. This can be used to calculate the voltage gradient at any point.

Using MKS units, the density of electric flux is equal to the permittivity of the medium ϵ times the electric field intensity in volts per meter. The curvilinear squares have effectively equal length and width. Considering 1 meter depth, the total electric flux in one flux tube is given by $\epsilon V/N_p$. The capacity of a condenser is defined as the charge stored per unit potential difference, and in unrationalized units each coulomb of charge produces 4π units of flux. We can thus write

$$C = \frac{\text{total electric flux}}{4\pi V}$$

$$= \frac{\epsilon}{4\pi} \frac{N_f}{N_p} \quad \text{farads per meter depth,} \tag{630}$$

where N_f is the number of flux tubes. The permittivity of free space is $\epsilon_0 = 1.113 \times 10^{-10}$ in MKS unrationalized units, and the relative permittivity or dielectric constant is defined as $K = \epsilon/\epsilon_0$. Equation (630) can be written as

$$C = \frac{1.113K}{4\pi} \frac{N_f}{N_p} \times 10^{-10} \quad \text{farads per meter depth.} \tag{631}$$

As a specific example, consider Fig. 110, for which $N_f/N_p = 6.5$. Assume that the medium is air, for which the dielectric constant is approximately unity. From Eq. (631)

$$C = \frac{1.113 \times 1}{4\pi} \times 6.5 \times 10^{-10} = 5.75 \times 10^{-11} \text{ farad per meter depth}$$

$$= 0.575 \quad \mu\mu\text{f/cm. depth.}$$

Magnetic Fields.—A plot of the magnetic field around the pole of a machine is shown in Fig. 112. If there are N turns in series on each pole, the total magnetomotive force across the air gap is $F = 4\pi NI$ pragilberts ($0.4\pi NI$ gilberts), where I is the current in amperes. The mmf across one potential tube is, therefore, $\Delta F = 4\pi NI/N_p$. Considering a depth of 1 meter normal to the plot, the amount of flux in each flux tube is

$$\Delta\phi = \frac{4\pi NI\mu}{N_p} \qquad \text{webers per meter depth,} \qquad (632)$$

where μ is the permeability of the medium, expressed in unrationalized MKS units ($\mu = 10^{-7}$ for free space).

The inductance of the winding can be expressed as the flux linkages (weber-turns) per ampere:

$$L = \frac{\psi}{I} = \frac{\Sigma N\phi}{I} \qquad \text{henrys.} \qquad (633)$$

The magnetic flux per tube can be found by Eq. (632), after which the flux linkages can be summed and placed in Eq. (633) to find the inductance.

As an example, consider the plot of Fig. 112. Take a unit block to be one of those to the left of the pole tip, *i.e.*, there will be four potential tubes. Each block under the pole therefore consists of two units. Counting flux tubes from the center line of the pole downward to the current sheet we find 20.5 tubes, contributing a linkage of $20.5 \Delta\phi \cdot N$ weber-turns. The remaining 0.5 tube links on the average about 95 per cent of the coil, contributing a linkage of $0.5 \Delta\phi \times 0.95N$. The middle of the next tube comes at about 0.80 of the height of the winding and adds a linkage of $\Delta\phi \times 0.80N$. Continuing in this manner and summing the linkages, we obtain for one side of one pole:

$$\begin{aligned}\psi &= (20.5 + 0.5 \times 0.95 + 0.80 + 0.55 + 0.25 \times 0.20)N\,\Delta\phi \\ &= 22.4N\,\Delta\phi \qquad \text{weber-turns per meter depth.}\end{aligned}$$

The other side of the pole is symmetrical; so for the entire pole the flux linkages are $\psi = 44.8N\,\Delta\phi$ weber-turns per meter depth.

Recalling that we chose $N_p = 4$, we substitute from Eq. (632) into our expression for flux linkage and from there into Eq. (633) and obtain

$$L = \frac{44.8N \left(\dfrac{4\pi NI \cdot 10^{-7}}{4}\right)}{I} = \begin{aligned}&1.41 \times 10^{-5}N^2 \qquad \text{henry/meter} \\ &4.30 \times 10^{-6}N^2 \qquad \text{henry/foot,}\end{aligned}$$

where L is the inductance of one pole of the machine per unit stacking length normal to the plot. Thus, for a machine with

9-in. stacking length and 450 turns per pole, the inductance would be

$$L = 4.30 \times 10^{-6} \times (450)^2 \times \tfrac{9}{12} = 0.653 \qquad \text{henry per pole,}$$

and for a two-pole machine with both field windings in series the total field inductance would be $2 \times 0.653 = 1.31$ henrys.

Three-dimensional Field Plotting.—It is possible to plot three-dimensional fields that have an axis of symmetry. In a two-dimensional plot the equipotential and flux lines represent the traces of surfaces that extend in a direction normal to the paper, but in a three-dimensional plot the lines are drawn so that when

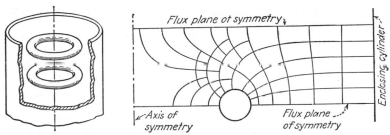

Fig. 116.—Example of three-dimensional plot with axis of symmetry; grid of charged rings. (*Reproduced from H. Poritsky, Graphical Field Plotting Methods in Engineering, Trans. A.I.E.E., Vol. 57, pp. 727–732, (1938), by courtesy of the author and publisher.*)

rotated around the axis of symmetry they yield tubes of flux and potential, each of the flux tubes containing the same amount of flux and all adjacent equipotential lines having the same potential difference.

When the lines are rotated about the axis of symmetry, the curvilinear blocks that are farther from the center will have a greater mean circumference. Hence the ratio of the width of the potential tubes to the width of the flux tubes will have to increase linearly with the radius. An axially symmetric plot for the field of a charged grid consisting of circular rings is shown in Fig. 116.

The fact that the ratio of width to length of the blocks continually changes with the radius is the main difference between this and two-dimensional plots. The two-dimensional plot is easier to make and in general yields better accuracy than a three-dimensional plot of comparable complexity.

Problems

1. Given the partial differential equation

$$\frac{\partial^2 z}{\partial x^2} + \frac{\partial^2 z}{\partial y^2} = 0.$$

Show by partial differentiation and substitution that this equation is satisfied by the solutions $z = f_1(x + jy)$ and $z = f_2(x - jy)$, where f_1 and f_2 are any functions and $j = \sqrt{-1}$. Then show by the same method that $z = f_1(x + jy) + f_2(x - jy)$ is also a solution of the equation.

2. An elastic string of length L has a weight w per unit length and is stretched with a tension F. One end of the string is fixed at $x = 0$ while the other end at $x = L$ is driven with a transverse motion $y = Y \sin \omega t$.

a. Using a product solution of the partial differential equation, find the steady-state displacement y as a function of x and t. What does this solution reduce to as $\omega L/a$ becomes very small?

b. If $L = 12$ in., $F = 0.50$ lb, and $w = 0.0012$ lb/in., find the phase velocity for traveling waves on the string and also the first three natural frequencies.

c. Using the data in (*b*) and $Y = 0.1$ in., plot y vs. x at $\omega t = \pi/2$ for driving frequencies which make the length of the string equal to $\frac{1}{8}$ wave length, $\frac{1}{4}$ wave length, 0.45 wave length, and 0.95 wave length.

3. An elastic string with tension F and weight per unit length w has its ends fixed at $x = 0$ and $x = L$. The string initially has zero displacement at all points.

a. At $t = 0$ the string is given an initial velocity $B_n \sin n\pi x/L$. Find the displacement y as a function of t and x.

b. At $t = 0$ the string is struck at the one-third point so that it is given the initial velocity shown in Fig. P3. Expand the initial velocity in a

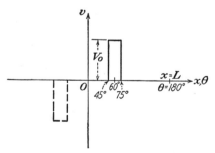

Fig. P3.—Initial velocity of string.

Fourier series as an odd function, and use this together with the results of part (*a*) to find the displacement as a function of t and x. Find the amplitude of the first six harmonic components of displacement and observe the absence of certain harmonics.

4. A string with length L, tension F, and weight per unit length w has its ends fixed at $x = 0$ and $x = L$. It is immersed in a medium that provides a viscous damping force. The damping force per unit length is equal to a coefficient D times the transverse velocity.

Set up the partial differential equation for the system and solve for the initial conditions of zero initial displacement and an initial velocity of $V_0 \sin n\pi x/L$. Show that the result is an exponentially decreasing vibration with the natural frequency

$$f_n = \frac{1}{2\pi} \sqrt{\frac{n^2\pi^2 a^2}{L^2} - \beta^2},$$

where $a^2 = Fg/w$ and $\beta = Dg/2w$.

5. Show that the partial differential equation for small longitudinal vibrations of a rod is

$$\frac{Eg}{w} \frac{\partial^2 u}{\partial x^2} = \frac{\partial^2 u}{\partial t^2},$$

where x is measured along the rod, u is the displacement in the x-direction of any particle from the unstressed position, E is the modulus of elasticity, and w is the weight per unit volume. Neglect gravity forces.

Note: The tensile strain at any point is given by $\partial u/\partial x$. Therefore the elastic force on any cross-sectional area A is $EA\, \partial u/\partial x$.

6. Using the differential equation of Prob. 5, find the phase velocity for the propagation of sound in a steel rod. Use $w = 0.28$ lb/in.^{3} and $E = 29 \times 10^6$ lb/in.^{2}

7. *a.* A certain helical spring of length L has a spring constant K and a total weight W. Assuming that it can be replaced for purposes of analysis by an elastic rod with the same weight and spring constant, write the differential equation of Prob. 5 in terms of K, W, and L.

b. The spring is fixed at $x = 0$, and at $x = L$ it is given the sinusoidal displacement $U \sin \omega t$. Find the steady-state displacement u as a function of x and t. What does this reduce to as $\omega \sqrt{W/Kg}$ becomes very small?

c. Using the results of part (*b*), find the natural frequencies of a spring for which $L = 10$ in., $K = 48.0$ lb/in., and $W = 1.10$ lb.

d. Using $U = 0.2$ in. and the data above, plot displacement u vs. distance x at $\omega t = \pi/2$ for frequencies equal to 0.05, 0.50, 0.90, and 1.90 times the first natural frequency. For each of these frequencies compute the maximum force that the spring exerts at the driven end, recalling that this force is proportional to $(\partial u/\partial x)_{x=L}$, and compare this force with that which would be exerted by an ideal spring with zero mass.

8. Find the general solutions of the following homogeneous equations:

a. $\dfrac{\partial^2 y}{\partial x^2} - \dfrac{\partial^2 y}{\partial x\, \partial t} - 2\dfrac{\partial^2 y}{\partial t^2} = 0.$

b. $\dfrac{\partial^2 y}{\partial x^2} - 2\dfrac{\partial^2 y}{\partial x\, \partial t} + \dfrac{\partial^2 y}{\partial t^2} = 0.$

9. A certain heated metallic rod is well insulated so that relatively little heat escapes from its surface. The rod has a length L, a conductivity k, a specific heat c, and a mass density ρ.

a. At $t = 0$ the rod has a temperature distribution given by

$$\theta = A_n \cos \frac{n\pi x}{L}.$$

Find the temperature distribution as a function of x and t.

b. At $t = 0$ the rod has a linear temperature distribution given by $\theta = \theta_m x/L$ for $0 < x < L$ (see Fig. P9). Expand the initial temperature distribution in a Fourier series as an even function, and use this together with the results of part (*a*) to find the temperature as a function of x and t.

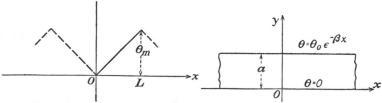

FIG. P9.—Initial temperature distribu-   FIG. P10.—Cross section of plate.
tion in rod.

10. Figure P10 shows the cross section of a large plate of uniform thickness a. One face is maintained at a temperature $\theta = 0$, while the other face is maintained at a temperature distribution given by $\theta = \theta_0 \epsilon^{-\beta x}$. The temperature is independent of z.

a. Find the steady-state temperature distribution as a function of x and y.

b. Using $\beta = \pi/2a$, plot lines of constant temperature, showing $\theta = \theta_0/4$, $\theta_0/2$, $3\theta_0/4$, and θ_0. Sketch lines of heat flow normal to these.

11. A cross section of a long solid cylinder of radius a is shown in Fig. P11. The surface is maintained at a temperature distribution given by

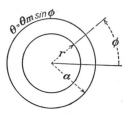

FIG. P11.—Cross section of cylinder.

$\theta = \theta_m \sin \phi$, independent of distance along the axis. The problem is to find the steady-state temperature distribution as a function of r and ϕ.

Note: Use the partial differential equation in polar form, and assume a solution of the form $\theta = R(r) \cdot \Phi(\phi)$. Then show that R satisfies Euler's differential equation (see Sec. 59, Chap. VI), and that the solution is of the form $R = Ar^k + Br^{-k}$. Observe that, since θ must be finite at $r = 0$, the last term of this solution is not applicable, so $B = 0$.

12. Many high-frequency electrical transmission lines that are physically short but electrically long can be treated most simply and with good accuracy by neglecting dissipation ($R = 0$ and $G = 0$).

a. Write the expressions for the propagation constant α and the characteristic impedance $\bar{Z}_0$ for a dissipationless line.

b. Write the steady-state vector solutions (616) and (617) for a dissipationless line in terms of trigonometric functions of the real argument $\sqrt{LC} \, \omega x$ (see Eqs. 262, Sec. 53, Chap. VI).

c. Using the results of part (*b*), find an expression for the input impedance of a dissipationless line terminated in any output impedance $\bar{Z}_R$.

d. Using the results of (*c*), show that a dissipationless line terminated in its characteristic impedance $\bar{Z}_0$ has an input impedance equal to the characteristic impedance, independent of frequency or the length of the line.

e. A dissipationless line is short-circuited at its "receiving" end. Show that the input impedance is a pure reactance. Plot the ratio

$$\frac{\text{input reactance}}{\text{characteristic impedance}}\quad\text{vs. the length of the line in wave lengths.}$$

Use lengths from 0 to 1.25 wave lengths.

13. In an investigation of the contact resistance of carbon brushes, it has been found necessary to compute the resistance of the brush itself. The shape of brush used in this experiment is shown in Fig. P13. Obtain by means of a field plot the resistance between the tip of the brush and a plane (normal to the axis of the brush) $1\frac{1}{2}$ in. above the tip.

Data: The depth of the brush normal to the plane of the drawing is $\frac{3}{8}$ in. The resistivity of the brush material is 0.0019 ohm-in.

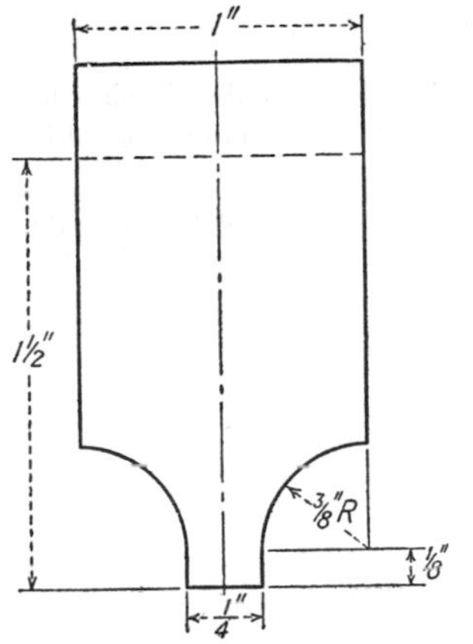

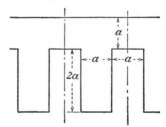

Fig. P13.—Carbon brush.

Fig. P14.—Air gap between a field pole and a slotted armature.

14. Figure P14 shows a portion of the air gap between a field pole and a slotted armature. Make a field plot of the magnetic flux between these two surfaces and find the ratio between the flux that passes across this gap (per unit depth for one slot pitch) to the flux that would pass across a uniform gap of width *a*.

15. Figure P15 shows a set of long, uniformly spaced cylinders located midway between two parallel planes. The cylinders are at one potential, and the planes are at another potential. Plot the resulting field and make the following computations:

a. The space between the cylinders and plates is filled with ground cork with a thermal conductivity of 0.026 Btu/ft-hr-°F. If the cylinders are at a temperature of 150°F and the plates are at a temperature of 60°F, find the rate of heat conduction from each cylinder to the plates, expressed in Btu/hr per foot depth.

b. The cylinders and plates form opposite elements of an electric condenser, and the dielectric between them is air. Find the capacitance per cylinder per unit depth.

If the potential difference between the plates and cylinders is 1,000 volts and $a = \frac{1}{8}$ in., find the maximum potential gradient in volts per inch.

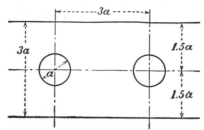

FIG. P15.—Cylinders between parallel plates.

16. A drawing of the commutating pole of a d-c machine is shown in Fig. P16, considerably idealized. The tip of the pole is rounded to obtain the proper distribution of flux.

a. Plot the field, assuming a current sheet on the surface of the pole. Neglect the small air gap beneath the main poles and assume that the main poles are unexcited.

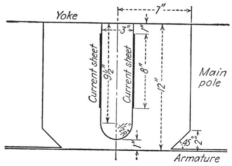

FIG. P16.—Commutating pole of d-c machine.

o. The commutating pole carries an mmf of 9,000 ampere-turns. Plot a graph of flux density at the armature surface (lines per square inch) vs. distance measured from the center line of the pole.

c. The commutating pole is 18 in. in axial length and the winding has 14 turns per pole. Find the self-inductance of the commutating winding in millihenrys per pole.

INDEX

A

Absolute value, of complex number, 184
Acceleration, of gravity, 15
Action and reaction, 13
Adequate physical equations, 234
Admittance, 191
Air resistance, on airplane wing, 230–234
  on falling body, 156
Algebra, of complex numbers, 182–186
Algebraic equations, roots of, 109
Algebraic signs, in electrical equations, 51–53
  meaning of, 48–50
  in mechanical equations, 57–59
Alternating currents, 182–196
  combined with transient, 194–196
  nonsinusoidal, 239
Amplitude, of forced oscillation, 190
  of free oscillation, 102
Amplitude spectrum, 267, 274
Analogies, 28, 67–70
  assumptions in, 68
  duality in, 69
  electric cable and heat flow, 313
Analysis, harmonic, 258–265
Angular momentum, 20–22
Angular velocity, 21, 57
  natural, 102
Antinode, 293
Assumptions, in electrical systems, 51
  in lumped-constant systems, 280
  in mechanical systems, 56
  use of, 3–5

B

Ber and bei functions, 176
Bessel functions, 168–179
  derivatives of, 173
  of fractional order, 174
  of imaginary argument, 175
  modified, 175
  of negative integral order, 175
  of positive integral order, 172
  of zero order, 169
  zeros of, 170
Bessel's equation, 169
Boundary conditions, 287
  applied by Fourier series, 296
  in field plotting, 323–325
  for quenched slab, 303
  for vibrating string, 291
Branch currents, 47
Buckingham π theorem, 219

C

Cable, electric, 313
Capacitance, from field plot, 329
Cauchy-Riemann equations, 321
Cauchy's equation, 167
Change, of dependent variable, 134-137
  of units, 218–219
Characteristic dimension, 231
Characteristic equation, 97, 109
Characteristic impedance, 316
Characteristic modes, 294
Charge resonance, 200
Checking, dimensional, 207–213
  limiting case, 214–215
Circuits, alternating-current, 182-196
  analogies to, 67–70
  coupled, 25, 31, 55

337

Circuits, dimensional analysis of, 208, 229
  with distributed constants, 280, 311–317
  duals of, 63–67
  Fourier-integral analysis of, 266–275
  mesh currents in, 47
  nonlinear, methods for, 75–89, 155, 229
  with nonsinusoidal voltage, 239, 251, 257
  setting up equations for, 50–56
  with time-varying parameter, 162
  voltages in, 23–26, 51
Coefficient of restitution, 34
Coefficients, Fourier, 241–243
  of inductance, 24–25
Complementary function, 118
Complete physical equations, 234
Complex Fourier series, 254–258
Complex numbers, 182–186
  absolute value of, 184
  algebraic operations on, 183–186
  vector representation of, 183
Complex roots, in characteristic equation, 101, 109–110
Condenser, capacitance, by field plot, 329
  energy stored in, 12
  reactance of, 194
  voltage across, 51
Conduction, of electricity, by field plot, 328
  of heat, analogy to cable, 313
    in cylinder, 176–179
    equation for rate of, 301
    by field plot, 317–328
    in quenched slab, 300–305
    steady, 307, 309–311
    variable, 300–308
Conformal mapping, 328
Conjugate functions, 321
Conservation of angular momentum, 20–22
  of energy, 11–13
  of momentum, 19–20
Constant, dimensional, 234

Constant, propagation, 317
  time, 99
Constant-current network, 72
Constant flux linkages, principle of, 26–30, 163
Convergence of Fourier series, 249
Coordinates, choice of, 45–48
Correlation of data by dimensional analysis, 226–229
Cosine, hyperbolic, 145
Coupled circuits, energy stored in, 31
  flux linkages in, 25–26
  force between, 32
  setting up equations for, 51, 55
  voltage induced in, 25–26, 51, 55
Coupling of rotating systems, 22
Critical damping, 103–104, 108
Cubic equation, roots of, 109–110
Current, alternating, 182–196, 239
  induced, 29
  mesh, 47
  nonsinusoidal, 239, 251, 257
  transient, 40
Curvilinear squares, 320

D

D'Alembert's principle, 18, 56
Damped oscillations, 102, 106, 122
  of elastic string, 333
Damping, critical, 103, 108
  effect of, on resonance, 197–201
  force of, 56–57
  solid and viscous, 56
Damping constant, in oscillatory solution, 102
  as system parameter, 57
Damping factor, 102
De Moivre's theorem, 186
Degree, of differential equation, 95
  of freedom, 46–47
Dependent variable, change of, 134–137
  in electrical systems, 47
  in mechanical systems, 45, 58
Derivatives, of Bessel functions, 173
  of Fourier series, 250
  of hyperbolic functions, 148

Derivatives, initial, 113–114, 132
   operator method, 137–145
   partial, 282–285
   of rotating vectors, 187–188
Differential, exact, 159
   total, 283–284
Differential equation, Bessel's, 169
   Cauchy-Riemann, 321
   Cauchy's, 167
   with constant coefficients, 97–149
   degree of, 95
   Euler's, 167
   exact, 159
   general solution, defined, 96
   graphical solution of, 86–89
   homogeneous, of first order, 157
   homogeneous linear, 96–117, 167
      of first order, 97–100
      of general order, 109–110
      of second order, 100–109
      systems of, 110–117
   initial conditions for, 43, 96, 113, 132
   operator method, 137–145
   linear, with constant coefficients, 97–149
      defined, 96
      general first-order, 161
      homogeneous, 96–117
      nonhomogeneous, 96, 117–134, 161
      (*See also* Differential equation, nonhomogeneous linear)
      systems of, 110–117, 130–134
   nonhomogeneous linear, 96, 117–134, 161
      general method, 127–130
      reduction to homogeneous, 119–127
      with several driving forces, 130
      systems of, 130–134
   with nonsinusoidal driving forces, 251–254, 257
   normal form of, 84
   numerical solution of, 82–86
   order of, 44, 95
   ordinary, 95–179

Differential equations, oscillatory solutions of, 101, 106, 122
   partial, 95, 280–331
   (*See also* Partial differential equations)
   particular integral of, 117
   particular solution defined, 96
   setting up, 45–70
   simultaneous, 110–117, 130–134
   with sinusoidal driving forces, 124, 188–193
   with variable coefficients, 161, 167–179
   with variables missing, 164–166
   with variables separable, 155
Differential operator, algebraic properties of, 111
   in partial differential equations, 298
   in systems of equations, 112, 131
   in writing equations, 54
Differentiation, of Fourier series, 250
   partial, 282–285
Dimension, characteristic, 231
   fundamental, 207, 211
Dimensional analysis, 218–235
   in changing units, 218
   correlation of data, 226–229
   derivation of formulas, 219–224
   of force on airplane wing, 230
   of heat transfer, 226
   in model theory, 230–234
   of nonlinear transient, 229
   in plotting analytical results, 222
   of velocity of sound in gas, 224
Dimensional checking, 207–213
Dimensional constants, 234
Dimensional formulas, table of, 212
Discontinuity, convergence at, 249
Displacement impedance, 192
Distributed constants, 280–331
Driving force, 118
   constant, 121
   nonsinusoidal, 239–275
   sinusoidal, 124, 182–201
   two or more present, 130
Driving-point impedance, 191
Dual equations, 63

Dual systems, 63–67
  in analogies, 69

E

Elastic mounting, of machines, 204
Electric fields, plotting of, 317–331
Electrical energy, 12
  stored in inductive circuits, 30
Electrical momentum, 27
Electrical systems, on a-c voltage,
    182–196
  analogies for, 67–70
  choice of variables in, 47
  dimensional analysis of, 208, 229
  with distributed constants, 280,
    311–317
  duals of, 63–67
  Fourier-integral analysis of, 266–
    275
  nonlinear, methods for, 75–89,
    155, 229
  with nonsinusoidal voltage, 239,
    251, 257
  setting up equations for, 50–56
  with time-varying parameter, 162
  voltages in, 23–26, 51
Electrical transmission lines, 311–
    317
Electromechanical system, 73
Energy, calculation of forces from,
    31–34
  kinetic, 11, 21
  law of conservation of, 11–13
  stored, in condenser, 12
    in coupled circuits, 31
    in linear inductance, 31
    in nonlinear inductance, 30
    in rotating systems, 21
    in spring, 11–12
Equations, adequate, 234
  Bessel's, 169
  Cauchy-Riemann, 321
  Cauchy's, 167
  characteristic, 97, 109
  checking of, 206–215
  cubic, 109–110
  dual, 63

Equations, Euler's, 167
  gravity forces in, 58
  Laplace's, 307, 309, 321
  ordinary differential, 95–179
    (*See also* Differential equations)
  partial differential, 280–331
    (*See also* Partial differential
    equations)
  roots of algebraic, 109–110
  setting up, 45–70
    (*See also* Setting up equations)
Equipotential lines, 318
Error function, 164
Euler's equation, 167
Euler's formula, 102
Even function, 245
Even harmonics, effect of, 244
Exact differential equations, 159
Expansion, in Fourier series, 239–
    275
  in interval, 249

F

Factor, damping, 102
  integrating, 161
Factorial, 174
Field, of charged rings, 331
  of conductor near iron surface, 326
  near slot, 324
  of poles of machine, 324
Field plotting, 317–331
  boundary conditions in, 323–325
  calculations in, 327–331
  method of, 321–325
  superposition in, 325
  three-dimensional, 331
Filter, 74, 278
Fischer-Hinnen harmonic analysis,
    258–263
Flux function, 318
Flux linkages, 23
  analogy to momentum, 28
  in coupled circuits, 26
  in linear inductance, 24
  in nonlinear inductance, 29
  principle of constant, 26–30, 163
Flux plotting, 317–331

Force, on airplane wing, 230–234
  analogy to voltage, 26, 67
  between coils, 32
  damping, 56–57
  as dependent variable, 69, 136
  inertia, 15–16, 57
  nonsinusoidal, 239
  sinusoidal, 124, 182
  of spring, 11–12, 57
  units of, 15
  by virtual displacement, 31–34
Forced oscillation, 124, 182
  combined with free oscillation, 122, 124–127
  of mass on spring, 196–201
  nonsinusoidal, 251–254, 266–268
Formula, Euler's, 102
  recursion, 172, 174
Fourier coefficients, 241, 242–249
  complex, 256
  for even and odd functions, 245 247
Fourier integral, 266–275
Fourier series, 239–275
  applied to boundary conditions, 296, 304
  complex form of, 254–258
  convergence of, 249–251
  differentiation of, 250
  estimation of harmonics, 264
  for even and odd functions, 245
  expansion by, in interval, 249
  integration of, 250
  numerical harmonic analysis, 258
  in terms of time or distance, 247
Fourier transform, 269
Free-body method, 61–63
Free oscillations, 100–103
  combined with forced oscillation, 122, 124–127
  of elastic string, 292–297
  of mass on spring, 106, 121
Freedom, degrees of, 46–47
Frequency, natural, 102
  of elastic string, 295
  resonant, 197
Frequency-doubling circuit, 278
Frictional forces, 56

Functions, ber and bei, 176
  Bessel's, 168–179
  complementary, 118
  conjugate, 321
  error, 164
  even, 245
  flux, 318
  gamma, 174–175
  harmonic, 307
  hyperbolic, 145–149
  odd, 246
  periodic, 239
  potential, 321
  propagation, 317
  pulse, 270
  of several variables, 282–285
  step, 273
Fundamental dimensions, 207, 211
Fundamental mode, 295
Fundamental wave, 241

G

Gamma functions, 174–175
General solution, defined, 96
Gibbs phenomenon, 250
Gradient, from field plot, 327, 329
Graeffe's root-squaring method, 109n.
Graphical field plotting, 317–331
Graphical integration, 80–82
Graphical solution of differential equations, 86–89
Gravity, acceleration of, 15
Gravity forces, in equations, 58
Gyration, radius of, 17

H

Harmonic analysis, 258–263
  by estimation, 264–266
Harmonic function, 307
Harmonics, 241, 295
  continuous spectrum of, 269
  effect of even, 244
  estimation of, 264–266
Heat flow, analogy to cable, 313
  conduction equation, 301

Heat flow, in cylinder, 176–179
  by field plotting, 317–328
  in quenched slab, 300–305
  steady, 307, 309–311
  storage equation, 301
  variable, 300–308
Heat transfer, dimensional analysis
    of, 226–229
Homogeneity, dimensional, 207
Homogeneous differential equations,
    96–117, 157, 167
  partial, 297–300
Hyperbolic functions, 145–149
  of complex argument, 148
Hysteresis, 30

I

Imaginary number, 101, 183
  as exponent, 102, 145, 184
Impact, 20
  coefficient of restitution for, 34
  dissipation of energy in, 11
Impedance, characteristic, 316
  driving point, 191
  electrical, 191
    of RC series circuit, 194
  mechanical, 192
    of mass on spring, 196
  transfer, 191
Induced current, 29
Induced voltage, 23–26, 51, 55
Inductance, coefficients of, 24–25
  effect of, in switching, 26–29
  energy stored in, 12, 30–31
  by field plotting, 330
  mutual, 25, 51, 55
  nonlinear, 29, 30, 229
  self-, 24, 51–53
  variable, 162–164
Inertia, moment of, 17
Inertia force, 15, 16, 57
Inertia torque, 17, 58
Initial conditions, applied after
    change of variable, 135–136
  effect of, 43
  for mass on spring, 105, 123
  operator method, 137–141

Initial conditions, for RL circuit, 99
  relaxed, 137
  by superposition, 141–145
  for systems of equations, 113–114,
    132
Initial derivatives, method of, 113–
    114, 132
  operator method, 137–141
Integral, definite, 76
  Fourier, 266–275
  graphical evaluation of, 80–82
  numerical evaluation of, 76–79
  particular, 117, 162
Integral operator, 138
Integrating factor, 128, 161
Integration, of Fourier series, 250
  graphical, 80–82
  numerical, 76–79
  step-by-step, 82–84
Isoclines, method of, 86–89
Isolation, of vibration, 204

K

Kinetic energy, 11
  of rotation, 21
Kirchhoff's laws, 23
  in setting up equations, 50–53

L

Laplace's equation, 307, 309, 321
  field-map solution, 317–331
Law, of action and reaction, 13
  of conservation of energy, 11–13
  Kirchhoff's, 23, 50
  Newton's, 14–15
Limiting-case checking, 214
Linear damping, 56
Linear differential equations, with
    constant coefficients, 97–149
  (*See also* Differential equations)
  partial, 280–331
  (*See also* Partial differential
    equations)
  with variable coefficients, 161,
    167–179

Linear inductance, 24
  energy stored in, 12, 31
  flux linkages in, 24
  varying with time, 162
  voltage induced in, 25–26, 51
Linear spring, 12
Lines, transmission, 311–317
Linkages, flux, 23
Loop method, 50, 67
Loops and nodes, 293

M

Mach's number, 234
Magnetic field, energy in, 12, 30–31
  field plotting of, 317–331
Mapping, conformal, 328
  field, 317–331
Mass, 15
  inertia force of, 15, 16, 57
  kinetic energy of, 11
Mean-value theorem, 286
Mechanical energy, 11–12
Mechanical filter, 74
Mechanical systems, analogies to,
    67–70
  choice of coordinates for, 45
  damping in, 56–57
  with distributed constants, 280–
    300
  forced oscillations in, 124, 196
    combined with free oscillations,
      122, 124–127
    nonsinusoidal, 251–254, 266
  forces in, 57
  free oscillations in, 100–108, 121–
    123
    with distributed constants, 292–
      297
  impedance of, 192, 196
  nonlinear, methods for, 75–89,
    155, 218
  resonance in, 196–201, 295
  setting up equations for, 56–63
  torques in, 57–58
Membrane, equation for, 181
Mesh currents, 47
Models, use of, 230–234

Modes of oscillation, 294
Modified Bessel functions, 175
Moment of inertia, 17, 58
Momentum, analogy to flux linkage,
    28
  angular, 21
  conservation of, 19–22
  electrical, 27
Motion, critically damped, 103, 108
  Newton's laws of, 14–15
  nonsinusoidal, 239, 251–254, 266
  oscillatory, 101, 106, 122
    of elastic string, 292–296
  rectilinear, 16
  rotational, 16–18
  sinusoidal, 124, 186–201
Mutual inductance, 25, 51, 55

N

Natural frequency, 102
  relation of, to resonance, 200
  of vibrating string, 295, 333
Network (*see* Electrical systems)
Newton's laws of motion, 14–15
Node method, 66–67
Nodes, and antinodes, 293
Nonhomogeneous differential equa-
    tions, 96, 117–134
Nonlinear damping, 56, 77, 156
Nonlinear inductance, 24
  energy stored in, 30
  flux linkages in, 29
Nonlinear spring, 11
Nonlinear systems, analytical meth-
    ods, 155–161, 164–166
  dimensional analysis, 229–230
  isocline method, 86–89
  numerical methods, 75–86
Nonperiodic function, expanded in
    interval, 249
  Fourier-integral analysis of, 266–
    275
Nonsinusoidal waves, 239–275
Normal form, 84
Numbers, complex, 182–186
  imaginary, 183
  Mach's, 234
  Reynolds, 227, 232

Numerical harmonic analysis, 258
Numerical integration, 76–79
Numerical solution, of differential equations, 82–86

O

Odd function, 246
One-dimensional heat flow, 300–305
Operator, differential, 54, 111
    partial, 298
    in systems of equations, 112, 131
Operator method, for initial derivatives, 137–145
Order of differential equation, 44, 95
Ordinary differential equations, 95–179
    (*See also* Differential equations)
Oscillation, 100–103
    characteristic modes of, 294
    damped, 102, 106, 122
    forced, 124, 182
        combined with free oscillation, 122, 124–127
        of mass on spring, 196–201
        nonsinusoidal, 251–254, 266
    free, 100–103
        of elastic string, 292–297
        of mass on spring, 106, 122
    natural frequency of, 102
    of pendulum, 87
    self-excited, 93
    steady state, 124, 182
    undamped, 103, 108, 201
Overdamped, 103, 106
Overtones, 295

P

Partial derivatives, 282–285
Partial differential equations, 280–331
    applied to quenched slab, 300–305
    boundary conditions for, 291, 310
        by Fourier series, 296, 304
    defined, 95–96
    homogeneous, 297–300
    Laplace's, 307, 309, 321
        field-map solution, 317–331

Partial differential equations, product solution of, 289–292
    of steady heat flow, 305–311
    of transmission line, 311–317
    of variable heat flow, 300–308
        in polar coordinates, 308
    of vibrating string, 285–297
    for vibration of rod, 333
Particular integral, 117
Particular solution, 96
Pendulum, oscillation of, 87
Periodic function, 239
    nonsinusoidal, 239–268
    sinusoidal, 182–201
Phase angle, 102, 191
Phase shift, at resonance, 199
Phase spectrum, 274
Phase velocity, 293, 295, 314
Pi theorem, 219
Plotting of fields, 317–331
Polar coordinates, 307–309
Positive directions, 48–50
Potential function, 321
Primary quantities, 220
Principle, of action and reaction, 13
    of conservation of energy, 11–13
    of conservation of momentum, 19–22
    of constant flux linkages, 26–30
    D'Alembert's, 18, 56
    of duality, 63–67
    of superposition, 13–14
    of virtual displacement, 31–34
Product solution, 289–292
Propagation constant, 317
Prototype, 231
Pulse function, 270

Q

Quenched slab, 300–305

R

Radius of gyration, 17
Real part of complex number, 186
Rectifier voltage, harmonics in, 257
Rectilinear translation, 16
Recursion formula, 172, 174

Repeated roots, 103, 110
Report, 6–8
Resistance, 51
Resonance, 124, 197
   with harmonic, 251–254, 267
   of mass on spring, 196–201
   phase shift in region of, 199
   relation of, to natural frequency, 200
   of vibrating string, 295
Resonance curves, 198
Restitution, coefficient of, 34
Reynolds number, 227, 232
Rod, equation for vibration, 333
Roots, complex, 101, 110
   of equations, 109–110
Rotating systems, angular momentum of, 20–22
   coupling of, 22
   torques in, 57–58
Rotating vectors, 186
   representing harmonics, 255
Rotation of rigid body, 16–18
Rule, Simpson's, 78–79
   trapezoidal, 76–78

S

Saturation curves, 29, 30
Secondary quantities, 220
Self-excited oscillations, 93
Self-inductance, 24, 51–53
Separation of variables, 155–156
Series, Fourier, 239–275
Setting up equations, 45–70
   for coupled circuits, 55–56
   for distributed systems, 285–313
   for electrical circuits, 50–56
   free-body method, 61–63
   for mechanical systems, 56–63
Simpson's rule, 78
Simultaneous differential equations, 110–117, 130–134
Sine, hyperbolic, 145
Sinusoids, vector representation of, 182–201
Slug, 15
Small-squares plot, 318

Solid damping, 56
Solution, of differential equation, 96
   general and particular, 96
   steady state, 40, 117
   transient, 40, 118
Sound, velocity of, in gas, 224–225
Spectrum, amplitude, 267, 274
   phase, 274
Spring, as distributed system, 280
   energy stored in, 11–12
   linear, 12, 57
   nonlinear, 11
Spring constant, 12, 57
Square wave, applied to resonant system, 251–254, 267
   Fourier analysis of, 243, 257
Squares, curvilinear, 320
Standing wave, 293
Steady heat flow, 305–311
Steady-state solution, 40, 117
   nonsinusoidal, 251–254, 257–258
   sinusoidal, 124, 188–193
Step-by-step integration, 82–84
Step function, 273
String, vibration of, 285–297
Successive initial derivatives, 113, 132
   operator method, 137–145
Superposition, of driving forces, 130
   of field plots, 325
   of harmonics, 252, 257
   for initial conditions, 141–145
   principle of, 13–14
Systems, analogous, 67–70, 74
   of differential equations, 110–117, 130–134
   with distributed constants, 280–331
   dual, 63–67

T

Tangent, hyperbolic, 146
Theorem, Buckingham π, 219
   De Moivre's, 186
   mean value, 286
Three-dimensional field plotting, 331
Time constant, 99

Torque, inertia, 17
  in mechanical systems, 57–58
Tracing errors, 210
Transfer impedance, 191
Transform, Fourier, 269
Transient, 40, 118
  critically damped, 103, 108
  exponential, 99, 101, 105
  Fourier integral analysis of, 266–275
  nonlinear, methods for, 75–89, 155, 229
  oscillatory, 101–103
    combined with forced oscillation, 122, 124–127
    effect of damping on, 106
    of mass on spring, 106, 122
    overdamped, 104–106
  in *RL* series circuit, 98–100
  with sinusoidal driving force, 122, 124–127, 194–196
Transient heat flow, 300–308
Translation, rectilinear, 16
Transmissibility, 204
Transmission lines, 311–317
Trapezoidal rule, 76–78
Traveling waves, 293–295, 314
Triangular wave, Fourier analysis of, 247, 257
Trigonometric functions, 145
  with imaginary argument, 148
Trigonometric series, 239–275
Tuned flywheel, 204

U

Undamped oscillation, 103, 108, 201
Undetermined coefficients, 119
Unit step function, 273
Units, 207
  changing, 218–219
  of force and mass, 15
  of mechanical constants, 57–58

V

Variable heat flow, 300–308
Variable parameter, 162
Variables, change of dependent, 134

Variables, choice of, 45–48
  separation of, 155
Vector representation, of complex number, 183
  of harmonics, 255
  of sinusoids, 182–201
Velocity, angular, 21, 57
  of falling body, 155–156
  phase, 293, 295, 314
  of sound in gas, 224
Velocity impedance, 192
Vibration, damped, 102, 106, 122
  forced, 124, 182
    combined with free vibration, 122, 124–127
    of mass on spring, 196–201
    nonsinusoidal, 251–254, 267
  free, 100–103
    of mass on spring, 106, 122
  isolation of, 204
  of membrane, equation for, 181
  modes of, 294
  natural frequency of, 102, 295
  of rod, equation for, 333
  of string, 285–297
Vibration absorber, 204
Vibration instrument, 203–204
Virtual displacement, 31–34
Viscous damping, 56
Voltage, analogies to, 68–69
  as dependent variable, 135
  induced, 23–26, 51
    in coupled circuits, 25–26, 51, 55
    across lumped impedances, 51
Voltage gradient, by field plot, 329

W

Wave, standing, 293
  traveling, 293–295, 314
Wave length, 295
  on transmission line, 314
Wind-tunnel testing, 233
Wing, force on, 230–234
Work, 31

Z

Zeros of Bessel functions, 170